Collins Advanced Modular Sciences

Microbes, Medicine and Biotechnology

Ken Mannion and Terry Hudson

Centre for Science Education
Sheffield Hallam University

Series Editor: Mike Coles

Collins Educational
An Imprint of HarperCollinsPublishers

**Northern
Modular Science Scheme**

Published by Collins Educational
An imprint of HarperCollins*Publishers* Ltd
77–85 Fulham Palace Road
Hammersmith
London
W6 8JB

First published 1996

Reprinted 1996

ISBN 0 00 322392 2

Series design by Ewing Paddock at PearTree Design
Layout and composition by Newton Harris

Edited by Penelope Lyons

Picture research by Caroline Thompson

Illustrations by Barking Dog Art, Jerry Fowler, Fraser
Williams, Peter Harper, Illustrated Arts

Printed and bound in Hong Kong

Contents

Acknowledgements

Text and diagrams reproduced by kind permission of:
Advisa Medica, Harcourt Brace & Company Ltd, John Murray (Publishers) Ltd,
Office for National Statistics, Oxford University Press,
Which? Ltd.

Crown copyright is reproduced with the permission of the controller of HMSO.

Every effort has been made to contact the holders of copyright material, but if any have been inadvertently overlooked the publishers will be pleased to make the necessary arrangements at the first opportunity.

The publishers would like to thank the following for permission to reproduce photographs (T = Top, B = Bottom, C = Centre, L = Left, R = Right):

Advertising Archives 55, 64, 80T, 82T;
Allsport/G Mortimore 113;
Allsport/D Cannon 169;
Ancient Art and Architecture Collection 71;
Barnaby's Picture Library 84B, 93;
Biophoto Associates 11B, 12B, 13, 37, 76, 80(inset), 85, 103, 148(inset);
John Birdsall Photography 57TL, 98T;
J Heseltine/Anthony Blake Photo Library 65TL;
Chris Bonington Photo Library 9;
University of Bradford/Department of Archeological Sciences 82CL;
Lauros-Giraudon/Bridgeman Art Library, London 9(inset);
Mike Benner/CAMRA 21;
N Tomalin/Bruce Coleman Ltd 75L;
Mary Evans Picture Library 84T, 124T,TC&B;

Geophotos/Tony Waltham 101B;
Ronald Grant Archive 46T, 47, 144T;
Sally and Richard Greenhill 95;
Michael Holford 22;
N Cattlin/Holt Studios International 30, 80C;
Hulton Deutsch Collection Ltd 48C, 110, 142T, 148R, 157;
Illustrated London News Picture Library 144B;
Roger and Nina Lacey 31B;
Pennie Lyons 89;
Mirror Syndication International 156;
National Library of Medicine 59;
S Dalton/NHPA 75C;
G Bernard/NHPA 143L;
Robert Opie Collection 44;
C Bromhall/OSF 11C;
P Barker/Panos Pictures 23;
H Wilson/Panos Pictures 28;
P M Smith/Panos Pictures 32C;
J C Tordai/Panos Pictures 34;
S Sprague/Panos Pictures 38;
P Fryer/Panos Pictures 65TC;
C Stowers/Panos Pictures 149;
Pfizer Ltd 60;
Popperfoto 163T;
Rank Hovis Ltd 46C;
Redferns 96;
Rex Features Ltd 98CL, 138, 139;

SCR Photo Library 31T;
Science Photo Library 8, 11R, 12T, 15, 36T, 48T, 51, 57C, 65R, 66, 77, 86, 87, 92, 98R, 99, 105, 108, 111, 116, 119, 120, 125, 127, 133, 137, 153, 163C, 170, 171;
Science and Society Photo Library 6;
Roger Scruton 27;
SHOUT 35T, 115, 128, 134, 146;
H Giraudet/Still Pictures 143R;
Tony Stone Images 16, 19, 24, 32B, 43, 70, 75T, 101T, 102, 129, 167;
C and S Thompson 35C, 65L;
The Wellcome Institute Library, London 82C, 124BC, 142C, 145;
Mike Williams 36CL;
Zefa Pictures Ltd 14.
Cover photograph supplied by Tony Stone Images.

To the student

This book aims to make your study of advanced science successful and interesting. The authors have made sure that the ideas you need to understand are covered in a clear and straightforward way. The book is designed to be a study of scientific ideas as well as a reference text when needed. Science is constantly evolving and, wherever possible, modern issues and problems have been used to make your study interesting and to encourage you to continue studying science after your current course is complete.

Working on your own
Studying on your own is often difficult and sometimes textbooks give you the impression that you have to be an expert in the subject before you can read the book. I hope you find that this book is not like that. The authors have carefully built up ideas, so that when you are working on your own there is less chance of you becoming lost in the text and frustrated with the subject.

Don't try to achieve too much in one reading session. Science is complex and some demanding ideas need to be supported with a lot of facts. Trying to take in too much at one time can make you lose sight of the most important ideas – all you see is a mass of information. Use the learning objectives to select one idea to study in a particular session.

Chapter design
Each chapter starts by showing how the science you will learn is applied somewhere in the world. Next come learning objectives which tell you exactly what you should learn as you read the chapter. These are written in a way which spells out what you will be able to do with your new knowledge, rather like a checklist – they could be very helpful when you revise your work. At certain points in the chapters you will find key ideas listed. These are checks for you to use, to make sure that you have grasped these ideas. Words written in **bold type** appear in the glossary at the end of the book. If you don't know the meaning of one of these words check it out immediately – don't persevere, hoping all will become clear.

The questions in the text are there for you to check you have understood what is being explained. These are all short – longer questions are included in a support pack which goes with this book. The questions are straightforward in style – there are no trick questions. Don't be tempted to pass over these questions, they will give you new insights into the work which you may not have seen. Answers to questions are given in the back of the book.

Good luck with your studies. I hope you find the book an interesting read.

Mike Coles, Series Editor
University of London Institute of Education, June 1996

Microbes in focus

Fig. 1 The beginnings of microbiology

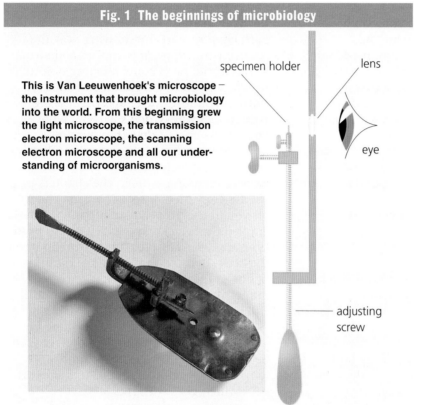

This is Van Leeuwenhoek's microscope – the instrument that brought microbiology into the world. From this beginning grew the light microscope, the transmission electron microscope, the scanning electron microscope and all our understanding of microorganisms.

specimen holder

lens

eye

adjusting screw

People have known about the effects of microbes for thousands of years. Microbes make bread rise, turn fruit juice into alcohol, and milk into cheese and yoghurt. Even the most primitive societies could treat certain illnesses. The ancient Egyptians used a collection of preservatives to stop the bodies of their dead kings and queens from decaying even though they knew nothing about decay-causing microbes. In all these situations, people knew about the *effects* of microorganisms but not about the organisms themselves. Nobody had seen microbes or even thought they might exist because microbial effects could be explained in other ways. What we now call biotechnology probably began as a kind of magic thousands of years ago. It took a huge leap towards becoming a science in the 1670s when a Dutch microscope maker called Anton van Leeuwenhoek looked at a sample of his own saliva (Fig. 1).

1.1 Learning objectives

After working through this chapter, you should be able to:

- **explain** the significance of the development of the microscope;

- **describe** the eukaryotic features of yeast and a typical filamentous fungus;

- **describe** the major functions of fungal cell wall, membrane and nucleus;

- **list** the prokaryotic features of a typical bacterium;

- **classify** bacteria according to their shape;

- **describe** Gram's staining technique and identify bacteria as Gram-positive or Gram-negative;

- **describe** the functions of the bacterial cell wall, capsule, membrane, flagellum, mesosome, nuclear zone, ribosomes, and plasmids;

- **describe** the features of viruses such as HIV, TMV and bacteriophages;

- **explain** the major functions of viral nucleic acid, capsid, capsomere and envelope;

- **recognise** the major features of fungi, bacteria and viruses as seen in electronmicrographs;

- **interpret** and evaluate microbial growth patterns.

1.2 Development of microscopes

Microorganisms are so small that they can only be seen clearly using a microscope; the better the resolution of the microscope, the clearer the image. There is a direct correlation between the development of the microscope and the understanding of organisms that are too small to be seen with the naked eye.

Anton van Leeuwenhoek was a man with no scientific training who published no books or scientific papers. He made microscopes that were very simple and consisted of a single tiny lens, but his observations and drawings show clearly that he understood that what he saw were living organisms. He described them as 'little animals or animalcules'. Here is his description of a specimen of his own saliva:

I now saw very plainly that these were little eels or worms, lying all huddled up together and wriggling; just as if you saw, with the naked eye, a whole tubful of very little eels and water, with the eels a-squirming among one another; and the whole water seemed to be alive with these multifarious animalcules. This was for me, among all the marvels that I have discovered in nature, the most marvellous of all.

1 a How do you think people would have reacted to what van Leeuwenhoek described?
   b How could you explain what he saw to them?

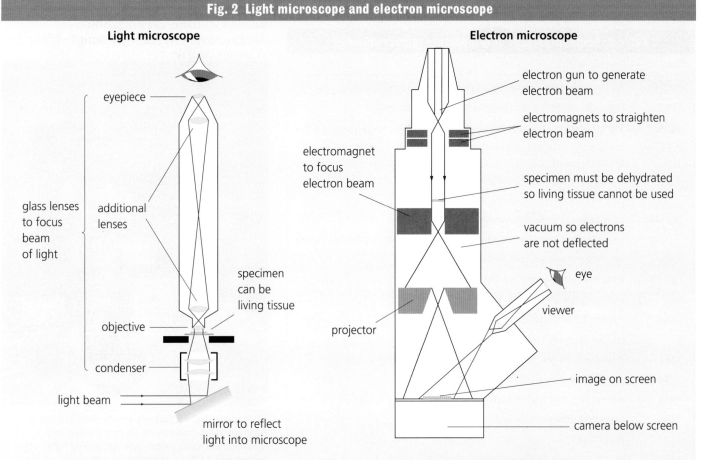

Fig. 2 Light microscope and electron microscope

Light microscope

eyepiece

glass lenses to focus beam of light

additional lenses

specimen can be living tissue

objective

condenser

light beam

mirror to reflect light into microscope

Electron microscope

electron gun to generate electron beam

electromagnets to straighten electron beam

electromagnet to focus electron beam

specimen must be dehydrated so living tissue cannot be used

vacuum so electrons are not deflected

eye

viewer

projector

image on screen

camera below screen

Source: adapted from Clegg and Mackean, *Advanced Biology: principles and applications*, John Murray, 1994

But the study of these 'animalcules' made no progress until the 1800s because no-one else could make microscopes as well as van Leeuwenhoek. Many of his microscopes have survived and we know

they could magnify up to 300 times and could resolve objects as tiny as one-millionth of a metre. Microscopes of such high quality were not generally available until the nineteenth century when new lenses and techniques to section, fix and stain specimens made the microscopic world clear to many. However, by the beginning of the twentieth century, light microscopy had almost reached the limit of its capabilities and progress slowed until the development of the electron microscope (EM) in the 1930s (Fig 2).

2 Why did nothing happen in the study of microorganisms until the 1800s?

3 Can you see viruses with a light microscope?

Understanding structure often provides a good basis for understanding function, which is why progress in understanding microorganisms depended on developments in the microscope (Table 2).

Table 1 Microscope resolution and visibility of specimens

Resolution to	Instrument limits	What can be seen
0.1 mm		
	limit of the eye's unaided resolution	
0.01 mm		most cells
0.001 mm (1 µm)		
		bacteria, some cell organelles
0.1 µm	limit of light microscope resolution	
		viruses
0.01 µm		plasma membranes
0.001 µm (1 nm)	limit of electron microscope resolution	molecules
0.1 nm		
		atoms
0.001 nm		
mm = millimetre	µm = micrometre	nm = nanometre

Table 2 Some important developments in microbiology

Date	Development
1675–85	van Leeuwenhoek makes microscopes, examines specimens and makes drawings
1700s	Spallanzani investigates the appearance of decay organisms in food
1800s	better microscopes become available
mid to late 1800s	Pasteur works on microorganisms and establishes that yeast is needed for fermentation and that decay is caused by 'germs' in the air; publishes his germ theory of disease and develops vaccines for rabies and anthrax
	Lister uses disinfectant in surgery and wound care
late 1800s	Gram develops stain for identifying bacteria
	Ivanovsky shows tobacco mosaic disease caused by an organism smaller than bacteria
1900s	light microscope developed to the limit of its resolution
early 1900s	developments in chemotherapy (vaccines, penicillin)
1932	electron microscope makes more detail visible than ever before
1935–40	crystallisation of tobacco mosaic virus by Stanley
	penicillin isolated by Chain and Florey
1940s	streptomycin isolated
1950s	animal cell cultures developed
1960s	enzymes for cutting DNA investigated
1970s	monoclonal antibodies developed
	DNA cloned
1980s	genetic engineering to produce enzymes, hormones, antibiotics

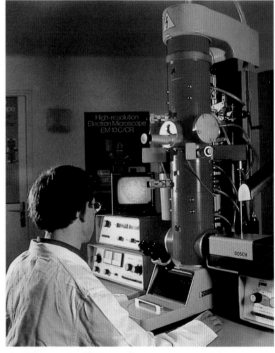

The transmission EM revealed a much more detailed and elaborate microscopic world. Its magnification and resolution are much greater than those of the light microscope (Table 1). The operating console here has a TV monitor.

1.3 Pasteur makes the link

Although microbial effects had been known for thousands of years, and although microbes were first observed in the seventeenth century, it was not until the middle of the nineteenth century that Louis Pasteur made a connection between them.

Many scientists of Pasteur's time believed in **spontaneous generation**. This was the belief that microorganisms just appeared when food decayed. This theory was not new. The ancient Chinese, Babylonians and Egyptians thought it explained where organisms came from and it was an alternative to the belief that life was specially created in all its forms by one or more gods.

Pasteur experimented with wine because he suspected that microbes were the cause of wine souring. He heated the wine to 50–100 °C to destroy the microbes. This method was successful and is familiar to us now as **pasteurisation** (moderate heating) – the process used to make milk safe to drink.

4 What is pasteurisation and why is it used to preserve certain foods?

Pasteur applied his ideas on microbes to disease, and claimed that microorganisms caused infectious diseases. He discovered that hens could be made immune to chicken cholera by giving them a mild dose of the cholera bacterium. He also vaccinated sheep against anthrax. Pasteur's work was important because it encouraged attempts to prevent and cure disease.

5 Study the photograph. How did Pasteur's results suggest that the organisms that spoiled the broth did not appear spontaneously?

Pasteur exposed 20 flasks of boiled broth to the Paris air and then resealed them. He took another 20 to the top of Mont Blanc where they were opened in the pure mountain air and then resealed. All the flasks exposed to the Parisian air went bad, but only 4 of the flasks opened on the mountain did.

Key ideas

- The effects of microbes have been known for thousands of years but microorganisms were not seen until the late 1600s. The understanding of microbes is closely related to the development of microscopes.

- Scientific light microscopy began in the 1800s and by the early 1900s the light microscope was fully developed. The EM came into use in the 1930s and revealed more detail.

- The light microscope shows bacteria and the larger organelles of eukaryotic cells. The EM can show viruses, plasma membranes and large molecules.

- Louis Pasteur demonstrated that microorganisms are in the air and cause certain diseases. He developed some vaccines and also used heat treatment (pasteurisation) to destroy microorganisms in wine.

9

1.4 Fungi

Fungi are eukaryotic organisms (Fig. 3). Many grow large enough to be seen without a microscope and detailed structures can be seen with a light microscope. Moulds, yeasts, mildews, and rusts are all fungi. Fungi exhibit **heterotrophic nutrition** (they require organic nutrients like carbohydrate as a carbon source) and many are **saprobiontic** (they feed on dead organic matter). Others are parasites, especially of plants. Some fungi are unicellular, like yeast, while others are complex multicellular systems.

6 List the structures that show fungi are eukaryotes.

Fungal structure

Yeasts are single cells with a cell wall made mainly of chitin. The wall serves to protect the contents of the cell. Inside the wall is the **plasma membrane**; it controls the flow of small molecules in and out of the cell. The nucleus has a double membrane and contains the genetic material; chromosomes appear when the nucleus divides. Also present are **mitochondria** and an **endoplasmic reticulum**. As in plant and animal cells, the mitochondria are the site of ATP production, and the endoplasmic reticulum is lined in places with **ribosomes**. These attached ribosomes are the site of protein synthesis.

Fig. 3 Features of eukaryotic and prokaryotic cells

Source: adapted from Phillips and Chilton, *A Level Biology*, Oxford University Press, 1989

Eukaryotic cells	Prokaryotic cells
large cells (10–100 μm)	small cells (1–10 μm)
DNA divided into chromosomes and combined with histone to form chromatin	DNA in a loop
nucleus bounded by double membrane	nuclear zone with no nuclear membrane
mitochondria, chloroplasts, centrioles, endoplasmic reticulum, microtubules	no membrane-bound organelles, no centrioles, no microtubules
large ribosomes	small ribosomes
cell walls in plant and fungal cells only	cell walls present and different from eukaryotic cell walls
complex cilia and flagella of tubulin and other proteins	simple flagella of flagellin
cell division by mitosis, spindle formed	cell division by simple fission, no spindle
sexual reproduction by meiosis and fertilisation common	sexual reproduction rare; genetic material passes from donor to recipient
many shared metabolic pathways, almost all aerobic	varied metabolic pathways using unusual energy sources, many anaerobic forms

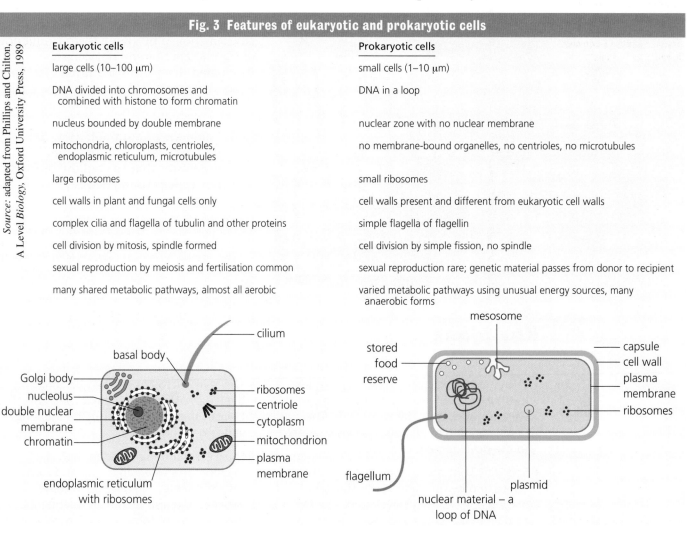

The body of a multicellular fungus is called a **mycelium** and consists of fine, colourless and branching threads called **hyphae**. Hyphae may be either **septate** which means they have cross-walls, or **aseptate** which means they are without dividing walls (Fig. 4). The older hyphae contain less cytoplasm and often have a large vacuole. The internal arrangement is **coenocytic** which means that the hyphae are not divided into cells each with a nucleus. Instead, many nuclei appear together and collect at the growing tips of the hyphae (Fig. 4). All these structures can be seen with a light microscope.

The misty 'bloom' on the skins of these grapes is yeast. The yeast cells ferment the grape juice into alcohol and also add their own subtle flavours to the wine.

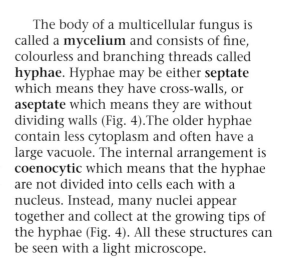

In Périgord (France) an unusual, underground fungus grows. It is called a truffle and is not connected to the chocolate truffles we see in confectioners. Fungal truffles are hunted for with pigs because pigs can smell them out. Truffles are regarded as a delicacy and are very expensive.

Fig. 4 Fungal hyphae

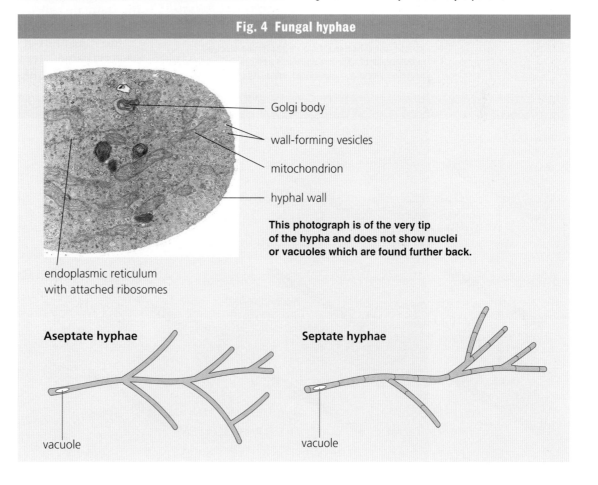

- Golgi body
- wall-forming vesicles
- mitochondrion
- hyphal wall

This photograph is of the very tip of the hypha and does not show nuclei or vacuoles which are found further back.

endoplasmic reticulum with attached ribosomes

Aseptate hyphae

vacuole

Septate hyphae

vacuole

1.5 Bacteria

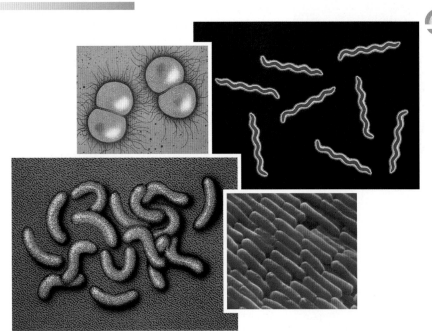

Coloured transmission electron micrographs of: *Neisseria gonorrhoeae* (blue), paired coccal bacteria covered with hairlike projections called pili; *Borrelia burgdorferi* (red and yellow), spiral bacteria. Coloured scanning electron micrographs of: *Bacillus anthracis* (red/orange), rod-shaped bacteria; *Vibrio cholerae* (pink), small curved bacteria.

7 Bacteria are prokaryotes. Using the information in Figure 3, summarise the difference between prokaryotes and eukaryotes.

Bacterial shape can be seen with a light microscope so their characteristic shapes have always been used to identify bacteria.

There are four major shapes:
- spherical (**coccus**) with an average diameter of 1 µm or less;
- rod-shaped (**bacillus**) which are 2–5 µm long;
- spiral (**spirillum**) which are a similar size to bacilli;
- curved (**vibrio**).

In 1884, Christian Gram developed a staining technique that divides bacteria into two groups whose cell walls are structurally different. Those that take up the stain are called **Gram-positive**, those that do not are **Gram-negative** (Fig. 5).

Identification of individual species of bacteria came later with improved microscopic techniques and procedures.

Fig. 5 Gram staining

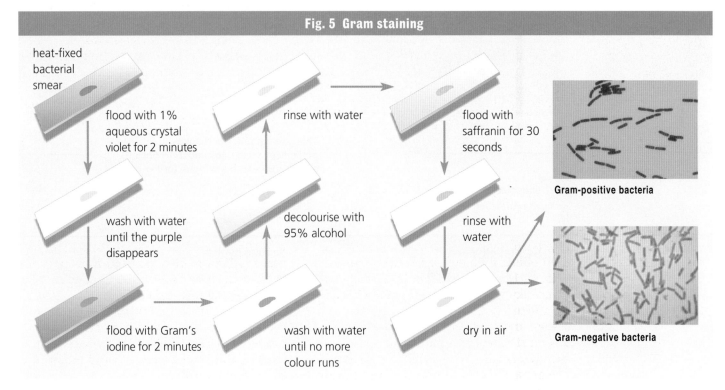

heat-fixed bacterial smear

flood with 1% aqueous crystal violet for 2 minutes

wash with water until the purple disappears

flood with Gram's iodine for 2 minutes

wash with water until no more colour runs

decolourise with 95% alcohol

rinse with water

flood with saffranin for 30 seconds

rinse with water

dry in air

Gram-positive bacteria

Gram-negative bacteria

Bacterial structure

Bacteria have a rigid cell wall for protection and to maintain their shape. Gram-positive bacterial cell walls are thick and are over 40% peptidoglycan. There is very little protein or lipid present. Gram-negative bacteria have a two-layered cell wall which is much thinner but more complex than a Gram-positive cell wall. The inner layer is rigid with little peptidoglycan and the outer layer is a membrane of proteins, lipids and lipopolysaccharides. Some Gram-negative bacteria have projections on their surfaces called **pili** or **fimbriae**. These are cylindrical rods of a protein called pilin. They allow bacteria to link to each other, to other cells and to the substrate.

Outside the cell wall of some bacteria is a slimy layer of polysaccharides or polypeptides called a **capsule**. The capsule protects the cells and allows them to attach to objects.

Some bacteria have **flagella**. These are long fine projections that enable movement. Bacterial flagella have a complicated structure of fibres composed mainly of a contractile protein called flagellin.

The plasma membrane (or cytoplasmic membrane) is the thin lipid and protein layer that encloses the cell contents. The membrane controls the flow of small molecules in and out of the cell. The membrane inside the cell wall may be extended into **thylakoids** in photosynthetic bacteria. Folding gives the membrane a larger surface area which is important since it is the site of much metabolic activity.

The genetic material in bacteria is contained in a folded, tight mass of DNA and RNA called the **nuclear zone**. The DNA in this zone is usually a single circular strand of approximately 4000 genes and contains the information required for cell metabolism, growth and reproduction.

Features that become visible under the electron microscope include ribosomes and **plasmids**. Ribosomes are spherical structures found in the cytoplasm. They are composed of proteins and RNA and are involved in protein synthesis. Plasmids are circular pieces of DNA found in bacterial cells in addition to the DNA of the nuclear zone. Some plasmids have only a few genes, others have hundreds, but these genes are not essential to the survival of the cell in normal circumstances. However, plasmids often carry genes for resistance to antibiotics and can be passed from one bacterium to another (Chapter 11, p. 151).

8 **List the structures which only become visible when bacteria are viewed under the EM.**

The plasma membrane may be extended into folds called *mesosomes* near the site of cell division.

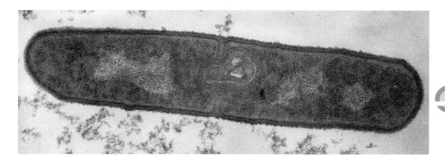

1.6 Viruses

Like bacteria, viruses were known through their effects long before the first virus was seen. In 1852, a Russian botanist called Ivanovsky made an extract from tobacco plants suffering from tobacco mosaic disease and passed it through a disk of unglazed porcelain to filter out any bacteria. He discovered that this bacteria-free extract could still transmit the disease to unaffected tobacco plants. He concluded that something infectious and smaller than bacteria must be causing the disease. In 1898, a Dutchman called Beijerink coined the term 'virus' (Latin for poison) to describe the tiny infectious agent. Later, chemical studies revealed that viruses are combinations of nucleic acid and protein called **nucleoproteins**.

In 1935, the first virus was purified and studied by a scientist called Wendell Stanley. He squeezed the juice from about 900 kg of tobacco leaves and extracted a residue that he purified to form needle-like crystals. The crystals were then dissolved in a neutral solution that could cause the disease when applied to tobacco leaves. Crystals are clearly not living cells, but later tests and the EM showed rod-shaped particles made of more than 2000 identical protein molecules forming a coat around a core of RNA. The particles were named tobacco mosaic virus (TMV). Stanley had isolated the agent that Ivanovsky had discovered nearly a century before.

Strictly speaking, viruses are not microorganisms since they are not cellular, contain no organelles and have no metabolism of their own. Are viruses even alive? Viruses are made of nucleic acid (DNA or RNA) enclosed within a protein coat. Some are also enveloped in a lipid membrane. Until they enter a host cell they are metabolically inert, and once they do enter a cell they are completely dependent on it for their replication. This level of dependence on a host makes them **obligate intracellular parasites**. All groups of living organisms are parasitised by viruses; viruses that attack bacteria are called **bacteriophages**. Although many viruses cause disease in their host, not all do.

9 a What argument would you use to explain that a virus is a living organism?
b What arguments would you use to explain that a virus is not alive?

Virus structure

Viruses range from 20 nm to 3000 nm in diameter, although many are around 100 nm or so across. The polio virus is small at 20–30 nm in diameter, the measles virus is much larger at 150–300 nm in diameter. The nucleic acid component of a virus is the genetic material and is either DNA or RNA. It can be single or double stranded, circular or linear, non-segmented or segmented, and diploid or haploid. The amount of genetic material, sometimes known as the **genome**, ranges from less than 10 000 nucleotides in the tiny polio virus to more than 200 000 nucleotides in the herpes virus. The average human gene is about 1000 nucleotides.

The nucleic acid is contained by a protein coat called a **capsid**. Because viruses have very few genes, they cannot encode many proteins and the capsid is built of many identical sub-units called **capsomeres** that link together to form a symmetrical structures. The size and form of the capsid is determined by the shape and interaction of the capsomeres. There are two types of capsid symmetry – **helical** and **icosahedral**. The capsomeres in a helical capsid can form a tight cylindrical rod (as in TMV and rabies virus), or they can form a looser more flexible structure (as in the measles and influenza viruses). Icosahedral capsids are almost spherical polyhedral structures with 20 triangular faces, 12 vertices and 20 edges. Polio and herpes viruses have icosahedral capsids. There are some viruses which incorporate both basic structures. For example, the T4 bacteriophage has an icosahedral head and a helical tail (Fig. 6). The capsid protects the DNA or RNA of the virus when outside host cells and plays a vital role in attaching the virus to the host.

TMV causes mottling of tobacco plant leaves and weakens the plants. It is a serious problem for tobacco companies as it means reduced profits. This has stimulated funding for research into microbes affecting tobacco plants.

Fig. 6 T4 bacteriophage

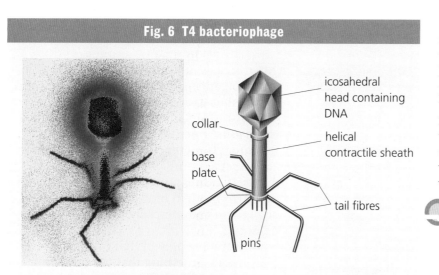

icosahedral head containing DNA

collar

helical contractile sheath

base plate

tail fibres

pins

Some viruses have an outer membranous **envelope** that is derived from the host as the newly assembled virus leaves the cell. The envelope contains proteins and virus glycoproteins. It helps the virus to penetrate the host cell membrane. The glycoproteins are also targets for the host immune system (Chapter 10). Human immunodeficiency virus (HIV), measles virus and influenza virus are enveloped viruses.

10 **Summarise the similarities and differences between bacteria and viruses.**

False colour transmission electron micrographs of the herpes virus and the rabies virus. The herpes virus has an icosahedral capsid (orange) surrounded by an envelope (orange and green) with a fringe of surface spikes. The rabies virus is bullet-shaped with a helical capsid (yellow) around which is an envelope (red).

Key ideas

- Fungi have eukaryotic cells. Some fungi, the yeasts, are single cells, others are multicellular organisms. Fungi can be clearly seen with a light microscope, including internal structures like the nucleus.

- Bacteria are prokaryotes. With a light microscope it is possible to see four basic shapes: cocci, bacilli, spirilla and vibrios.

- Bacteria are also referred to as Gram-negative or Gram-positive according to how their walls react to Gram's stain. Gram-negative bacteria have a thinner but more complex wall than Gram-positive bacteria. Some bacteria are covered with a capsule, and some have flagella for movement.

- The plasma membrane inside the bacterial cell is often folded into mesosomes or thylakoids. Genetic material is in an area called the nuclear zone. Plasmids also contain genes.

- Viruses can only be seen with an EM and consist of a core of nucleic acid within a protein coat. The coat or capsid is made of repeating sub-units called capsomeres arranged either helically or icosahedrally. Some viruses, like the T4 bacteriophage, have both arrangements.

- Viruses can only replicate within a living host cell. Viruses that attack bacteria are called bacteriophages.

1.7 Microscopes and biotechnology

Fig. 7 Asexual reproduction in yeast

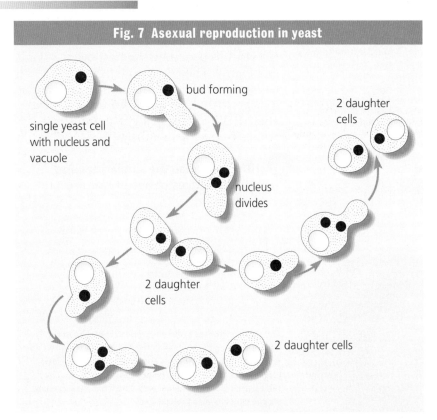

single yeast cell with nucleus and vacuole

bud forming

nucleus divides

2 daughter cells

2 daughter cells

2 daughter cells

When John Keats, a young English poet, had tuberculosis (TB) in 1820 there was no treatment other than to go somewhere where 'the air was better'. Keats went to Rome where he died in 1821. In 1908, a vaccine for TB was developed and in 1944, streptomycin – an antibiotic active against the bacterium that causes TB – was isolated from its microbial source.

Microscopes not only enabled us to see microorganisms for the first time, they also enabled us to count the number of organisms in particular cultures by using a specialised microscope slide called a **haemocytometer** (Fig. 8). From this grew an understanding of growth patterns. Understanding growth patterns is essential to much modern biotechnology. Microbes are grown commercially for one of two reasons:

- we want a supply of that organism;
- we want something that the organism produces while it is growing (Table 3).

Growth and asexual reproduction

A single yeast or bacterial cell produces two daughter cells when it divides (Fig. 7). These in turn produce four cells, then eight, sixteen, thirty-two and so on (Table 4). This continued doubling of numbers is called an **exponential increase** in population. The population descended from each cell after a number of generations of growth in favourable conditions can be estimated by the equation:

population in the nth generation = 2^n

So, after four generations the population will be:

$$2^4 = 2 \times 2 \times 2 \times 2$$
$$= 16 \text{ cells}$$

Table 3 Some important products from microorganisms

Product	Microorganism
yoghurt and fermented milk products	*Lactobacillus* and *Streptococcus* spp.
vinegar	*Acetobacter aceti*
antibiotics	*Actinomycetes* and various fungi
lactic acid	*Lactobacillus* spp.
steroids	*Mycobacteria*
enzymes	*Bacillus* spp.
beer and wine	*Saccharomyces cerevisiae*
soy sauce (shoyu)	*Aspergillus oryzae*
vitamins	various yeasts
single cell protein	*Fusarium graminearum*

Table 4 Growth of a microbial colony			
Time hours	Number of cells in colony	Time hours	Number of cells in colony
0	1	3.0	64
0.5	2	3.5	128
1.0	4	4.0	256
1.5	8	4.5	512
2.0	16	5.0	1024
2.5	32		

11 In Table 4, how many cells would there be after another 5 hours?

Counting cells

When cells get into a suitable environment, there is a brief period in which the cells adapt to their new conditions. Then the cells divide every 30–60 minutes or so for as long as conditions remain favourable. Favourable conditions include a suitable temperature, an adequate supply of nutrients and the absence of accumulated waste products. The cell population is measured using a haemocytometer at specific time intervals (Fig. 8). Counts are usually done in triplicate and an average count is then calculated.

Fig. 8 Equipment for culturing a population and performing a total cell count

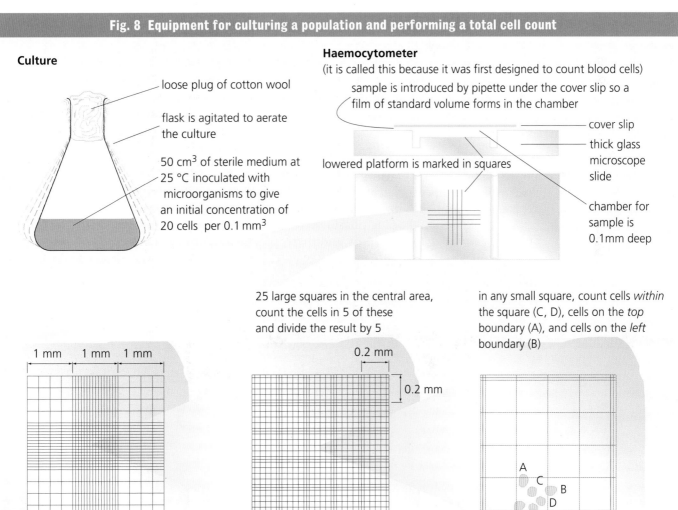

Culture

loose plug of cotton wool

flask is agitated to aerate the culture

50 cm³ of sterile medium at 25 °C inoculated with microorganisms to give an initial concentration of 20 cells per 0.1 mm³

Haemocytometer
(it is called this because it was first designed to count blood cells)

sample is introduced by pipette under the cover slip so a film of standard volume forms in the chamber

cover slip

thick glass microscope slide

lowered platform is marked in squares

chamber for sample is 0.1mm deep

1 mm   1 mm   1 mm

25 large squares in the central area, count the cells in 5 of these and divide the result by 5

0.2 mm

0.2 mm

in any small square, count cells *within* the square (C, D), cells on the *top* boundary (A), and cells on the *left* boundary (B)

A
C
B
D

when small squares have a triple rule along one side, the cell boundary is the *middle* line on the top and left sides, and the *inside* line on the bottom and right sides

Colorimetry provides an alternative method. The more cells there are in a culture, the more **turbid** (cloudy) it is, and the more light it absorbs. Samples of the culture are taken at regular intervals and the absorbance of the samples measured in a colorimeter. Cell counts are also made on the samples. Absorbance can then be plotted against cell numbers (Fig. 9). This plot is called a **calibration curve** and it can be used to convert future absorbance readings of similar cultures to the total number of cells in that sample. For viable cell counts, see Chapter 2, p. 25.

Population growth patterns

For most microbes, there are four phases of population growth (Fig. 10).

In the lag phase, the cells are active but there is little increase in number. The cells take in water, synthesise ribosomes and produce enzymes. The length of this phase depends on the medium used and whether or not the cells were growing in a similar medium before. At first, large cells are produced but the **generation time** (the life span of a cell) gets shorter as the cells reproduce at a smaller size.

In the exponential or log phase, nutrients are in plentiful supply and there is ample space. The cells are very active and reproduce at the fastest rate. This is called the log phase because if the logarithm of the number of cells is plotted against time, a straight line is obtained. When the cells are multiplying at their maximum rate they are said to be in a state of **balanced growth**. In every generation there is a doubling of cell components, and all measures of cell growth (increase in dry weight, DNA content and protein content) increase in the same proportion. The **carrying capacity** is the maximum population an environment can support.

In the stationary phase, the cells alter the culture medium as they grow. Nutrients become depleted and there is a fall in pH as carbon dioxide, acids and other metabolites build up. The reproductive rate falls and cells die in greater numbers leaving only those better able to survive in the increasingly difficult conditions. This is known as **environmental resistance**.

In the death phase, more cells die than are produced, so the number of living cells declines. The causes of cell death include starvation, shortage of oxygen, and toxicity of the environment due to waste products.

Factors affecting growth

Factors called **limiting factors** influence the growth of cells in culture:
- nutrient availability;
- temperature;
- pH;
- oxygen;
- build up of toxic material.

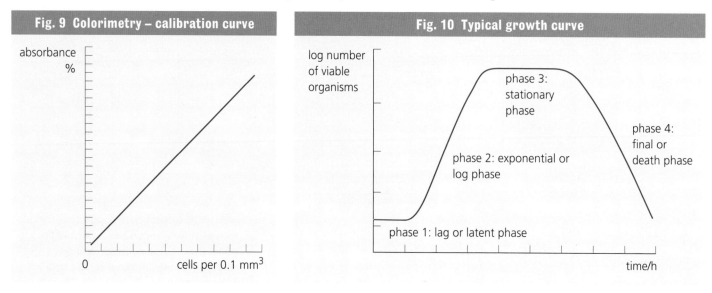

Fig. 9 Colorimetry – calibration curve

absorbance %

0   cells per 0.1 mm³

Fig. 10 Typical growth curve

log number of viable organisms

phase 3: stationary phase

phase 2: exponential or log phase

phase 4: final or death phase

phase 1: lag or latent phase

time/h

Fig. 11 Changes in cell numbers and pH of a population over 40 hours

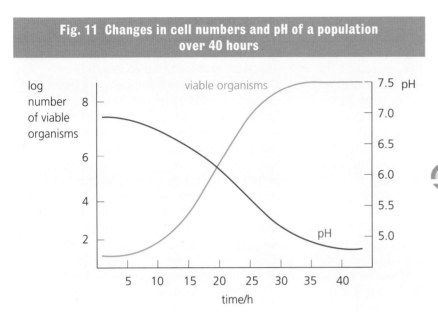

A microbial population increases logarithmically until one or more limiting factors inhibit growth. For instance, when the concentration of an essential nutrient (carbon, hydrogen, oxygen, nitrogen, sulphur or phosphorus) is increased, growth increases until the effect of one or more of the other factors causes the growth rate to tail off.

12a In Figure 11, assuming there is plenty of nutrient and the temperature is favourable, what do you think is causing the pH to drop?

b Relate the changes in the growth curve from 10 to 20 hours and from 30 to 40 hours to pH changes.

1.8 Commercial biotechnology

Commercial production of microorganisms used to be by **batch culture** – a culture was set up and after a period for growth it was harvested. A more recent method is to grow the organisms in **continuous culture** – a long-term operation over many weeks, during which time nutrient medium is added as fast as it is used and the overflow is harvested (Fig. 12).

13 How do you think the apparatus in Figure 12 works?

Fig. 12 Apparatus for continuous culture

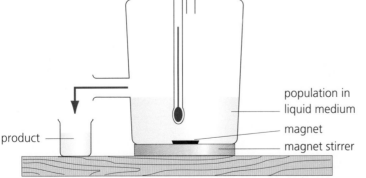

Making wine is one of the oldest biotechnologies of all and has changed very little over the centuries except in scale. Yet great estates and much wealth rest on the simple fact that single-celled yeasts can turn grape juice into wine.

Biotechnology is the use of biological agents to produce or process some other material. It has been practised for thousands of years, but the name and the scale on which it is now practised are new. Many of the early techniques were batch processes for producing or preserving food. Today, both batch and continuous processes are used in the food industry (Chapters 2–4, 6). Healing is another aspect of microbial action that ancient civilisations practised and modern techniques have continued to exploit (Chapters 7–12). However, we also now use microorganisms for purposes that are new, for instance in biological washing powders (Chapter 5), in diagnosis (Chapter 11), and in producing medicines and food (Chapters 4–6, 11).

Tomorrow's world

It is over 300 years since van Leeuwenhoek first saw the world of microorganisms on which we now depend so heavily. Biotechnology has brought us vaccines, medicines, and more reliable methods of fermenting food and drink. Microbiologists are ready to move into a world of genetically engineered microbes that can make anything from human immunity proteins to biodegradable plastics. But is this advisable? Do we really know where we are going? There are ethical questions to consider as well as the scientific and economic ones.

14 '**Genetic engineering**' **is a term that frightens many non-scientists. Why do you think this is so?**

Key ideas

- Cells in a culture can be counted using a microscope and a haemocytometer.

- There are four phases to a growth curve. In the latent phase, cells are getting used to where they are. In the exponential phase, cells are growing and dividing very rapidly. In the stationery phase there are so many cells that they are affecting the medium. In the death phase, more cells die than are produced.

- Growth is affected by nutrient availability, temperature, pH, and available oxygen. These are called limiting factors and an unfavourable level of any of them can slow down or stop growth.

- Commercially, continuous culture is used to produce microorganisms. When microbes are used to produce something else, the process involved may be batch or continuous culture.

Fermenting food and drink

CAMRA is the Campaign for Real Ale. Members of CAMRA are convinced that traditional methods of brewing and storing beers create beers with better flavours. They call these beers 'real ales'. They say that although modern brewing processes produce large quantities of beers and lagers more cost-effectively, they are gassy, low quality drinks. Where do you stand in the traditional methods versus new technologies argument?

2.1 Learning objectives

After working through this chapter, you should be able to:

- **explain** the importance of monitoring the quality of raw materials used in food and drink fermentations;

- **use** dilution plating and total viable count techniques;

- **explain** the difference between primary and secondary metabolic products.

- **describe** the importance of yeast in biotechnology;

- **relate** the nutritional requirements of yeast to the feed stocks used to produce beers and breads;

- **describe** the development of soured milks, including yoghurt, as dairy products;

- **list** the organisms used in fermented dairy products;

- **list** the factors that affect the growth of bacteria in milk.

2.2 Traditional fermented foods

People have been brewing and baking and making cheese and yoghurt for thousands of years. These processes involve **fermentation** – using microorganisms to **metabolise** a carbon **substrate** under **anaerobic conditions**, i.e. in the absence of oxygen. Biotechnologists have extended this definition of fermentation to include **aerobic conditions**, i.e. when oxygen is present (Fig. 1). This means that the definition of fermentation now includes all commercial productions using microbes. Some producers still use traditional fermentation methods, but many now produce fermented foods and drinks on a massive scale using modern biotechnological methods. Whatever the method, the basis of the fermentations remains the same: microorganisms produce metabolites that change the original foodstuff into a more valuable fermented product. Crucial to the quality of the fermented product are:

* the type of microorganism;
* the quality of the raw material;
* and, some say, whether the fermentation is carried out by traditional or modern methods.

The first fermentations were probably accidental; for example, if fruit is left in warm and moist conditions, microbes on the skin grow and ferment the fruit. Whether a fermented food is regarded as acceptable or spoiled is a matter of taste.

Many civilisations used fermentation to preserve foods. In the fermented form the foods did not 'go off' so quickly and could be stored. This is very valuable in hot countries where some foods rapidly become inedible; preserved foods can be eaten when fresh food is not available. But one fermentation product is consumed for its intoxicating effects as well as for its flavour – alcohol. Ethanol is popular but it affects brain processes and can alter mood, balance, heart rate and other physiological functions.

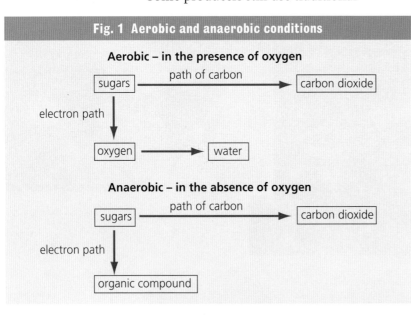

Fig. 1 Aerobic and anaerobic conditions

Aerobic – in the presence of oxygen

sugars → (path of carbon) → carbon dioxide

electron path ↓

oxygen → water

Anaerobic – in the absence of oxygen

sugars → (path of carbon) → carbon dioxide

electron path ↓

organic compound

The production of fermented fruit juices and vinegar began before 3000 BC, and there is good evidence that vines were cultivated before 2000 BC. This Roman ceiling shows the harvesting and treading of grapes for wine. Beer appears to have been developed later, the Sumerians, Babylonians and Egyptians all record brewing beer around 200–300 BC.

Q1 Why do you think the UK has laws forbidding the sale of alcohol to under-18s?

Q2 Why was fermentation important for early civilisations?

Foods produced on a commercial scale by microbes include:
* tempe and shoyu (soy sauce) from soy beans;
* beers from cereal;
* breads from cereal flour;
* yoghurt and cheese from milk.

2.3 Soy beans

Tempe is popular in Indonesia, Surinam and New Guinea (Fig. 2). It must be eaten soon after fermentation has reached a level where the tempe is solid. Later, ammonia is produced and gives the food an unpleasant taste.

Q 3 What are some of the changes that occur during the fermentation of soy beans to produce tempe?

Q 4 Tempe has one unusual characteristic for a fermented food. What is it?

Fig. 2 Soy bean processing for tempe and shoyu

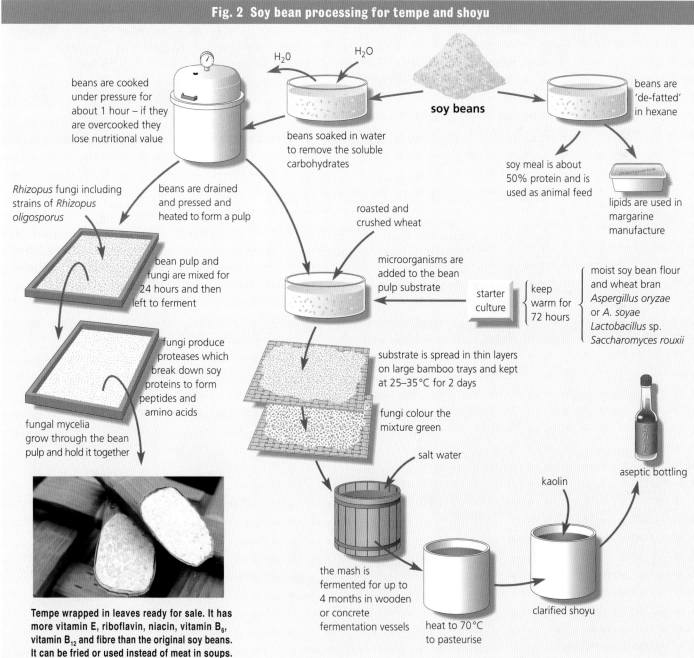

H_2O

H_2O

soy beans

beans are cooked under pressure for about 1 hour – if they are overcooked they lose nutritional value

beans soaked in water to remove the soluble carbohydrates

beans are 'de-fatted' in hexane

soy meal is about 50% protein and is used as animal feed

lipids are used in margarine manufacture

Rhizopus fungi including strains of *Rhizopus oligosporus*

beans are drained and pressed and heated to form a pulp

roasted and crushed wheat

bean pulp and fungi are mixed for 24 hours and then left to ferment

microorganisms are added to the bean pulp substrate

starter culture

keep warm for 72 hours

moist soy bean flour and wheat bran
Aspergillus oryzae or *A. soyae*
Lactobacillus sp.
Saccharomyces rouxii

fungi produce proteases which break down soy proteins to form peptides and amino acids

substrate is spread in thin layers on large bamboo trays and kept at 25–35°C for 2 days

fungal mycelia grow through the bean pulp and hold it together

fungi colour the mixture green

salt water

kaolin

aseptic bottling

the mash is fermented for up to 4 months in wooden or concrete fermentation vessels

heat to 70°C to pasteurise

clarified shoyu

Tempe wrapped in leaves ready for sale. It has more vitamin E, riboflavin, niacin, vitamin B$_6$, vitamin B$_{12}$ and fibre than the original soy beans. It can be fried or used instead of meat in soups.

Soy sauce is also called shoyu. There are many varieties and soy sauces are common in China, Japan, Vietnam, Korea, the Philippines and Thailand. In some cases the soy beans are mixed with wheat or rice or both in order to alter the final taste and alcohol content. The production of shoyu is thought to have started in the sixth century AD.

5 What affects the final flavour of shoyu?

6 Why is it important not to cook the soy bean substrate too much?

No Japanese meal is complete without a bottle of shoyu. It has been estimated that the average consumption of shoyu per person in modern Japan is about 10 dm³ per year.

2.4 Yeasts and biotechnology

Yeasts are probably the most important microorganisms used in biotechnology. They are cultured on a very large scale to provide sufficient stocks for a number of industries.

Yeasts are used:
- as a food substance in their own right;
- to produce beers, ales, lagers and wines;
- in bread manufacture;
- to produce alcohol as a biofuel.

Fig. 3 Ethanol production and biomass production

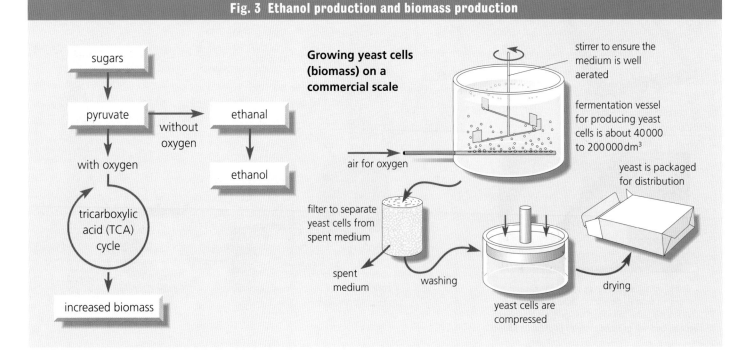

24

Fig. 4 Primary and secondary metabolite production

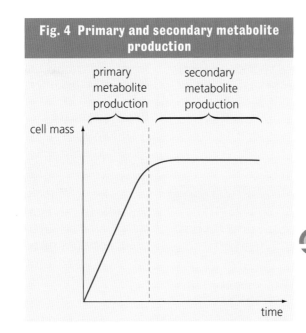

The growth conditions needed when using yeast in fermentations differ from the growth conditions needed to produce yeast cells in large numbers. For fermentations, the yeast cells are grown anaerobically so that the sugars are eventually converted to alcohol and carbon dioxide. When yeasts are grown for **biomass** i.e. to promote maximum growth of the cells, this is done in aerobic conditions. The same or similar types of yeast are used, but the growth vessel is stirred and aerated to provide oxygen (Fig. 3).

7 Explain why growing yeast aerobically does not produce alcohol.

Primary and secondary metabolites

Substances that are produced by organisms as part of the normal pattern of growth and synthesis of cell materials are called **primary metabolites**. These substances include amino acids, nucleotides, enzymes and the end products of fermentations such as acids and ethanol. Many vital biotechnological products, including foods and drinks, are dependent on the production of primary metabolites.

Microorganisms also produce chemicals that are not directly involved in normal growth and production of cell materials. These substances are called **secondary metabolites** and many are very valuable to us. For example, most antibiotics are secondary metabolites. So, primary metabolites are formed during active growth; secondary metabolites are produced after the main growth period is completed (Fig. 4).

Counting the cells

Microbial cell counts can be made by a total viable count using the dilution plate technique (Fig. 5). In this method, the individual colonies that are counted are assumed to have arisen from a single cell. The number of colonies is multiplied by the dilution factor to give a total viable cell count for the original sample. Compare this technique with the total count using a haemocytometer (Chapter 1, p. 17).

Fig. 5 Total viable count using dilution plate technique

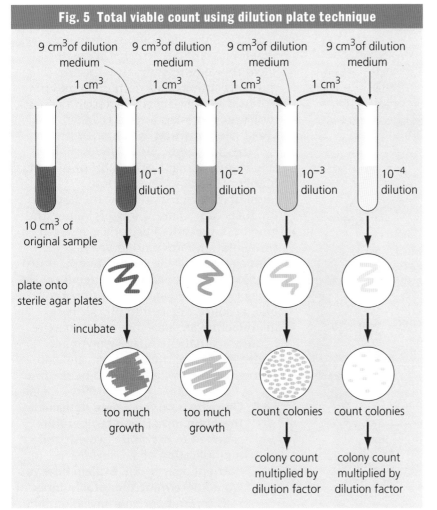

2.5 Brewing and baking

The most commonly used species of yeast, especially *Saccharomyces cerevisiae*, have been cultured for hundreds of years. Over this time, the most desirable strains for particular functions such as brewing and baking have been selected. Now, genetic engineering is also used to develop improved strains that produce more alcohol or grow at lower temperatures.

Brewing yeasts

Alcoholic drinks are produced from a number of raw materials including cereals, fruits and sugar crops (Fig. 6). Only a very few types of yeast are used; they are strains of *S. cerevisiae* or closely related species. These yeasts are not able to hydrolyse starch, so if a starch-rich nutrient is to be used, enzymes such as amylase must be added to break down the starch to sugars. In brewing, the yeast cells use a range of sugars:

- sucrose;
- fructose;
- maltose;
- maltotriose.

Alcoholic fermentations are mainly anaerobic, but some oxygen is needed to allow the yeast to synthesise specific nutrients such as some fatty acids and sterols not provided by the raw material. However, if oleic acid or olenoic acid is added, the yeasts can grow well with no oxygen.

Like most fungi, yeasts prefer slightly acidic environments with a pH of 4–6. At higher pH values, there is more fermentation but some unwanted by-products can occur. At low pH values, the growth of unwanted bacteria is reduced. Fermentation rates tend to increase with temperature, but the specific temperature selected for a fermentation depends on the type of yeast used and the nature of the final product. The conditions for beer manufacture are a balance between conditions that encourage growth and multiplication of the organism, and those that encourage the production of alcohol.

Q 8 Describe how you would determine the optimum pH and temperature required to maximise growth and multiplication of *S. cerevisiae* in nutrient agar broth. Explain how you would determine the total number of cells throughout your investigation.

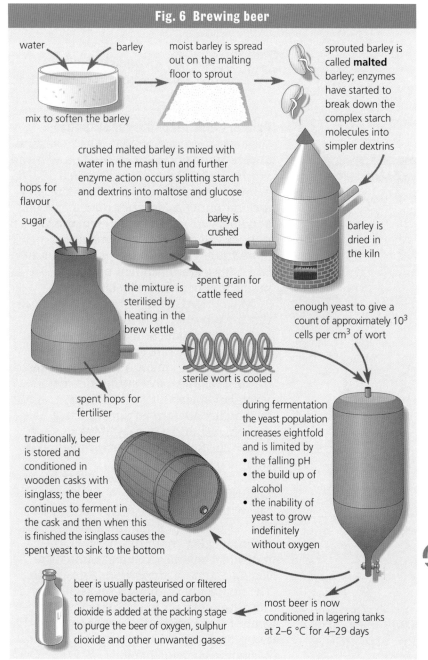

Fig. 6 Brewing beer

water — barley

mix to soften the barley

moist barley is spread out on the malting floor to sprout

sprouted barley is called **malted** barley; enzymes have started to break down the complex starch molecules into simpler dextrins

crushed malted barley is mixed with water in the mash tun and further enzyme action occurs splitting starch and dextrins into maltose and glucose

hops for flavour

sugar

barley is crushed

barley is dried in the kiln

the mixture is sterilised by heating in the brew kettle

spent grain for cattle feed

enough yeast to give a count of approximately 10^3 cells per cm^3 of wort

sterile wort is cooled

spent hops for fertiliser

traditionally, beer is stored and conditioned in wooden casks with isinglass; the beer continues to ferment in the cask and then when this is finished the isinglass causes the spent yeast to sink to the bottom

during fermentation the yeast population increases eightfold and is limited by
- the falling pH
- the build up of alcohol
- the inability of yeast to grow indefinitely without oxygen

beer is usually pasteurised or filtered to remove bacteria, and carbon dioxide is added at the packing stage to purge the beer of oxygen, sulphur dioxide and other unwanted gases

most beer is now conditioned in lagering tanks at 2–6 °C for 4–29 days

Brewing

Beer is brewed from barley, but barley contains complex starches and proteins that are not suitable for fermentation. The processes of **malting** and **mashing** serve to break down the complex starches and proteins to simple sugars. The liquid so produced is call **wort** and contains glucose (Fig. 6).

Any oxygen in the wort is quickly used up and adding oxygen later in the process affects flavour. After fermentation the yeast should settle out. Modern yeast strains clump together (**flocculate**) and this aids settling which in turn helps the clearing of the beer. Chilling will also make the beer clear faster. Other methods of clearing beer include filtration, centrifugation, or adding a **fining agent** such as isinglass to settle the yeast. All beers require a period of storage and conditioning after fermentation – this period is called **lagering**.

Traditionally, there is a distinction between top-fermenting yeasts (e.g. *S. cerevisiae*) and bottom-fermenting yeasts (e.g. *S. uvarum*). The top-fermenters function best at 15–22 °C and rise to the top of the fermenter vessel near the end of the fermentation time so they can be skimmed off. Top-fermenters are used in ale production. The bottom-fermenters function best at 8–15 °C and sink to the

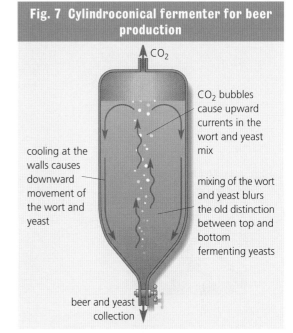

Fig. 7 Cylindroconical fermenter for beer production

CO_2

CO_2 bubbles cause upward currents in the wort and yeast mix

cooling at the walls causes downward movement of the wort and yeast

mixing of the wort and yeast blurs the old distinction between top and bottom fermenting yeasts

beer and yeast collection

bottom of the fermenter vessel towards the end of the fermentation process. Bottom-fermenters are used to brew beer and lager. In modern fermenters, the distinction between top and bottom fermenters has become less clear (Fig. 7).

The brewing industry is of major importance worldwide; over 84 billion dm^3 of beer are produced each year. New developments in automation and strain improvement have increased yields, but the basic process would still be familiar to the early Babylonians, Sumerians and Egyptians of 4000 years ago.

9 What is the difference between top and bottom fermenting yeast?

10 Why are the fermenters used in brewing beers not highly aerated and stirred?

Baking yeast

Bread is a very ancient food and, like beer and wine, its manufacture depends on yeast cells. The yeast is usually called baker's yeast and is a strain of *S. cerevisiae*. The production of bread is an aerobic process that produces more carbon dioxide and less alcohol than brewing (Fig. 8).

This brewery uses traditional methods to produce a popular real ale.

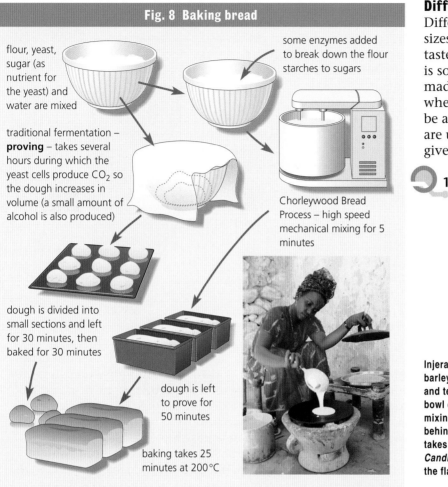

Fig. 8 Baking bread

flour, yeast, sugar (as nutrient for the yeast) and water are mixed

some enzymes added to break down the flour starches to sugars

traditional fermentation – **proving** – takes several hours during which the yeast cells produce CO_2 so the dough increases in volume (a small amount of alcohol is also produced)

Chorleywood Bread Process – high speed mechanical mixing for 5 minutes

dough is divided into small sections and left for 30 minutes, then baked for 30 minutes

dough is left to prove for 50 minutes

baking takes 25 minutes at 200°C

Different breads

Different types of breads have different sizes, shapes, composition, texture and taste. One of the most interesting of these is sourdough bread. Sourdough breads are made from rye flour or a mixture of rye and wheat flour. The yeasts for this bread must be acid tolerant because lactic acid bacteria are used to create acidic by-products which give the bread its sour flavour.

Q 11 Ethanol and carbon dioxide are produced when bread dough rises. The carbon dioxide creates the texture of the bread, what happens to the ethanol during the rest of the bread-making process?

Injera is a bread-like product made from maize, wheat or barley in Ethiopia and Somalia. It has a similar appearance and texture to pancakes. The flour is mixed with water in a bowl called a bohaka. Bohakas are not fully cleaned after mixing because traces of fermented dough that are left behind help to inoculate the following batch. Fermentation takes 1–3 days and the fermenting organism is the yeast *Candida guilliermondii* but other bacteria and fungi add to the flavour.

Key ideas

- Traditional fermentations have been known and used for thousands of years.

- Traditionally, fermentation is the process by which microorganisms metabolise carbon under anaerobic conditions. Biotechnologists have extended this definition to include aerobic conditions.

- Soy beans are fermented by fungi to produce tempe and shoyu.

- Yeast cells are grown anaerobically to convert sugar to alcohol and carbon dioxide. Yeasts are grown aerobically for biomass.

- Traditional and modern methods of fermentation are both in existence.

- In baking and brewing, the development of improved strains of *S. cerevisiae* has resulted in greater yields.

- There has been much research into factors affecting beer conditioning and packaging.

- Traditional ales are brewed using methods that would be familiar to a brewer from almost any time in history.

- There are many different sorts of bread depending on the raw materials used.

2.6 The dairy industry

Fermented dairy products have been known all over the world for many centuries. Many thousands of different products are now consumed for their range of distinctive flavours without people realising that fermentation was originally a way to preserve milk (Table 1). The production processes for all fermented milk products are very similar and involve the same basic biotechnology but modern dairies draw on state-of-the-art developments.

Table 1 Some fermented milk products	
Product	Fermenting organism
yoghurt	*Streptococcus thermophilus*
	Lactobacillus bulgaricus
kefir	*Lactobacillus lactis*
	Lactobacillus bulgaricus
	Saccharomyces spp.
sour cream	*Lactococcus* sp.
	Leuconostoc sp.
buttermilk	*Lactococcus lactis*
	Leuconostoc cremoris
butter	*Lactococcus lactis*

Milk as a raw material

The milk most commonly used in dairy products in the UK is cows' milk (Table 2).

Table 2 Composition of cows' milk		
Component	Whole milk g dm^{-3}	Skimmed milk g dm^{-3}
carbohydrate	55	58
protein	40	42
fat	45	1.3
calcium	1.4	1.5

Cows' milk is widely used because it contains many minerals and vitamins that are essential for humans, and 98% of the protein can be digested by humans. However, some people are allergic to cows' milk. These people are usually recommended to try goats' milk. The carbohydrate in milk is lactose and is sometimes called 'milk sugar'. Lactose is broken down to glucose and galactose by lactase. Milk is an **emulsion** of tiny fat droplets in water but fat floats in water so there is a tendency for the fat droplets to collect at the top of the container.

Some milk proteins are used in other industries (Table 3).

Table 3 Uses of milk proteins	
Protein	Use
lactalbumin (whey protein)	food source
lactoglobulin (whey protein)	food source
caseinogen	production of junket and hard cheeses
casein	reacted with menthanal to make casein plastic

12 Where is most of the fat in a bottle of milk found? Why?

Contamination problems

Milk is an excellent growth medium for many bacteria and this can cause problems. Bacteria like *Escherichia coli* ferment the lactose in the milk to produce a mixture of acids and gases that spoil the milk. *E. coli* is one of the **coliform bacteria**. These are Gram-negative bacteria that normally grow in the colon and are passed out in faeces. Some coliform bacteria are human **pathogens**, so they cause illness as well as ruin milk supplies. There are two main ways that coliform bacteria enter milk supplies:

- poor handling techniques, for example farm workers not washing their hands;
- contamination by cow faeces.

Moulds are also a problem. Mould growth gives milk a musty aroma and looks very unsightly. Moulds are spread by air-borne spores so contamination of milk usually indicates poor storage conditions. Yeasts can cause problems in milk products by converting the sugars in milk to alcohol and carbon dioxide.

Table 4 Heat treatments for milk		
Heat treatment	Conditions	Resultant shelf life of milk
pasteurisation	71.7 °C for at lest 15 seconds	4–5 days
sterilisation	104–113 °C for 15–40 minutes	2–3 months
ultra heat treatment (UHT)	132.2 °C for at least 1 second	several months
high temperature short time (HTST) – also called flash pasteurisation	72 °C for at least 15 seconds or 90 °C for at least 1 second	4–5 days
low temperature long time (LTLT)	63 °C for at least 30 minutes	4–5 days

Quality control of milk

The dairy industry carefully monitors the quality of the milk it uses. Milk is usually sterile when it leaves the cow, but it is easily contaminated. Properly collected and handled raw milk should contain fewer than 10 000 microorganisms per cm^3 of which fewer than 700 per cm^3 are coliform bacteria. If milk is carelessly handled or dirty vessels are used, the number of coliforms alone may rise to over 10 000 per cm^3. Milk is heat treated before any dairy process to reduce the risk of contamination by microorganisms (Table 4).

13 Describe how you would investigate the keeping qualities of milk that has had different types of heat treatment.

14 It is possible to buy completely untreated milk. What are some of the health hazards of drinking this milk?

Testing milk quality

Most dairies routinely test milk supplies by:
- bacterial counts on milk samples from farm and dairy storage tanks;
- checking taste and smell;
- monitoring the percentage of water and the fat content;
- monitoring the antibiotic content.

There are two common hygiene tests used, the resazurin test and the total viable bacterial count (Fig. 9). The resazurin test is often called the rejection test as it is quick and easy to do on milk samples as they arrive at the dairy. The result is known within a few minutes and if the milk is contaminated it can be rejected straight away.

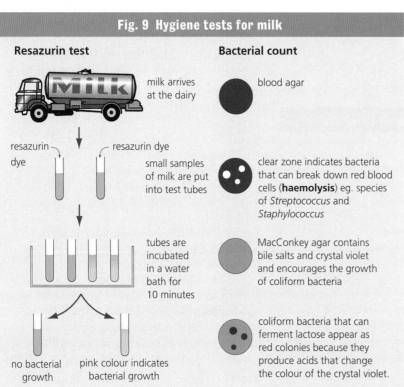

Fig. 9 Hygiene tests for milk

Resazurin test

milk arrives at the dairy

resazurin dye / resazurin dye

small samples of milk are put into test tubes

tubes are incubated in a water bath for 10 minutes

no bacterial growth / pink colour indicates bacterial growth

Bacterial count

blood agar

clear zone indicates bacteria that can break down red blood cells (**haemolysis**) eg. species of *Streptococcus* and *Staphylococcus*

MacConkey agar contains bile salts and crystal violet and encourages the growth of coliform bacteria

coliform bacteria that can ferment lactose appear as red colonies because they produce acids that change the colour of the crystal violet.

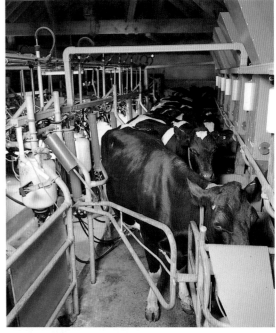

In order to reduce the risk of milk being contaminated with potentially harmful microorganisms, most farmers clean milking equipment with hyperchlorite or iodine detergents and milk is stored under refrigerated conditions.

Yoghurt

Yoghurt and its related products are extremely popular and have many different names throughout the world.

Yoghurt is made from concentrated milk (Fig. 10). Concentrating the milk by skimming and adding back the solids as powder enables manufacturers to standardise the starting point of their process despite small variations in the quality of the milk supply. The lactose in the milk is fermented to lactic acid by lactic acid bacteria, for example *Lactobacillus bulgaricus*. The lactic acid gives yoghurt its tangy flavour. It is essential that no antibiotic has entered the milk (for example, from a cow being treated for infected udder) as the antibiotic could inhibit the growth of the starter culture.

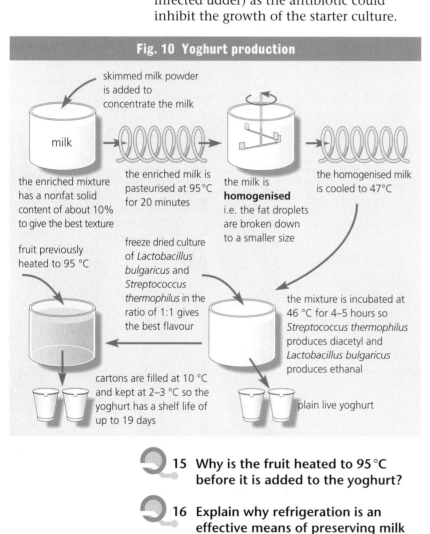

Fig. 10 Yoghurt production

skimmed milk powder is added to concentrate the milk

milk

the enriched mixture has a nonfat solid content of about 10% to give the best texture

the enriched milk is pasteurised at 95 °C for 20 minutes

the milk is **homogenised** i.e. the fat droplets are broken down to a smaller size

the homogenised milk is cooled to 47 °C

fruit previously heated to 95 °C

freeze dried culture of *Lactobacillus bulgaricus* and *Streptococcus thermophilus* in the ratio of 1:1 gives the best flavour

the mixture is incubated at 46 °C for 4–5 hours so *Streptococcus thermophilus* produces diacetyl and *Lactobacillus bulgaricus* produces ethanal

cartons are filled at 10 °C and kept at 2–3 °C so the yoghurt has a shelf life of up to 19 days

plain live yoghurt

15 Why is the fruit heated to 95 °C before it is added to the yoghurt?

16 Explain why refrigeration is an effective means of preserving milk and yoghurt.

Kefir is a foaming fermented milk drink that has been produced in the Caucasus Mountains since 4000 BC. Many Russian farm workers in this area claim to be between 100 and 120 years old and attribute their long life to kefir.

Goats' milk yoghurt is usually made traditionally. The milk is concentrated by boiling then a small amount of a previous batch of yoghurt is added and the mixture is left to ferment.

Cheese manufacture

There is a tremendously wide range of cheeses, almost every part of the world has its own characteristic cheese. Making cheese is different from making yoghurt because:

- the microorganisms used are different;
- the milk must be separated into solid and liquid components prior to cheese making (Fig. 11).

The starter culture used depends on the type of cheese being manufactured. Specific starter cultures determine the biochemical reactions that take place. For cheddar cheese the culture is a mixture of several strains of *Streptococcus lactis* and *S. cremoris*. Mixtures of starter cultures are particularly useful as the bacteria in these starter cultures can be infected with a virus that causes them to die. If a starter contains only one sort of bacterium, an infection would mean that all was lost. With mixed cultures there is a good chance that some of the strains will be immune to the bacteriophage attack.

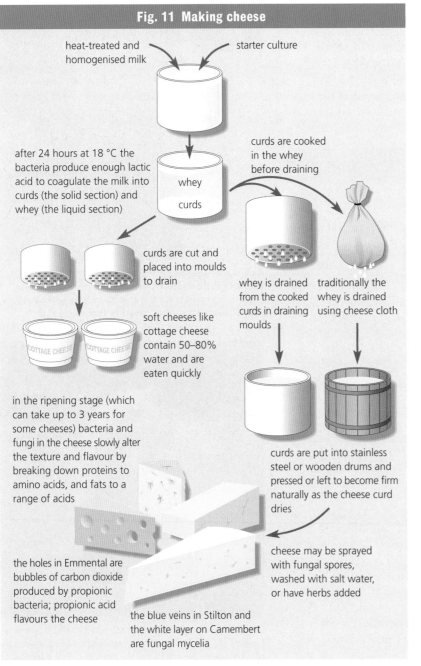

Fig. 11 Making cheese

heat-treated and homogenised milk → starter culture

after 24 hours at 18 °C the bacteria produce enough lactic acid to coagulate the milk into curds (the solid section) and whey (the liquid section)

whey
curds

curds are cut and placed into moulds to drain

soft cheeses like cottage cheese contain 50–80% water and are eaten quickly

curds are cooked in the whey before draining

whey is drained from the cooked curds in draining moulds

traditionally the whey is drained using cheese cloth

in the ripening stage (which can take up to 3 years for some cheeses) bacteria and fungi in the cheese slowly alter the texture and flavour by breaking down proteins to amino acids, and fats to a range of acids

curds are put into stainless steel or wooden drums and pressed or left to become firm naturally as the cheese curd dries

cheese may be sprayed with fungal spores, washed with salt water, or have herbs added

the holes in Emmental are bubbles of carbon dioxide produced by propionic bacteria; propionic acid flavours the cheese

the blue veins in Stilton and the white layer on Camembert are fungal mycelia

All over the world, some cheeses are made on a small scale in the kitchen while others are produced by the thousand on automated production lines.

Sometimes chymosin is added to help coagulate the milk. Chymosin is also known as bovine rennet as it is obtained from the stomachs of calves. Milk for vegetarian cheeses is coagulated using the starter culture only, or using chymosin produced by the mould, *Mucor mieleli*. Cottage cheese is coagulated using only chymosin, so it is not very acidic. This means it spoils quickly if not refrigerated.

17 **What is the difference between curds and whey?**

18 **Why are the finishing cultures, such as the fungal spores, only added towards the end of the cheese-making process?**

19 **How does the manufacture of vegetarian cheese differ from that of non-vegetarian cheese?**

Ripening can take over a year. It is the process that gives different cheeses their characteristic look and taste. Traditionally, some cheeses are ripened in caves because they are dark and have a constant temperature. In some countries, enzymes extracted from microorganisms are used to reduce the maturation time for cheddar cheese from a year to only 3 months. The enzymes promote the breakdown of proteins in the cheese to amino acids more quickly than the natural ripening process. This commercial example of new developments being used to make traditional processes more economical is not in use in the UK.

20 a **Decide where you stand in the traditional versus modern debate and give your reasons.**
   b **Do you think it is acceptable that you often have to pay more for traditionally produced cheese or bread or yoghurt than for the versions that are made in modern factories?**

Key ideas

- Fermented dairy products have been known all over the world for many centuries.

- Fermenting milk was originally a means of preserving it.

- The production processes for all fermented milk products are very similar and involve the same basic biotechnology.

- Even the most modern plants for food and drink fermentations still rely on basic biotechnology known for thousands of years.

- Many different organisms can grow by utilising a substrate such as milk, yet some spoil the milk and others ferment it to make desirable substances.

- Products such as cheeses vary enormously depending on the nature of the microorganisms used in manufacture.

- Careful control of raw materials and starter cultures, and of production, storage and handling methods is vital to prevent contamination.

Adding acids

Citrus fruits contain 7–9% citric acid and there are some small factories in Mexico and South America that extract the acid from unripe lemons and limes. Many tonnes of fruit are used.

Many people like tangy drinks and lots of people put vinegar on their chips. The 'tang' comes from citric acid and vinegar is the common name for ethanoic acid. Many food additives are acids – but don't worry, acids are not necessarily dangerous. For many years citric acid was extracted from citrus fruits – oranges, lemons and limes. As demand for citric acid increased it was manufactured chemically, but there was also interest in other approaches. Scientists discovered in 1893 that **filamentous fungi** produced citric acid and in 1929 the world's first biotechnological citric acid was put on sale. Sales have increased ever since (Table 1). Vinegar has always been made by bacteria acting on wine, beer or cider.

Table 1 World production of citric acid	
Year	Tonnes of citric acid
1910	2 000
1929	5 000
1953	50 000
1979	220 000
1994	350 000

3.1 Learning objectives

After working through this chapter, you should be able to:

- **list** some of the uses of citric acid and vinegar;

- **recall** that growth may be affected by oxygen availability;

- **describe** techniques for investigating oxygen requirement;

- **recall** that industrial fermentations may be aerobic or anaerobic;

- **explain** the distinction between submerged and surface fermentations;

- **relate** the structure of an industrial fermenter to the growth requirements of the microorganisms;

- **explain** how environmental factors may change during fermentation, and how these changes may be monitored and controlled;

- **describe** the major problems involved in scaling from pilot laboratory models to full scale industrial production;

- **describe** the industrial production of citric acid and vinegar;

- **list** some microorganisms that are cultured on an industrial scale to make useful products.

3.2 Uses of citric acid and vinegar

Citric acid and vinegar are sold in bulk and are relatively inexpensive. For example, in 1995 a kilogram of citric acid cost about 50p whereas a kilogram of vitamin B_{12} cost about £6000.

Citric acid
Citric acid is used by:
- the pharmaceutical industry;
- the food and drink industry;
- the chemical industry.

Q 1 How many of the uses of citric acid shown in the photograph have you seen most recently?

About 10% of the citric acid produced annually is used by the pharmaceutical industry, often in the form of a citrate (Fig. 1). Iron citrate is used as a preservative in ointments, tablets and blood products. During blood transfusions, the blood is

Fig. 1 Structure of citric acid and citrate

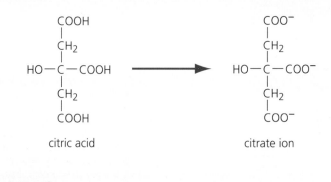

citric acid → citrate ion

Producing fizz

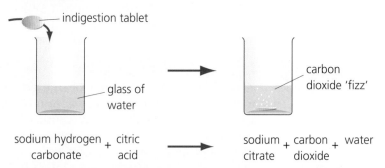

indigestion tablet

glass of water

carbon dioxide 'fizz'

sodium hydrogen carbonate + citric acid → sodium citrate + carbon dioxide + water

prevented from **coagulating** by the addition of sodium citrate.

Citric acid is used in soluble aspirin and fizzy indigestion treatments. The latter contain sodium hydrogen carbonate (bicarbonate) and citric acid which react to produce sodium citrate, water and carbon dioxide. The carbon dioxide bubbles off as the 'fizz' (Fig. 1).

The food and drink industry uses over 60% of the citric acid produced every year. Citric acid is used to:
- lower pH and so aid setting in marmalade and jam;
- give tangy flavours to confectionery, ice cream, soft drinks and fruit juice;
- help preserve food by reacting with the tiny amounts of **trace elements** that would otherwise make the food go rancid;
- prevent vitamin C from being lost during the manufacture of baby food, edible oils and dairy products.

Each year, the chemical industry uses approximately 25% of the citric acid produced. The chemical processes include:

- making anti-foam agents and water softeners;
- metal extraction;
- manufacturing detergents.

 2a Which use of citric acid is a result of its 'acidic' taste?

b Which use of citric acid depends on its ability to react with trace metals?

Vinegar

Vinegar is one of the most common food additives, it's not just for splashing on chips. World output of vinegar exceeds 1500 million dm^3 per year. It is used extensively by food manufacturers to flavour foods, to make pickles and chutneys and to preserve foods. Some people still like to drink very dilute flavoured vinegars.

Polyphosphates were added to detergents to clean away dirt and to soften the water. Unfortunately, polyphosphates cause this white pollution, so chemists looked for a chemical to do the same job but not damage the environment. Citric acid was the answer. Although it is more expensive than polyphosphates, it has now replaced them.

In 1665, the village of Eyam in Derbyshire was isolated from the neighbouring populations because plague broke out in the village. It had been brought by fleas in fabric sent from London. The Eyam villagers decided to stay within the village to prevent the plague spreading, but they had to buy food from outside traders. The villagers left money for the food in a bucket of vinegar at the village boundary. Without knowing the cause of the disease, the villagers correctly believed that the acid nature of the vinegar would sterilise the coins.

3.3 Fungal citric acid

Citric acid is produced in the **tricarboxylic acid (TCA) cycle** (Fig. 2). It is an additive to the food industry, but it is a natural product of most cells.

Many strains of fungi excrete small amounts of citric acid. Since the start of commercial citric acid production only

Aspergillus niger strains have been used and a great deal of genetic manipulation has led to the high-yield strains now in use. The only United Kingdom company producing citric acid spent years selecting and genetically manipulating over 150 000 strains. Citric acid has recently been

Fig. 2 The TCA cycle

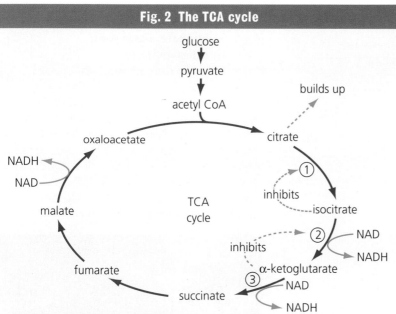

glucose
↓
pyruvate
↓
acetyl CoA

builds up ↗

oxaloacetate → citrate

NADH ↖
NAD ↖

① inhibits ----→ isocitrate

TCA cycle

malate

② NAD → NADH

inhibits ----→ α-ketoglutarate

fumarate

③ NAD

succinate → NADH

It is thought that in *Aspergillus niger*, enzyme 3 is faulty and does not efficiently catalyse the change from α-ketoglutarate to succinate. This causes a build-up of α-ketoglutarate which inhibits enzyme 2 and causes a build-up of isocitrate. The isocitrate in turn inhibits enzyme 1 and results in a build-up of citrate. This leads to the excretion of citric acid.

Aspergillus niger

Table 2 Some important aerobes and anaerobes

Microorganism	Oxygen requirement	Importance
Azotobacter spp.	obligate aerobes	free living nitrogen fixers
Bacillus spp.	obligate aerobes	industrial enzyme producers
		some cause disease e.g. anthrax
Lactobacillus spp.	obligate aerobes	ferment milk to yoghurt
Rhizobium spp.	obligate aerobes	symbiotic nitrogen fixers
Penicillium spp.	obligate aerobes	penicillin producers
Escherichia spp.	facultative anaerobes	symbiotic gut bacteria
Salmonella spp.	facultative anaerobes	cause food poisoning
Clostridium spp.	obligate anaerobes	cause disease e.g. tetanus, gangrene
Treponema spp.	obligate anaerobes	cause syphilis

produced from *Candida* species of yeast, but although this is an easier organism to culture, production has not yet reached commercial levels.

3 Study Figure 2. Which enzyme does not work well in *A. niger* strains used to produce citric acid? Why?

Anaerobic and aerobic growth

When citric acid is produced, **nicotinamide adenine dinucleotide (NAD)** is reduced to **NADH**. The NADH must be re-oxidised to NAD by a series of oxidation and reduction reactions called the **electron transfer chain**. These reactions allow hydrogen and electrons, taken from food, to pass down the electron transfer chain to a **final acceptor**. In aerobic respiration, the final acceptor is oxygen. As the hydrogen and electrons pass down the chain, **adenosine triphosphate (ATP)** is formed from **adenosine diphosphate (ADP)**.

Some microorganisms that use aerobic respiration must have oxygen as the final acceptor and are called **obligate aerobes**. There are other microorganisms that cannot survive when oxygen is present; they use an alternative final acceptor and are called **obligate anaerobes**. So, obligate aerobes are obliged to use oxygen and obligate anaerobes are obliged to avoid it. There is also a third group of microorganisms that can carry out both aerobic and **anaerobic respiration**, but they grow better in the presence of oxygen. These are called **facultative anaerobes** (Table 2). Most fungi are aerobic, but some species are facultative anaerobes.

4 How can some microorganisms grow without oxygen?

Oxygen requirement

In order to design a suitable vessel in which *A. niger* can produce citric acid on an industrial scale, it is important to know about the organism's **oxygen requirement**, i.e. whether it is aerobic, anaerobic or a facultative anaerobe. Oxygen requirement can be determined by stab culture or by molten culture (Fig. 3).

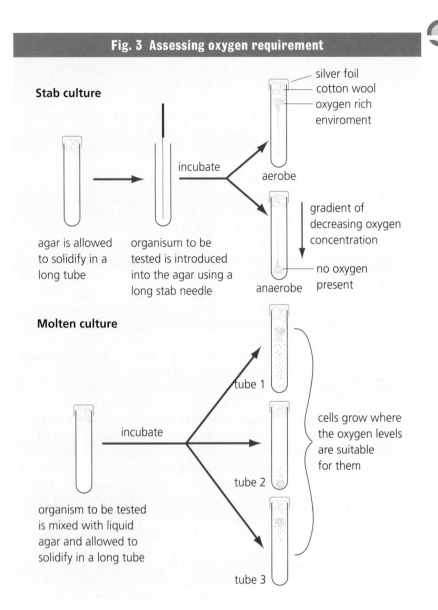

Fig. 3 Assessing oxygen requirement

Stab culture

agar is allowed to solidify in a long tube

organism to be tested is introduced into the agar using a long stab needle

incubate

silver foil
cotton wool
oxygen rich enviroment

aerobe

gradient of decreasing oxygen concentration

no oxygen present

anaerobe

Molten culture

organism to be tested is mixed with liquid agar and allowed to solidify in a long tube

incubate

tube 1

tube 2

tube 3

cells grow where the oxygen levels are suitable for them

5 Examine Figure 3 and decide which molten culture tubes contain:
a) obligate anaerobes;
b) obligate aerobes;
c) facultative anaerobes.

Fermentation is the term used by biotechnologists to describe any process by which microorganisms break down a substance (Chapter 2, p. 22). Citric acid is produced as *A. niger* breaks down glucose. Because *A. niger* is an aerobe, the production of citric acid is called an **aerobic fermentation**.

This woman is using a *biogas* **generator in Nepal. Biogas is a mixture of methane gas and carbon dioxide and is produced by** *anaerobic fermentation*. **Biogas is produced from concentrated sewage by anaerobic bacteria called the** *methanogenic bacteria*. **The process takes place in the absence of oxygen in tanks called digesters. Not only is biogas a useful and inexpensive fuel, its production from sewage is cheaper than other methods of sewage treatment.**

Key ideas

* Citric acid has many uses in the food, pharmaceutical and chemical industries.
* Vinegar is widely used by food manufacturers.
* A fault in the TCA cycle of the fungus *Aspergillus niger* leads to a build up and excretion of citric acid. This makes *A. niger* suitable for the commercial production of citric acid. Special high-yielding strains of *A. niger* have been selected and isolated.

* Obligate aerobes require oxygen for growth; obligate anaerobes cannot survive if oxygen is present. Facultative anaerobes can survive with or without oxygen, but do better with it.
* Fermentation is the process by which microorganisms break down a substance; fermentations can be aerobic or anaerobic.
* *A. niger* is an aerobe and produces citric acid by aerobic fermentation.

3.4 Fungal fermentation – citric acid

Surface culture

The first design of surface fermenter system for citric acid was developed in 1923. It used shallow porcelain trays approximately a metre square which were stacked on top of one another in dust-free rooms. Today, **surface culture** is used for about 20% of citric acid production and is carried out using acid-resistant metal trays (Fig. 4). After about 6 days at 30 °C all the sugar in the medium has been fermented by the fungus which floats on top of the medium as a thick white layer.

6 How does the surface fermentation process ensure that sufficient oxygen is available to support the growth of the fungi?

Submerged culture

About 80% of the world's citric acid is produced by submerged processes. **Submerged culture** systems take up less space than surface culture and give better control over factors such as aeration. The medium for submerged culture is a low-viscosity liquid because the fungus grows beneath the surface and it must be easy to stir and bubble air through the medium. The most commonly used carbohydrate sources are:

- potato starch (plus amylase to assist the fungal amylase in breaking down the starch to sugar);
- glucose syrups, sugar cane syrup;
- sugar cane molasses, sugar beet molasses.

The initial fermenter is filled with the sterile medium and additional nutrients are added. Sterile air is blown through. This process is called **sparging** and it creates an air-rich medium. Next the *A. niger* spores are introduced. The fungus will not survive if oxygen is deficient. Oxygen is not highly soluble in the liquid medium, and the growing organism would soon use it up, so the medium is continuously **aerated**. After about 24 hours, the mixture of medium and fungus is transferred to the main fermentation vessel. This is likely to be up to ten times the volume of the first step fermenter. The initial growth phase is to ensure that there is no contamination by unwanted organisms and to allow the fungal spores time to germinate. There are two main types of submerged process reactors (Fig. 5):

- airlift fermenters;
- stirred fermenters.

7 Study Figure 5. Describe and give reasons for the main differences between stirred and airlift fermenters.

Fig. 4 Surface culture fermentation of citric acid

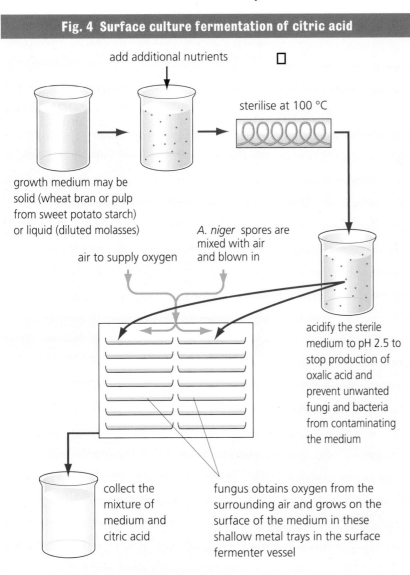

add additional nutrients

sterilise at 100 °C

growth medium may be solid (wheat bran or pulp from sweet potato starch) or liquid (diluted molasses)

A. niger spores are mixed with air and blown in

air to supply oxygen

acidify the sterile medium to pH 2.5 to stop production of oxalic acid and prevent unwanted fungi and bacteria from contaminating the medium

collect the mixture of medium and citric acid

fungus obtains oxygen from the surrounding air and grows on the surface of the medium in these shallow metal trays in the surface fermenter vessel

In both airlift and stirred systems, fermenters are made from stainless steel or coated in protective plastic to minimise the risk of corrosion by the medium which has a pH of 1–2. Corrosion damage is costly to repair and releases trace amounts of metals which inhibit citric acid production in the fermenter. Temperature, carbon dioxide and dissolved oxygen levels are constantly monitored and the level of citric acid production is checked by titration. After about 8 days, the citric acid is extracted.

8 What is sparging and what is its purpose?

The medium is likely to foam in all submerged systems, so anti-foam agents such as oils are added. It is also possible to disperse foams by mechanical agitation.

Comparing fermentation processes

In both surface and submerged culture techniques, it is important to monitor metal ions in the medium. For example, iron is needed for fungal growth, but too much iron inhibits the production of citric acid and promotes the production of oxalic acid. For optimum growth there should be about 2 p.p.m. iron, but for optimum citric acid production there should be 0.05–0.5 p.p.m. iron. Adding small amounts of copper reduces the inhibitory effect of iron so high growth and high citric acid yield can be obtained. A chemical such as ferrocyanide can also lower iron concentration by forming a complex with the iron.

There are advantages and disadvantages to both surface and submerged processes (Table 3). Surface processes are usually used in small plants; submerged processes are preferred for large-scale production.

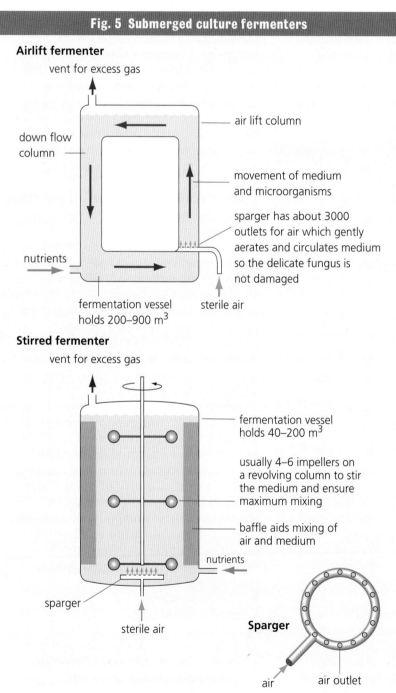

Fig. 5 Submerged culture fermenters

Airlift fermenter

vent for excess gas

air lift column

down flow column

movement of medium and microorganisms

sparger has about 3000 outlets for air which gently aerates and circulates medium so the delicate fungus is not damaged

nutrients

fermentation vessel holds 200–900 m³

sterile air

Stirred fermenter

vent for excess gas

fermentation vessel holds 40–200 m³

usually 4–6 impellers on a revolving column to stir the medium and ensure maximum mixing

baffle aids mixing of air and medium

nutrients

sparger

sterile air

Sparger

air   air outlet

Table 3 Advantages and disadvantages of surface and submerged processes	
Surface processes	Submerged processes
low investment cost for reactor	high investment cost for reactor
low energy costs	high energy costs
high labour costs	low labour costs
simple technology	complex technology
low training costs	high training costs
low overall yield	high overall yield

9 Why are submerged processes preferred for the large-scale production of citric acid?

Fermentations and scaling-up

The development of fermentation processes and the isolation of suitable strains of microorganisms to obtain a good yield of product take many years (Chapter 5, p. 58). At the same time it is necessary to develop cost-effective media, to measure any additives and their effects, to design and test the reactor and to investigate aeration, stirring, pH and growth temperature. This may lead to a fermentation system that works well in the laboratory, but that doesn't mean it will work well on a larger scale. When tonnes of microorganisms are involved they may not behave in the same way as when there are a few grams. Solving these problems and moving from a laboratory system to full-scale production is the next challenge. This is usually done in a series of carefully monitored steps, each step being a ten-fold increase on the previous one. Each time, the optimum growth conditions are determined. In this way the final fermenter size is reached.

In established industrial fermentations, it is still necessary to move through these stages to ensure that there are enough actively growing organisms to put into the final fermentation vessel. This is called **scaling-up** and without this process the time taken for the organisms to increase in number so that they efficiently ferment the material in the final vessel would make the fermentation uneconomic (Fig. 6).

 10 **List some of the factors that might influence the design and size of a fermenter vessel.**

Fig. 6 Scaling-up

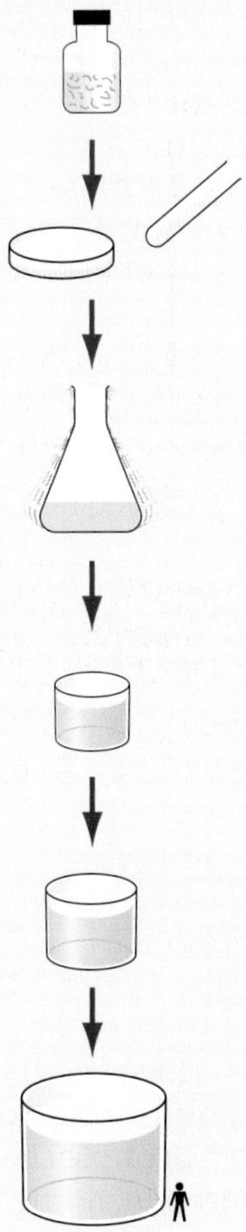

Starter culture
These freeze-dried bacterial or fungal cells have been carefully selected and isolated. The freeze-dried cells are kept in a tiny glass vial and can be stored in a refrigerator for many years. It is essential that great care is taken in handling the starter culture because contamination can be very expensive to correct later.

Agar plate or slope culture
These are kept at the optimum growth conditions for organism
long enough to provide a colony sufficient to inoculate the starter vessel.

Starter vessel or shake flask
This is kept at the optimum growth conditions for the particular strain used for 1–3 days (for bacteria) or 1–3 weeks (for slower-growing fungi). As bacteria can double their population every 1–2 hours, this starter phase increases the number of bacterial cells very quickly.

Seed fermenter
For the production of pectinases and proteases the starter vessel doesn't produce enough microbial cells to add to the main vessel. This seed fermenter is an intermediate vessel with a capacity of approximately 10 000 dm^3. The starter culture is poured in and grown on for a further 1–3 days (for bacteria) or 1–3 weeks (for fungi). This produces a tenfold increase in the total number of organisms.

Secondary fermenter
This intermediate vessel is required when the final fermentation vessel is so big that the seed fermenter cannot provide enough organisms to efficiently inoculate the medium in it.

Production fermenter
This is the main fermentation vessel and is where the production phase of the fermentation takes place. This vessel is about ten times larger than the vessel used for the previous stage.

Downstream processing

Recovering the product of a fermentation from the mixture in the fermenter is called **downstream processing** (Fig. 7).

 11 Lemons and limes contain citric acid (photograph on p. 34). Why don't we just crush up lemons to get the citric acid we need for industry?

Fig. 7 Downstream processing of citric acid

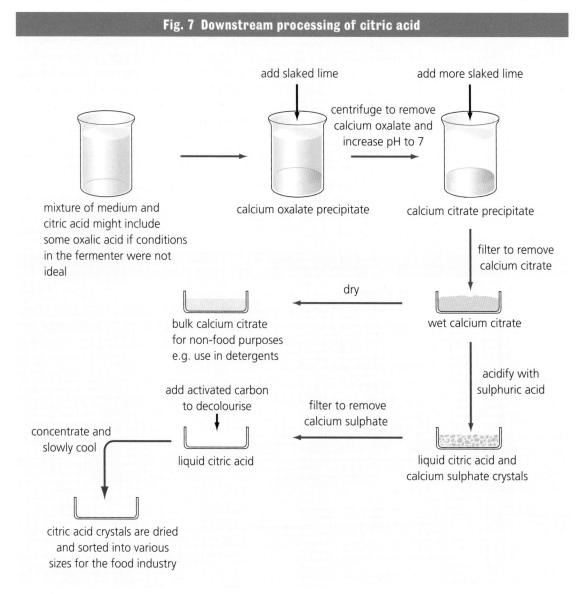

mixture of medium and citric acid might include some oxalic acid if conditions in the fermenter were not ideal

add slaked lime

centrifuge to remove calcium oxalate and increase pH to 7

calcium oxalate precipitate

add more slaked lime

calcium citrate precipitate

filter to remove calcium citrate

wet calcium citrate

dry

bulk calcium citrate for non-food purposes e.g. use in detergents

acidify with sulphuric acid

add activated carbon to decolourise

filter to remove calcium sulphate

liquid citric acid and calcium sulphate crystals

concentrate and slowly cool

liquid citric acid

citric acid crystals are dried and sorted into various sizes for the food industry

3.5 Bacterial fermentation – vinegar

Ethanoic acid is the organic acid that gives vinegar its taste. Ethanoic acid is also known as acetic acid and is formed by bacterial oxidation of ethanol. The word 'vinegar' comes from the French *vin aigre* which means 'sour wine'. However, the name is now applied to any sour liquid produced from fermented alcohol. There are several types of vinegar depending on the kind of alcohol fermented (Table 4).

Table 4 Main types of vinegar	
Name of vinegar	Characteristics
wine vinegar	made from wine and can be white or red
	some types (e.g. one made in Orleans) are stored in oak casks to add flavour
malt vinegar	made from beer
	dark colour and strong flavour
cider vinegar	made from cider
	light colour with a distinctive taste
distilled vinegar	very strong (12%)
	colourless
	often used for pickling and preserving foods

Vinegars are made from all kinds of alcoholic drink. There is an enormous range of colour and flavour. Some vinegars have added herbs, some are later coloured and flavoured by fruit.

Fig. 8 Bacterial production of ethanoic acid

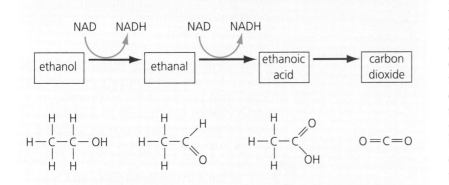

 12 Why is it impossible to produce vinegar from cola drinks?

Ethanoic acid is produced by many types of bacterium (Fig. 8). However, it is only produced in sufficient quantities for commercial production of vinegar by the acetic acid bacteria. Two closely related genera of acetic acid bacteria are used, the *Acetobacter* and *Gluconobacter*.

The strains of *Acetobacter* that are used commercially are:
- *Acetobacter aceti*;
- *A. pasteurianus*;
- *A. peroxidans*.

The *Gluconobacter* tend to oxidise the ethanoic acid to carbon dioxide and water, but one strain, *Gluconobacter oxydans*, does not and so has commercial value. These strains are acid tolerant and produce ethanoic acid by aerobic fermentation.

13 Why is acid tolerance important for commercially useful acetic acid bacteria?

The fermentation of ethanol to ethanoic acid generates NADH which is re-oxidised to NAD via the electron transfer chain. This generates ATP but requires oxygen. If oxygen is not present in sufficient amounts, the cells die; correct aeration of the fermentation is vital.

Trickle generator

Vinegar has been made from wine for as long as wine has been produced. Wine left in large, flat, open vats slowly developed a thin layer of bacteria on the surface; the bacteria turned the wine to vinegar. The production method for vinegar did not change much for hundreds of years, but during the nineteenth century methods that we would recognise as industrial were developed. One of these, a modified surface technique called the trickle generator process was further developed about 1949 (Fig. 9). The bacteria in the generator convert approximately 90% of the alcohol to ethanoic acid. After collection, the vinegar is usually stored for a while to enhance the flavour.

Fig. 9 Trickle generator

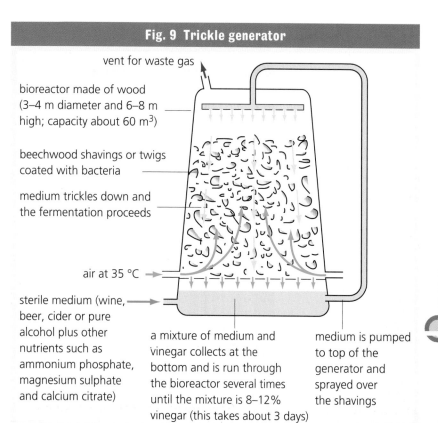

vent for waste gas

bioreactor made of wood (3–4 m diameter and 6–8 m high; capacity about 60 m³)

beechwood shavings or twigs coated with bacteria

medium trickles down and the fermentation proceeds

air at 35 °C

sterile medium (wine, beer, cider or pure alcohol plus other nutrients such as ammonium phosphate, magnesium sulphate and calcium citrate)

a mixture of medium and vinegar collects at the bottom and is run through the bioreactor several times until the mixture is 8–12% vinegar (this takes about 3 days)

medium is pumped to top of the generator and sprayed over the shavings

Fig. 10 Submerged fermenter for ethanoic acid production

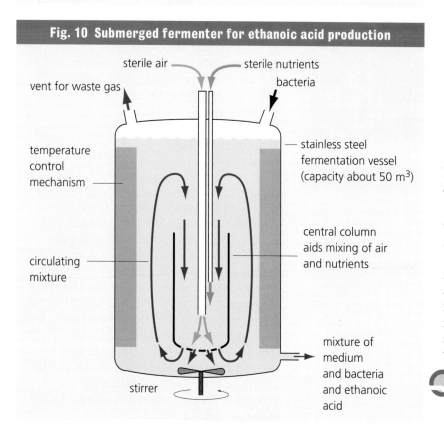

sterile air

sterile nutrients

bacteria

vent for waste gas

temperature control mechanism

circulating mixture

stirrer

stainless steel fermentation vessel (capacity about 50 m³)

central column aids mixing of air and nutrients

mixture of medium and bacteria and ethanoic acid

Vinegar for use in the home is still produced by the method first evolved when this advert was released – about 100 years ago.

14 Wine, beer and cider contain substances other than alcohol. Why are additional nutrients necessary when pure alcohol is used in the trickle generator?

Submerged fermentation

Vinegar is very cheap so there has been little interest in research and development to develop new equipment, processes or strains for producing it. However, pure ethanoic acid for use in industry is manufactured by a chemical process which starts with ethene as the raw material. Lately, the price of ethene has been rising steadily. At the same time, there have been general improvements in fermentation processes and feedstuffs have got cheaper. This all means that new techniques of submerged bacterial fermentation may be used to produce industrial ethanoic acid on a large scale in future.

The fermenters used for submerged fermentation of alcoholic brews to ethanoic acid (Fig. 10) are very similar to those used in citric acid production. The process requires careful monitoring to maintain steady production, but it is more efficient than the trickle generator.

15 Make a list of similarities and differences between the production of citric acid and vinegar.

3.6 Other food additives

Citric acid and vinegar are natural substances that are now produced in large amounts by fermentations and added to food and drink. Sales of food additives such as acidulants, thickeners and flavourings produced by fermentations are expected to exceed £2 billion by the year 2000 – the production of food additives is big business. Although many food additives are produced by fermentations (Table 5), many others are produced chemically or come from natural sources such as plant extracts. Much research is going on to improve microbial strains and production techniques so that more and more food additives can be produced by fermentations.

In 10 years it may be that most food additives come from fermentations. This is already causing some marketing problems in countries such as the USA where there are very strict laws about package labelling. Ingredients now have to be described as 'from a microbial source' and some advertising and marketing managers are worried that people will associate 'microbes' with 'germs'.

Table 5 Some food additives produced by fermentations	
Name	Uses
Amino acids	
L-glutamate	flavour enhancer
L-lysine	feed additive (cereal supplement)
Vitamins	
vitamin B$_{12}$	pernicious anaemia treatment
riboflavin	food colouring (E101)
Fats and oils	
linoleic acid	dietary supplement/prostaglandin production
Carbohydrates	
xanthan	gums and gelling
curdlan	gels and low calorie salad dressings
dextran	stabiliser in ice cream and confectionery

Q 16 How would you reassure a friend who doesn't like the idea that food contains 'things from microbes' that additives from microbial fermentations are safe?

Key ideas

- Commercial fermentations use either surface culture or submerged culture.

- Most citric acid is produced by submerged culture. Sparging supplies air.

- Scaling-up to large-scale production is done in a series of steps. Each step is a 10% increase on the step before.

- Scaling-up in established fermentations ensures there are enough actively growing organisms for the last fermentation vessel.

- Downstream processing is the name for recovering citric acid from the final mixture.

- Vinegar has always been produced from wine by bacterial oxidation of ethanol to ethanoic acid. Household vinegar is produced in the trickle generator.

- Ethanoic acid for industry is produced chemically, but in future ethanoic acid might be produced on a large scale by submerged fermentation.

- Many other food additives are produced by bacterial fermentation and the list is likely to go on getting longer.

More than mushrooms

I created the Rank film company and in the 1960s I was also Chairman of a large group of food production companies called Rank Hovis McDougall. At that time it was becoming clear that the world population was increasing faster than people had ever thought likely and scientists thought a worldwide protein famine would result if nothing was done. I decided to do something so I asked my research director, Dr. Arnold Spicer, to develop a program that would lead to the production of a new protein source.

When my research and development team took on the challenge we didn't think it would take about 20 years and cost many millions of pounds before our product was available. We hoped to find a way of growing a source of protein on starch because that was an abundant by-product from many of the Rank Hovis McDougall companies. We also hoped that the process would finance itself – or even make a profit. You can buy our product now, but the challenge isn't over yet.

J. Arthur Rank and (inset) Dr Arnold Spicer.

4.1 Learning objectives

After working through this chapter, you should be able to:

- **list** examples of microorganisms that are cultured on an industrial scale to make useful products;

- **explain** how to find the optimum growth conditions for fungi;

- **recall** the methods used to measure the growth of fungi in a range of liquid media;

- **relate** the nutritional requirements of fungi to the feedstocks used in mycoprotein and penicillin production;

- **understand** that penicillin is an example of a secondary metabolite;

- **describe** the industrial production of mycoprotein and penicillin and some of the uses of these products;

- **relate** the fermentation processes for the production of mycoprotein and penicillin to the growth requirements of the microorganisms used;

- **describe** the downstream processes used to separate mycoprotein and penicillin from the fermentation medium.

4.2 Initial research

Dr. Spicer and his team began with a number of criteria:

- since starch was cheap and available, the process must use starch as a starting point;
- the substrate, intermediate products and final product must be safe to eat;
- the product must be rich in protein;
- the product must taste good;
- the product should have a texture as close to meat as possible;
- the cost of the process should be as low as possible.

Microorganisms are the most efficient producers of protein (Fig. 1) so the team decided to look for a filamentous fungus that would grow rapidly on starch and produce cells with a high protein content.

1 a What other advantages does protein production by microorganisms have over protein production using cattle and chickens?

b How does a rapidly growing, filamentous fungus fit the criteria that Dr Spicer's team listed?

Rank Films distributed this movie. Dr. Spicer's team decided that the new product should resemble meat because meat had a high reputation as a protein source and it was thought that the fibrous texture would retain flavourings.

Microorganisms have been used as food for centuries – mushrooms have been eaten all over the world for hundreds of years. However, many people still associate bacteria and fungi with disease and decay. Despite this, the development team decided to press ahead and this brave decision has led to a range of microbial products on the shelves of most supermarkets. These products include vegetarian crispbakes, pies, and burgers. Along the way, the research and development teams had to solve many problems in fermentation, handling and harvesting.

Literature search

An important stage in research and development is to find out everything already known about the problem you are working on. Research scientists have to have an up-to-date knowledge of the science most relevant to their work, and top up this knowledge by searching books and journals for the latest ideas. This is called a **literature search**. Dr. Spicer and his colleagues looked for information about fermentations with fungi to learn all there was to know about the processes. At the time, the best known fermentation using a filamentous fungus was the process producing the first antibiotic, penicillin.

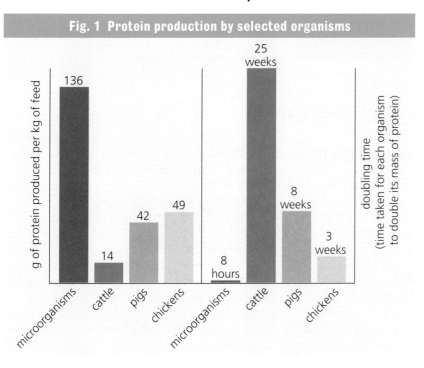

Fig. 1 Protein production by selected organisms

g of protein produced per kg of feed: microorganisms 136, cattle 14, pigs 42, chickens 49

doubling time (time taken for each organism to double its mass of protein): microorganisms 8 hours, cattle 25 weeks, pigs 8 weeks, chickens 3 weeks

Penicillins are produced by many different fungi, including *Penicillium* and *Aspergillus*. This *Penicillium* sp. is growing on a nectarine.

Learning from penicillin

Ernest Duchesne, a French medical student, first noted and described penicillin in 1896. However, this finding was forgotten and penicillin was rediscovered by Alexander Fleming in 1928. Fleming noticed that the fungus *Penicillium notatum* produced a chemical that killed a number of bacteria without harm to the fungus itself.

There were years of development between Fleming's discovery and the widespread use of penicillin. The original strain of *Penicillium* had a yield of penicillin of only 0.0012 g dm^3. Within 20 years, the yield was 50 g dm^3. The main change that led to this massive improvement was the switch to *Penicillium chrysogenum*. During the 1960s and 1970s, hundreds of new strains of *P. chrysogenum* were investigated following **mutation treatment** with X-rays, UV radiation or chemical mutagens, but since then work has concentrated on examining genetic crosses between mutants. Many high-yielding strains have resulted.

Penicillin research was stepped up during the Second World War and by 1941 was used to treat soldiers so that their wounds did not become infected.

4.3 Finding the microorganism

Dr Spicer's research team realised that the key to microbial protein production lay in the isolation of suitable organisms. So a massive **screening** program was started to look at fungi in various soil samples. In 1967, the team decided to search a sports field in Kent. They chose this ground because it is close to a factory producing wheat starch. At times the field was sprayed with surplus starch so they thought there was a good chance of fungi able to break down starch flourishing there. A *Penicillium* that could grow on starch was found and

was investigated but the total protein content of the cells was less than 30%. The organism was also difficult to grow under continuous culture. The search was widened in 1969 and soil from many countries was screened. These samples included ones from tropical regions because they might contain fungi with a rapid growth rate and able to survive high temperatures. In the end, the fungus actually chosen was found in soil from a garden only a few miles from the team's laboratories.

Isolating the fungus

During the original search, 20–30 strains were isolated from each soil sample (Fig. 2). These were purified by removing some spores and re-plating onto fresh agar plates. Eventually, following work on over 3000 strains, a possible organism was selected. It was a strain of *Fusarium graminearum*.

 2 How might the screening tests for a fungus for antibiotic production differ from screening tests for a filamentous fungus for protein production?

Having isolated a possible organism, Dr Spicer's team prepared **stock cultures** and **working cultures** from the **master cultures** (Fig. 3). The master cultures are freeze-dried (**lyphophilised**) and stored and subsequent stock cultures are made from these. This means that the original master cultures are not used up too quickly. Stock cultures are cultures that are maintained in the laboratory for study and reference. Working cultures are made from the stock culture by adding it to 400 cm³ of suitable medium and incubating for 96 hours. Working cultures are the ones actually used in fermentation processes. Both stock and working cultures can be stored at –20 °C for up to a year. They can be quickly thawed when needed.

3 What are some of the advantages of preparing and maintaining stock and working cultures rather than using master cultures?

Fig. 2 Isolation procedure

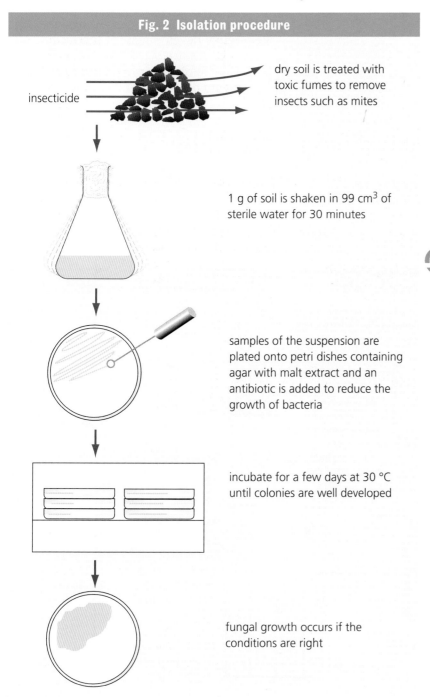

insecticide

dry soil is treated with toxic fumes to remove insects such as mites

1 g of soil is shaken in 99 cm³ of sterile water for 30 minutes

samples of the suspension are plated onto petri dishes containing agar with malt extract and an antibiotic is added to reduce the growth of bacteria

incubate for a few days at 30 °C until colonies are well developed

fungal growth occurs if the conditions are right

Fig. 3 Hierarchy of cultures

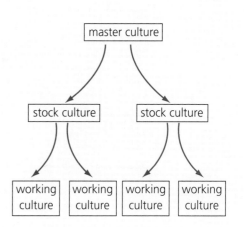

master culture

stock culture   stock culture

working culture | working culture | working culture | working culture

Fig. 4 Deuteromycete life-cycle

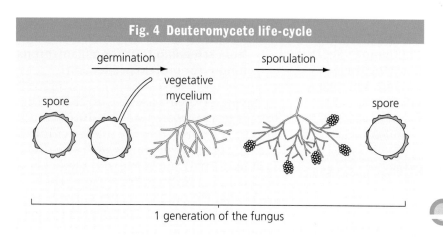

germination → vegetative mycelium → sporulation

spore → spore

1 generation of the fungus

The genus *Fusarium* belongs to the Deuteromycetes. These have a relatively simple life cycle (Fig. 4). It is important to keep checking that the plating and re-plating processes used to prepare usable cultures do not lead to subsequent generations that are different from the original. All biotechnological processes need to ensure that the organisms used as working cultures are identical to the master cultures used for the original development of products.

4 How might poor handling ruin the purity of a culture?

4.4 Industrial production of penicillin

Penicillin is produced by submerged fermentation in main fermentation vessels with a volume of 40–200 dm³ (Fig. 5). *Penicillium chrysogenum* is aerobic and needs a high oxygen level at all stages of the fermentation. This rules out the larger-scale fermenters because they are difficult to aerate effectively. Temperature must also be monitored. The optimum temperature range for penicillin production is 25–27 °C.

Fig. 5 Penicillin fermentation and downstream processing

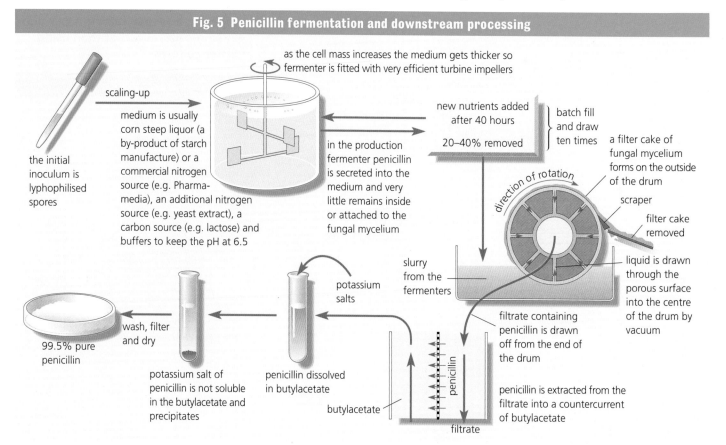

scaling-up

the initial inoculum is lyphophilised spores

medium is usually corn steep liquor (a by-product of starch manufacture) or a commercial nitrogen source (e.g. Pharma-media), an additional nitrogen source (e.g. yeast extract), a carbon source (e.g. lactose) and buffers to keep the pH at 6.5

as the cell mass increases the medium gets thicker so fermenter is fitted with very efficient turbine impellers

in the production fermenter penicillin is secreted into the medium and very little remains inside or attached to the fungal mycelium

new nutrients added after 40 hours

20–40% removed

batch fill and draw ten times

a filter cake of fungal mycelium forms on the outside of the drum

direction of rotation

scraper

filter cake removed

slurry from the fermenters

liquid is drawn through the porous surface into the centre of the drum by vacuum

filtrate containing penicillin is drawn off from the end of the drum

penicillin is extracted from the filtrate into a countercurrent of butylacetate

potassium salts

penicillin dissolved in butylacetate

butylacetate

penicillin

filtrate

potassium salt of penicillin is not soluble in the butylacetate and precipitates

wash, filter and dry

99.5% pure penicillin

Coloured scanning electron micrograph of the mycelium and fruiting bodies of *Penicillium* sp.

Approximately 10% of the carbon source is used in penicillin production, the rest is used for energy and growth. Most of the penicillin is produced after about 40 hours, i.e. after the main increase in fungal biomass (Fig. 6).This production phase can be extended to up to 180 hours by carefully adding additional nutrients to the fermenter. **Continuous fermentation** is the process of continually adding nutrient so that more product is obtained. This is not successful for penicillin production because the fungus uses the nutrient to grow, not to produce penicillin. A compromise position is used in which 20–40% of the contents of the fermentation vessel is removed and then fresh medium is added. This is called 'batch fill and draw' and may be carried out up to ten times before the fermentation vessel is completely emptied for cleaning.

5 a Study Figure 6. How long does it take for the carbon source to be used up?
  b Describe the relationship between biomass increase and penicillin production.

6 a Why are additional substances added to the penicillin fermenters after 40 hours, even though little further cell growth will occur?
  b Why is batch fill and draw more successful in producing penicillin than continuous fermentation?

Downstream processing

Initially, the cost of extracting penicillin from the medium was high compared to other costs of production, but efficient downstream processing has now reduced this. Penicillin is still expensive to produce, but downstream processing is not the main cost. This is unusual because, generally, the expensive fermentation products are the ones with high downstream processing costs (Table 1).

In the modern downstream processing of penicillin, the slurry that is run off from the main fermentation vessel is first filtered and then the filtrate is treated (Fig. 5).

Fig. 6 Utilisation rate of carbon source in penicillin production

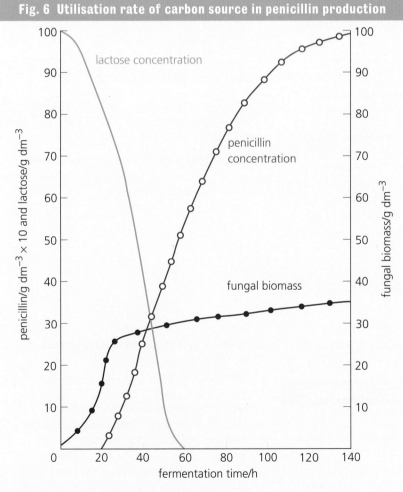

Source: adapted from Queene and Swartz in *Economic Microbiology*, Ed. Rose, London Academic Press, 1979

51

Table 1 Downstream processing costs as proportion of selling price		
Product	Approximate selling price in 1994/£ t^{-1}	Downstream processing cost as % of sale price
yeast biomass	300	20
xanthan	6 000	50
citric acid	960	30–40
ethanol	300	15
monosodium glutamate	1 500	30–40
penicillin G	18 000	20–30

7 a What do you think Dr Spicer's team could learn from the processes involved in producing penicillin?

b Where do you think the differences between penicillin production and protein production are likely to occur?

Key ideas

- Microorganisms are the most efficient producers of protein.

- You can find out about a new scientific process by studying a similar one. You start with a literature search.

- To find a microorganism with specific characteristics, you start a screening program. Since many fungi can be isolated from soil, this is a good place to start.

- Master cultures are cultures of the original isolated organisms; they are freeze-dried and stored. Stock cultures are made from master cultures. Working cultures are made from stock cultures. Care must always be taken that subsequent generations of an organism are identical to the master culture.

- Penicillin is produced by a fungus; it kills certain bacteria but does not harm the fungus.

- Penicillin is produced by submerged aerobic fermentation.

- Penicillin production occurs mostly after the main increase in fungal mass.

- Penicillin production is not suitable for continuous fermentation; the batch fill and draw method is used.

- The downstream processing of penicillin is efficient and is not the most expensive part of the production process.

4.5 Producing mycoprotein

The culture medium is a carbohydrate nutrient plus additional components (Table 2). Other substances added to the growth medium are ammonium phosphate, biotin (a vitamin), and the sulphates of zinc, copper and iron.

During the early development of the process, batch culture was used. This involved preparing a sterile medium, seeding it with *Fusarium*, waiting for the mycelium mass to increase and then stopping the fermentation to harvest the product. The development team realised that because they wanted a continuously increasing biomass, a continuous process would be possible and would have

Table 2 Sources of carbohydrate for mycoprotein production		
Carbohydrate	Source	Processing required
starch	wheat, potato, bean, maize	careful hydrolysis using food-grade enzymes is necessary
molasses (very cheap)	sugar cane or beet	inorganic salts and gums must be removed
glucose syrup	wheat, maize, potato	iron level must be determined because too much iron causes the mycoprotein to look grey

economic advantages. In particular, the number of close-downs and sterilisation phases would be reduced and the organisms could be grown at maximum rate for longer. Closing down an industrial process is expensive, and keeping production costs low was one of the original criteria set by Dr Spicer's team. The use of continuous culture is the major difference between the production of penicillin and mycoprotein.

Measuring growth rate

In order to make decisions about different culture types and growth conditions, it is necessary to measure the rate of growth of the fungus effectively and accurately. In the laboratory, this can be done in two ways:
- measure the mycelium diameter on a petri dish;
- measure the dry mass of mycelium.

One way to find the optimum temperature for the growth of *Fusarium* is to inoculate identical petri dishes of growth medium with spores of the fungus and incubate the plates at different temperatures but for the same time. A number of plates are incubated at each temperature and the experiment is repeated on a number of occasions. When the plates are examined, the diameter of each fungal colony is measured. A mean value for the diameter at each temperature is calculated. The temperature that shows the largest mean mycelial diameter is the optimum temperature for growth.

To determine the optimum level of nutrient concentration or optimum pH of the medium, the dry mass of the mycelium is measured. The net mass is determined by harvesting the mycelium from the liquid culture by centrifugation or filtration and then drying, usually overnight in an oven at 100–105 °C. The dried mycelium is then weighed. The optimum growth conditions are those which yield the greatest mass of mycelium.

Great care must always be taken when working with spore-forming fungi because the spores can easily become airborne and then inhaled. This can cause medical problems.

8 Why is the dry mass determination of mycelium growth in liquid medium preferred over the mycelium diameter method for determining optimum conditions for growth factors and pH?

9 How you would carry out an investigation to determine whether glucose, lactose, sucrose or maltose gave the best growth rate of *Penicillium* at 30 °C?

Scaling-up for mycoprotein production

Dr Spicer's development team made the first attempt at continuous culture with a filamentous organism in a pilot plant that was opened in 1971. The plant allowed constant automatic monitoring of all aspects of the fermentation process. It was possible to measure pH, media flow rates, temperature, nutrient types and concentrations, gas levels and aeration rates. Every result was logged and analysed. Many of the developments made at the pilot plant are now standard practice for control in highly automated fermentation processes in many biotechnology industries. The mycoprotein product was tested on a range of animals and, finally, humans. No ill effects from eating the mycoprotein have been recorded.

10 Briefly compare the advantages and disadvantages of batch and continuous culture.

By the early 1980s, the development team had a fully trialled pilot process and an apparently safe and efficiently produced mycoprotein. Before further scaling-up of production, the project had to receive clearance from the Ministry of Agriculture, Fisheries and Food (MAFF) for mycoprotein to be sold as a food; the application to MAFF ran to two million words. Permission to sell mycoprotein as a food was granted in 1985 and a range of new problems had to be faced. As important as the technical and scientific problems of moving to large-scale production were those of finance: the investment required was huge.

Raising the capital needed was proving very difficult when they had a stroke of luck. Fossil fuel prices rose in the 70s and early 80s and the increased cost of methane from the North Sea meant that a process for producing single cell protein (called Pruteen) for feedstuffs developed by ICI was no longer financially viable. The development of Pruteen had started at the same time as that of mycoprotein and had already reached large-scale production stages. In 1983 ICI gave up Pruteen production but still had the fermentation technology and plant available. In 1984 a partnership was announced between Rank Hovis McDougall and ICI and the large-scale production of mycoprotein was started. The company was called Marlow Foods.

Mycoprotein production today

The fermentation process used today is continuous (Fig. 7). The rate of flow of medium into the fermenter is very important. It is calculated by determining the **dilution rate**. This is the time taken for a volume of medium equal to the size of the fermenter to pass through the fermenter. It is given the symbol h and is measured in hours. A dilution rate of 20 h in a fermenter of 1500 dm^3 means that it takes 20 hours for 1500 dm^3 of medium to

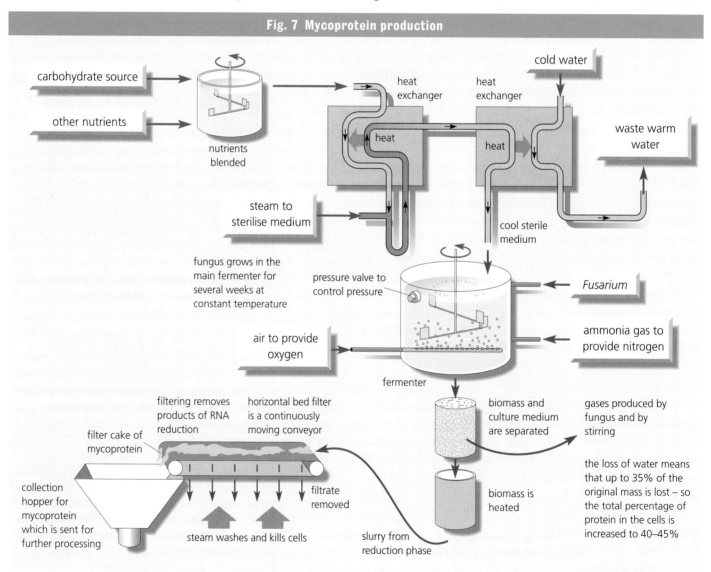

Fig. 7 Mycoprotein production

carbohydrate source

other nutrients

nutrients blended

heat exchanger

heat exchanger

cold water

heat

heat

waste warm water

steam to sterilise medium

cool sterile medium

fungus grows in the main fermenter for several weeks at constant temperature

pressure valve to control pressure

Fusarium

air to provide oxygen

ammonia gas to provide nitrogen

fermenter

filtering removes products of RNA reduction

horizontal bed filter is a continuously moving conveyor

biomass and culture medium are separated

gases produced by fungus and by stirring

filter cake of mycoprotein

collection hopper for mycoprotein which is sent for further processing

filtrate removed

biomass is heated

the loss of water means that up to 35% of the original mass is lost – so the total percentage of protein in the cells is increased to 40–45%

steam washes and kills cells

slurry from reduction phase

pass through the vessel. In order to achieve this, 75 dm^3 of culture medium must pass through the fermenter every hour. If medium enters and leaves at too high a rate, the fungus has very little time to grow and most of the medium leaves the vessel unused. If the dilution rate is low, the fungus will grow well but remain inside the vessel for a long time so productivity will be low. In mycoprotein fermentations, the dilution rate is a compromise between high productivity and good mycelial growth.

11 **Why is the dilution rate of the medium important in continuous fermentation?**

12 **Study Figure 7. Why does heating the biomass reduce the cell mass by up to 35% but increase the protein to 40–45%?**

The filter cake of mycoprotein is a pale brown, fibrous, moist sheet which would make an ideal growth medium for bacteria, so it is quickly frozen or dried. The cake can then be used in a number of food products. As the filtering process is not carried out under aseptic conditions, this part of the recovery process is regularly monitored for bacterial growth by total viable counts on samples taken from the filtration area.

13 **How would you carry out a total viable count on samples taken from the cloth cover of the horizontal bed filter?**

14 **How does the downstream processing of mycoprotein differ from that of penicillin?**

4.6 Marketing mycoprotein

Good news for chickens. A Korma made with Quorn.

Since the early development of the meat-like product, a new market has evolved. Over the past 20 years there has been a rapid increase in the number of people deciding to become vegetarian. These people, and those forbidden by their religion to eat meat, have increasingly bought alternatives to meat. Ironically, the producers of Quorn have been so successful in mimicking the texture and look of meat that some vegetarians refuse to eat it.

Mycoprotein was originally developed as a protein source to alleviate famine throughout the world. However, Marlow Foods decided that consumption of the new foodstuff in the UK should be encouraged because:

• it was thought unlikely that another country would accept a foodstuff that wasn't consumed in the country that produced it;

• increased production of mycoprotein would only be financially viable if a consumer market was created in the UK first;

• if people got used to mycoprotein as a meat substitute, new food products could then be developed.

So the marketing teams went to work and one of the first steps was to find an acceptable name. Market surveys had found that like term 'mycoprotein' was unpopular because it was too similar to 'microprotein'. Eventually the name 'Quorn' was chosen and registered as a trademark. The name was made-up so a new image could be created around it. Since 1985 the marketing strategy of the company has been to advertise and promote Quorn as a healthy meat alternative in familiar products such as curries. Now that Quorn is accepted by shoppers, more imaginative food products are being developed.

Famine and filamentous fungi

The declared aim of the manufacturers of Quorn is to increase production so that the price can be reduced and Quorn can be sent to countries in need of additional cheap protein. The development of this product has taken a long time, but a nutritious fungal foodstuff is now available. Whether or not this product can eventually contribute towards feeding the millions of people at risk from famine remains to be seen.

15 **What are some of the reasons why it took over 20 years for a new idea to appear as Quorn in the supermarkets?**

Key ideas

- Mycoprotein is produced by the fungus *Fusarium* growing on starch.

- The growth rate of a fungus can be determined by measuring the diameter of the mycelial mass or by measuring the dry mass of mycelium.

- A pilot plant for mycoprotein production was opened in 1971. In 1984 Rank Hovis McDougall and ICI formed a partnership called Marlow Foods to produce mycoprotein on a commercial scale.

- Mycoprotein is produced using a continuous fermentation process.

- The downstream processing of mycoprotein leads to a reduction in total mass but an increase in the percentage protein content.

- Mycoprotein is marketed as Quorn.

- Quorn does not yet provide a cost-effective famine relief, but a new market has developed due to the increase in vegetarianism.

Nature's catalysts

My gran has lots of problems with her hands. Her joints are very swollen and painful because of arthritis, so she finds it difficult to open and close her fingers. When she wants a cup of tea she can't open the lid of the tea caddy without a struggle. We help whenever we can, but we can't be there all the time. Gran says she is lucky, some of her friends have arthritis in their legs and hips and they can hardly walk. I read somewhere that young people can get arthritis too if they've had a bad injury.

Anna is obviously worried about her grandmother. The bad news is that there is no cure for arthritis, but the good news is that medicine can help to relieve some of the symptoms with anti-inflammatory drugs like cortisone. In the past, cortisone was produced by a very complicated process with a very low yield. This made it very expensive – a gram cost over £120. Each injection for Anna's grandmother used to cost approximately £60. A big step forward came when an enzyme isolated from a mould, *Rhizopus arrhizus*, enabled chemists to use a different, cheaper pathway to make cortisone. The cost of a gram of cortisone is now less than 50p.

Microbial enzymes are now used in enormous quantities in the food industry, in washing powders, in medicine, and in the production of other chemicals like cortisone.

5.1 Learning objectives

After working through this chapter, you should be able to:

- **explain** why microorganisms are particularly useful as a source of industrial enzymes;

- **describe** strain selection, substrate selection, fermentation and downstream processing in enzyme production;

- **describe** some uses of isolated enzymes;

- **describe** ways in which enzymes can be immobilised;

- **design** investigations using enzymes;

- **explain** the advantages of using isolated enzymes rather than whole microorganisms in industrial processes.

5.2 Selecting a strain

Enzymes are only produced by living cells. Microorganisms are used to produce enzymes on an industrial scale. The scope for detecting new and useful organisms is huge. For example, tens of millions of microorganisms of many different types exist in a gram of soil (Table 1). So far, less than 1% of the world's microorganisms have been researched.

Strain selection is necessary to find microorganisms that will produce an enzyme that will do exactly what is required (Fig. 1). Strains must not make human beings ill; some may be genetically altered. Organisms selected to produce enzymes that are used in the food industry have to comply to very strict rules and regulations. The responsibility for the safety of the final product lies with the product manufacturer.

1 Describe how you would select a strain of *Bacillus* that could produce proteases tolerant to pH 10 and a temperature of up to 60 °C.

Table 1 Microorganisms in soil	
Type of organism	Estimated numbers of individuals in 1 g of soil
bacteria	10^6–10^8
actinomycete spores	10^4–10^6
fungal spores	10^2–10^4

Fig. 1 Strain selection

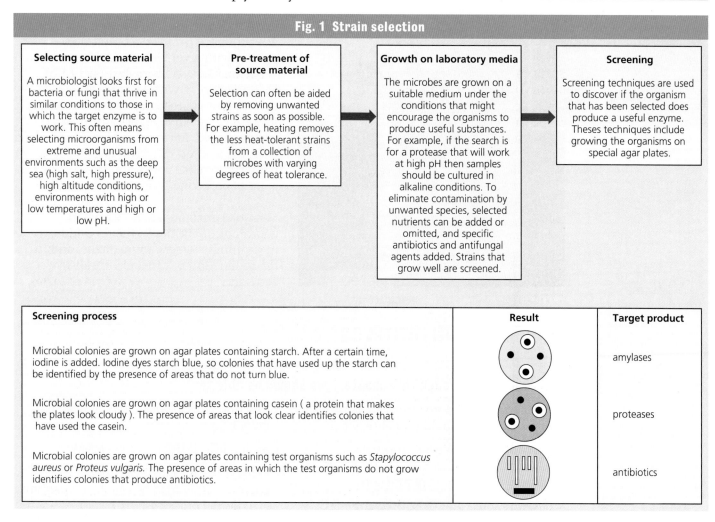

Selecting source material

A microbiologist looks first for bacteria or fungi that thrive in similar conditions to those in which the target enzyme is to work. This often means selecting microorganisms from extreme and unusual environments such as the deep sea (high salt, high pressure), high altitude conditions, environments with high or low temperatures and high or low pH.

Pre-treatment of source material

Selection can often be aided by removing unwanted strains as soon as possible. For example, heating removes the less heat-tolerant strains from a collection of microbes with varying degrees of heat tolerance.

Growth on laboratory media

The microbes are grown on a suitable medium under the conditions that might encourage the organisms to produce useful substances. For example, if the search is for a protease that will work at high pH then samples should be cultured in alkaline conditions. To eliminate contamination by unwanted species, selected nutrients can be added or omitted, and specific antibiotics and antifungal agents added. Strains that grow well are screened.

Screening

Screening techniques are used to discover if the organism that has been selected does produce a useful enzyme. Theses techniques include growing the organisms on special agar plates.

Screening process	Result	Target product
Microbial colonies are grown on agar plates containing starch. After a certain time, iodine is added. Iodine dyes starch blue, so colonies that have used up the starch can be identified by the presence of areas that do not turn blue.		amylases
Microbial colonies are grown on agar plates containing casein (a protein that makes the plates look cloudy). The presence of areas that look clear identifies colonies that have used the casein.		proteases
Microbial colonies are grown on agar plates containing test organisms such as *Stapylococcus aureus* or *Proteus vulgaris*. The presence of areas in which the test organisms do not grow identifies colonies that produce antibiotics.		antibiotics

5.3 Intracellular and extracellular enzymes

The enzymes are always produced inside the cells but many pass out through the cell walls into the growth medium. These are called **extracellular enzymes**. Enzymes that stay inside the cell are called **intracellular enzymes**. Most of the enzymes used in industrial applications are extracellular enzymes produced by microorganisms during fermentation; the process can be either surface or submerged culture.

Extracellular enzymes have three main advantages over intracellular ones:
- the enzyme is already outside the cell so there is no need to break open the cell – often a difficult and expensive process;
- only a limited number of enzymes are secreted into the growth medium so the task of isolating the desired enzyme(s) is much easier;
- extracellular enzymes are more robust and therefore less likely to be broken down by heat or chemicals than the intracellular ones.

2 Why are intracellular enzymes more difficult to isolate than extracellular enzymes?

Isolated enzymes are usually more efficient in biotechnology than whole cells because the enzyme concentration is higher and no unwanted enzymes are present.

5.4 Enzyme production

Surface and submerged techniques

In the 1880s, Dr Jokichi Takamine, a Japanese scientist, developed a method for preparing an enzyme from moulds grown on the surface of rice. This is called surface culture. The enzyme Dr Takamine produced was diastase. In 1917, Boidin and Effront used surface culture of microorganisms to produce amylase and diastase, and this technique is still in use today, especially in Japan.

Since 1917 there have been major developments in what is now called enzyme biotechnology. A range of procedures called submerged culture techniques were developed to increase yields during penicillin production, and have since been more and more widely used. In submerged culture techniques, the mould or bacterium producing the enzyme is grown throughout a liquid medium rather than on the surface of a solid medium. This means that more microbial cells are produced and there is a higher yield of enzyme – but aeration and stirring of the medium may be necessary and this leads to higher costs.

3 Explain why the early production of enzymes by fermentation was carried out using surface techniques.

In 1894, Dr Takamine's enzyme preparation was taken up by the firm Parke, Davis and Co. and sold under the trade name Takadiastase. It was used to treat patients who had digestive problems and were unable to break down starch to maltose.

Fermentation

Biotechnologists generally call the breakdown of substances by microbes fermentation (Chapter 2, p. 22). Industrial fermentations all require scaling-up (Chapter 3, p. 41) and aseptic techniques are rigorously followed throughout (Fig. 2). The purpose of scaling-up is to ensure that there is sufficient actively growing culture to add to the main vessel.

4 Why do you think the aseptic technique guidelines for staff at a research establishment handling commercial starter strains include instructions to:
   a work in a draught-free area?
   b allow heated nichrome loops to cool before placing them in a liquid culture?
   c not use unlabelled plates or culture bottles?

5 a Why is scaling-up important?
   b In Figure 2, what tests would you undertake to make sure that the microorganisms in the conical flask are only from the starter culture?

Aseptic technique guidelines

- Sterile gloves, masks and hats must be worn at all times.
- All staff must wear a freshly laundered laboratory coat.
- Always work in a draught-free area, preferably with the cultures inside a fume-cupboard.
- Ensure that benches are thoroughly washed with antiseptic before starting any aseptic work.
- Always flame the tops of bottles and culture vessels before transferring any culture.
- Use only sterile pipettes or flamed nichrome loops for transferring cultures.
- Allow flamed loops to cool before placing them into liquid cultures or onto agar gels.
- Make sure that any culture medium and agar plates are sterile before use.
- Never inoculate an unlabelled plate or culture bottle.
- Incubate all cultures in a sealed incubator.

Fig. 2 Scaling-up and aseptic technique

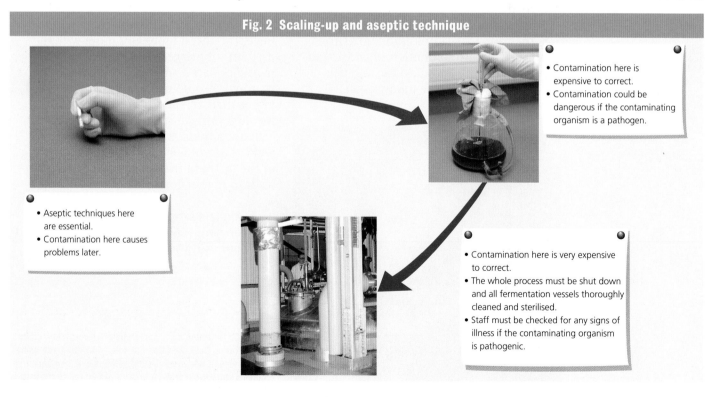

- Aseptic techniques here are essential.
- Contamination here causes problems later.

- Contamination here is expensive to correct.
- Contamination could be dangerous if the contaminating organism is a pathogen.

- Contamination here is very expensive to correct.
- The whole process must be shut down and all fermentation vessels thoroughly cleaned and sterilised.
- Staff must be checked for any signs of illness if the contaminating organism is pathogenic.

Cell growth and enzyme production

The microbial cells are encouraged into **exponential growth** in the **starter vessel** and **seed vessel**. This means that there is a rapid increase in the number of cells, so there are enough cells to go into the **main fermentation vessel**. In the industrial production of a protease, the microorganisms in the starter and seed vessels are given a rich nutrient medium with a lot of protein so that they can easily obtain the amino acids that they need for growth. Not much protease is produced because as soon as the enzyme leaves the cell it is in the presence of protein which it breaks down into amino acids that the bacterium can absorb (Fig. 3). This inhibits further production of protease.

In the fermentation vessel, the bacterial cells are allowed to grow for a further 1–8 days. The microorganisms commonly used for enzyme production require a source of organic carbon and nitrogen, as well as minerals, water and oxygen. The medium in the fermenter vessel is usually a relatively cheap feedstuff such as potato flour, cornsteep liquor, or soy bean meal, with added sugars and salts. It is important that the medium meets all of the basic nutritional needs of the microorganism that is being used. But the nutrient medium does not have much protein in it. Each bacterium produces a lot of protease because when the enzyme leaves the cell it does not immediately come into contact with protein that it can break down into amino acids for the bacterium to absorb – so each bacterium is producing more enzyme in order to maximise the harvest of amino acids from the small amount of protein available (Fig. 3).

Obviously, if the organisms are given too little in the way of nutrients then they will not survive at all. The task for the biotechnologists is to provide a medium that contains just sufficient nutrient to ensure that the microorganisms in the main fermenter produce the maximum amount of enzyme and continue to grow but without increasing the number of cells. This stage of population growth is called the **post-exponential phase**. It is also the production phase of the fermentation. As well as controlling the medium, it is important that other growth conditions such as oxygen level, pH and temperature, are also monitored and controlled. Maximum enzyme production is achieved when each of the growth conditions is maintained at its **optimum** (Fig. 4).

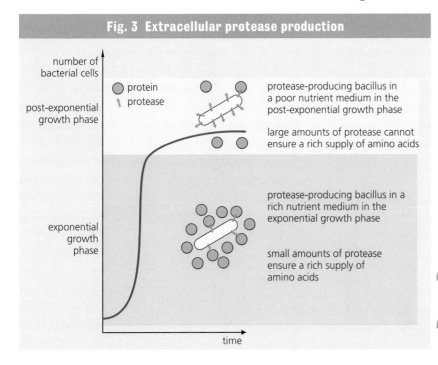

Fig. 3 Extracellular protease production

- protein
- protease

protease-producing bacillus in a poor nutrient medium in the post-exponential growth phase

large amounts of protease cannot ensure a rich supply of amino acids

protease-producing bacillus in a rich nutrient medium in the exponential growth phase

small amounts of protease ensure a rich supply of amino acids

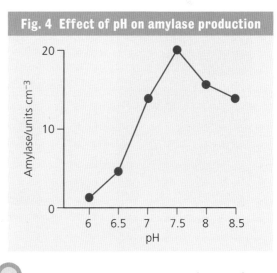

Fig. 4 Effect of pH on amylase production

6 **What is the optimum pH for amylase production?**

7 **What is the purpose of each step in fermentation?**

5.5 Downstream processing

After fermentation, the nutrient broth has become a mixture of enzyme, nutrients, waste materials and cells. The enzyme must be extracted and the process of doing this is called downstream processing (Fig. 5).

The aim of downstream processing is to purify the product as much as is required at the minimum cost. The cost of the process depends on many factors including:
- the nature of the original raw materials;
- the presence of undesirable by-products in the broth;
- the concentration of the desired product in the broth (Fig. 6).

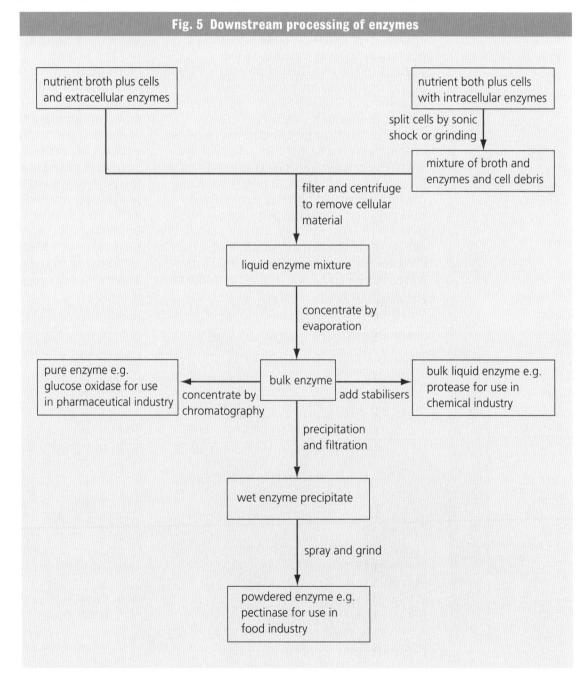

Fig. 5 Downstream processing of enzymes

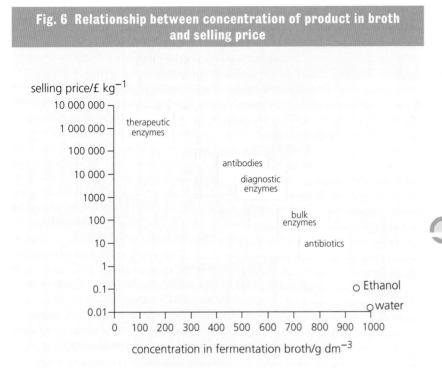

Fig. 6 Relationship between concentration of product in broth and selling price

selling price/£ kg^{-1}

concentration in fermentation broth/g dm^{-3}

Enzyme production is more efficient today than 100 years ago because:
- genetic manipulation of microorganisms has improved yields;
- low-cost nutrients and advanced monitoring have improved fermentation technology;
- new methods extract a greater proportion of the enzymes from cells;
- downstream processing techniques are more efficient;
- continuous production in special reactors is more efficient than batch processes.

8 a Other than ethanol and water, which type of product occurs in fermentation broths in the greatest concentration?

b Which three groups of product can cost more than £10 000 kg^{-1}?

c Explain why the concentration of product in the fermentation has an effect on final sale price.

Key ideas

- Industrial enzymes are produced from bacteria and microbial fungi by fermentation.
- Strains of microorganisms to produce enzymes are specially selected using specific growth media and genetic manipulation.
- Enzymes may be intracellular or extracellular; extracellular enzymes are cheaper to produce.
- Enzymes are produced using submerged techniques.
- Enzymes are produced on a commercial scale when the organism is in the post-exponential growth phase.
- The fermentation process involves scaling-up and downstream processing.

5.6 Uses of enzymes

Enzymes do not need the high temperatures or pressures of many industrial chemical processes, so reactions catalysed by enzymes are often cheaper than comparable chemical processes. Enzymes are very specific and can catalyse reactions between specific chemicals, even in mixtures. This means that less time needs to be spent in purifying mixtures. The industrial uses of microbial enzymes can be divided into three groups:
- food and industrial processes;
- diagnostic and analytical processes;
- treating disease.

Table 2 Some industrial enzymes			
Enzyme	Source	Use	World production in 1993 Tonnes
Bacillus proteases	*B. licheniformis* *B. subtilis*	detergents stain removers meat tenderisers	540
fungal proteases	*Aspergillus niger* *A. oryzae*	bread making chill-proofing beer	10
fungal amylases (turn starch to maltose)	*A. oryzae*	bread making desizing textiles	10
glucoamylases (turn starch to glucose)	*A. niger*	glucose manufacture	355
Bacillus amylases (turn starch to glucose)	*B. subtilis*	glucose manufacture	325
glucose isomerase	*Streptomyces* sp. *Bacillus* sp.	manufacture of high-fructose syrups to sweeten soft drinks	70
rennin	*Endothia parasitica* *Mucor* sp.	cheese making	26
pectinases	*A. niger* other fungi	clarifying fruit juices and wines retting flax	10

You don't have to wash your jeans with a load of rocks at the laundrette to get the 'stonewashed' effect. Microbial enzymes can do it for you.

Food and industrial processes frequently use large quantities of **protease**, **amylase** and **pectinase**. These enzymes are often referred to as **bulk enzymes** because they are used in such large quantities. In 1993, the total annual production of commercially produced enzymes was approximately 1350 tonnes (Table 2).

9 a Working from Table 2, approximately what percentage of the total enzyme production is made up of amylases?
  b What type of reaction does this group of enzymes catalyse?

Food production

Pectins occur naturally in the cell walls of fruits. Because pectin molecules have a branching structure they form a gel very easily. This is very useful in the production of jams and preserves; it is the pectin that makes these products set. However, the presence of pectin hinders the extraction of juice from crushed fruit because the gel traps the juice. To prevent this happening, the fruit is crushed and then pectinases are used to hydrolyse the pectin molecules so that they cannot form a gel and bind the fruit pulp together. This makes it easier to get the juice from the fruit and so increases the yield. Pectinases are also used to treat cloudy fruit juices. The cloudy appearance is usually caused by pectin gel in the juice; pectinases can break this down into soluble molecules so the juice becomes clear. In the case of grape juice (called 'must'), this is especially important because otherwise the gel remains in place throughout the fermentation and makes the wine cloudy.

Pectinase preparations make up about 1% of the total commercial enzyme production and actually contain many enzymes, each attacking a different part of the pectin molecule (Fig. 7). Pectinases are used commercially to:
• clarify fruit juices
• clarify grape must;
• extract olive oil;
• prepare fruit and vegetables for further processing.

This machinery is to separate water from the olive oil.

These olive trees are in the West Bank. After harvesting, pectinase is added to the olives to soften them and make extracting the olive oil easier. The pectinase also ensures the oil is clear.

Fig. 7 Production of pectinase and its use in fruit juice production

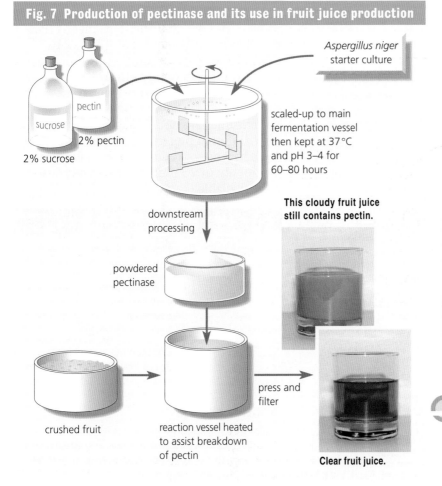

sucrose

pectin

2% sucrose

2% pectin

Aspergillus niger starter culture

scaled-up to main fermentation vessel then kept at 37 °C and pH 3–4 for 60–80 hours

downstream processing

This cloudy fruit juice still contains pectin.

powdered pectinase

crushed fruit

reaction vessel heated to assist breakdown of pectin

press and filter

Clear fruit juice.

Commercial pectinases are commonly produced from *Aspergillus niger* cultures, but *Aspergillus wentii* and *Rhizopus* species are also used. The powdered enzyme is added to the crushed fruit (Fig. 7).

10 The mixture of crushed fruit and pectinase is heated to aid the breakdown of pectins in the fruit. Describe how you would carry out an investigation to find out the optimum temperature for pectinase action.

Industrial processes

Proteases make up about 40% of the total enzyme production. These protein-digesting enzymes are the ones that 'digest even the stubbornest stains' during washing; their most common use is in detergents and washing powders. The reason why proteases are so useful in these products is that many of the stains that are difficult to wash away are proteins, e.g. milk, egg and blood. The enzymes in washing powders and liquids are very powerful: only small amounts are needed. Some are stable up to temperatures of 60–70 °C. The proteases can be grouped into three types based on the optimum pH at which they are active (Fig. 8).

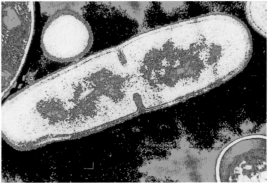

Coloured transmission electron micrograph of *Bacillus licheniformis*; bacteria like this make biological powders effective.

11 a Which organisms produce proteases used in detergents?
   b Why is temperature tolerance so important in washing powder proteases?

Fig. 8 Proteases and pH range

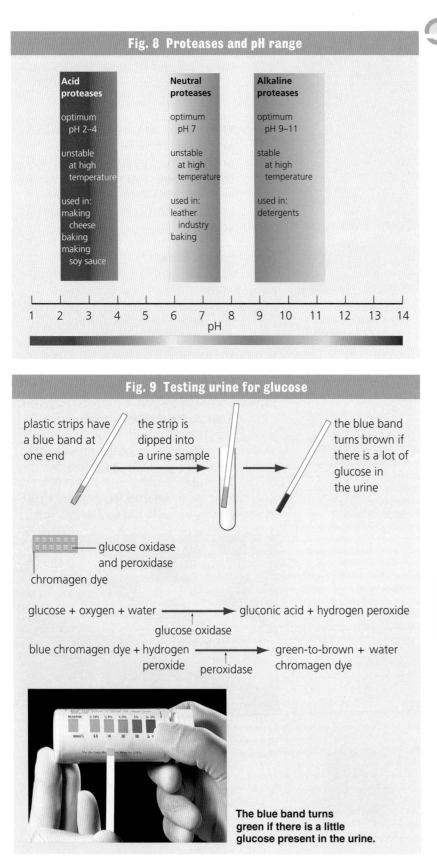

Acid proteases	Neutral proteases	Alkaline proteases
optimum pH 2–4	optimum pH 7	optimum pH 9–11
unstable at high temperature	unstable at high temperature	stable at high temperature
used in: making cheese baking making soy sauce	used in: leather industry baking	used in: detergents

pH: 1 2 3 4 5 6 7 8 9 10 11 12 13 14

Fig. 9 Testing urine for glucose

plastic strips have a blue band at one end

the strip is dipped into a urine sample

the blue band turns brown if there is a lot of glucose in the urine

glucose oxidase and peroxidase
chromagen dye

glucose + oxygen + water $\xrightarrow{\text{glucose oxidase}}$ gluconic acid + hydrogen peroxide

blue chromagen dye + hydrogen peroxide $\xrightarrow{\text{peroxidase}}$ green-to-brown + water chromagen dye

The blue band turns green if there is a little glucose present in the urine.

12 How would you determine whether a strain of *Bacillus* was likely to produce alkaline, neutral or acid proteases?

Diagnostic and analytic processes

Diagnostic enzymes can detect certain important chemicals in body fluids; they act quickly and are very reliable because they are extremely specific. These enzymes are often used in **biosensors**. Biosensors are tools for finding out information about the body without invading the body. For example, plastic strips specially coated with the enzymes glucose oxidase and glucose peroxidase and a dye can indicate the presence of glucose in urine by a colour change on the strip when it is dipped into a sample of urine (Fig. 9). In a healthy person, urine does not contain glucose. However, a person suffering from diabetes mellitus is unable to control the level of glucose in the blood; it gets so high that some passes out in urine. This means that the presence of glucose in urine can be used as a simple screening test for diabetes mellitus (*Biology Core*, p. 181).

Unfortunately, diagnostic enzymes have to be stored at a low temperature so that the enzymes are not damaged. Despite this, they are often preferred to other analytical tools because of their reliability. Biosensor kits for about 20 important compounds are now available (Table 3).

Table 3 Biosensors and their uses

Substance tested for	Diagnostic enzyme
urea	urease
cholesterol	cholesterol oxidase
glucose	glucose oxidase
aspartate	aspartase
lactate	lactate dehydrogenase
penicillin	penicillinase
alcohol	alcohol dehydrogenase

Treating disease

Enzymes that are used to treat disease are called **therapeutic enzymes**. Asparginase is an example; it is used in the treatment of acute lymphatic leukaemia.

5.7 Immobilised enzymes

Some commercially produced enzymes are used in industrial process that are designed to produce large quantities of another product. For example:
- fructose production;
- amino acid production;
- antibiotic production (Fig. 10).

In these processes, the enzymes may be used in batch cultures or in a continuous process. In batch cultures, the enzyme is used in its free state and has to be separated from the product after every batch. In continuous processes, enzymes (or sometimes whole microbial cells) are **immobilised** inside the reaction vessel. There are three different ways of immobilising enzymes (Fig. 11). Immobilisation in industrial processes dates from the 1940s.

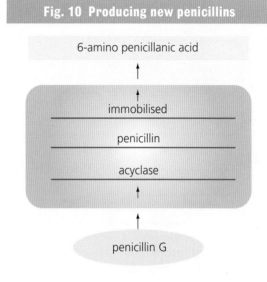

Fig. 10 Producing new penicillins

6-amino penicillanic acid

↑

immobilised

penicillin

acyclase

↑

penicillin G

13 **Explain the relative advantages and disadvantages of the three different ways of immobilising enzymes.**

Fig. 11 Immobilising enzymes

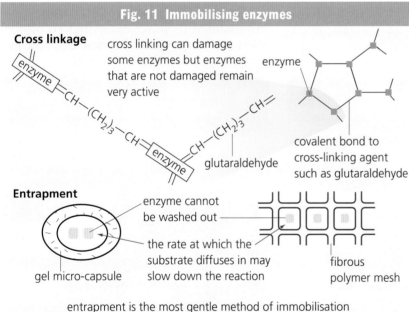

Cross linkage

cross linking can damage some enzymes but enzymes that are not damaged remain very active

enzyme

glutaraldehyde

covalent bond to cross-linking agent such as glutaraldehyde

Entrapment

enzyme cannot be washed out

the rate at which the substrate diffuses in may slow down the reaction

gel micro-capsule

fibrous polymer mesh

entrapment is the most gentle method of immobilisation and does not damage enzymes

Adsorption

enzyme held by weak forces and may become detached

adsorbing agent such as glass bead, carbon particle or collagen

adsorption makes it easy for the enzyme to come into contact with its substrate but the process is expensive

Problems with industrial enzymes

There have been some big problems with the use of enzymes on a large scale. For instance, there have been many reports of allergic reactions among workers involved in the process of adding powdered protease enzymes to washing powders. It is now thought that this problem was caused by the *powdered* enzyme coming into contact with the skin and/or being inhaled. As this problem created more and more publicity the production of proteases fell. Between 1969 and 1971 there was a drastic reduction in protease sales from £100 million to £35 million. Since then, special processing techniques have been introduced. Immobilised proteases are now added to detergents in particulate form, not as fine powders. To produce the particulate form, a wet paste of the enzyme is melted at 50–70 ºC with polyethylene glycol and then made into tiny solid spherical particles. In this form, the enzyme is called **micro-encapsulated** because it is trapped inside a micro-capsule. Allergies are now much less common and sales have recovered.

Fig. 12 Reactors for immobilised enzymes

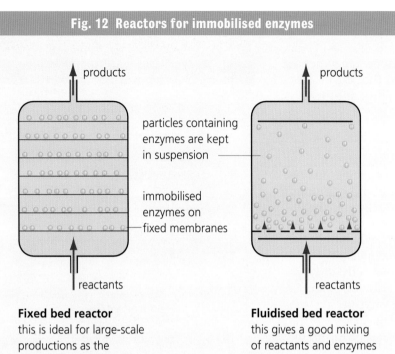

products

particles containing enzymes are kept in suspension

immobilised enzymes on fixed membranes

products

reactants

reactants

Fixed bed reactor
this is ideal for large-scale productions as the reactants pass slowly through the membranes

Fluidised bed reactor
this gives a good mixing of reactants and enzymes but it is difficult to do on a large scale

neither reactor is stirred because immobilised enzyme systems are fragile

14 Since 1971, the production of alkaline proteases has increased dramatically following a disastrous slump caused by reports of allergic reactions amongst workers. How has improved enzyme technology greatly reduced the problem of allergies?

Immobilised enzyme reactors

There are two main types of reactor for immobilised enzyme processes. One type is for processes that use enzymes immobilised on a fixed bed or membrane, the other is for processes where the enzymes are bound to or within particles (Fig. 12). There are, of course, pluses and minuses in immobilising enzymes (Fig. 13).

15 Why do you think a stirred fermenter is not used for immobilised enzyme systems?

Amino acids can be produced using immobilised enzymes and by batch culture; there is a considerable difference in cost between these methods (Fig. 14).

Fig. 13 Advantages and disadvantages of immobilisation of enzymes

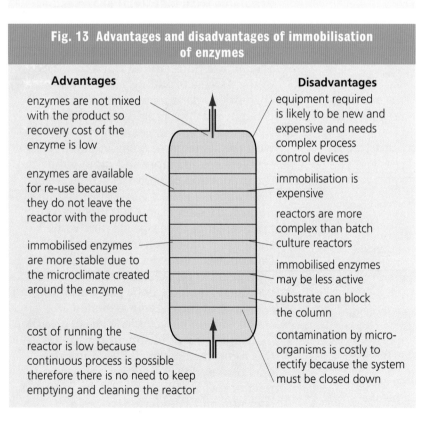

Advantages

enzymes are not mixed with the product so recovery cost of the enzyme is low

enzymes are available for re-use because they do not leave the reactor with the product

immobilised enzymes are more stable due to the microclimate created around the enzyme

cost of running the reactor is low because continuous process is possible therefore there is no need to keep emptying and cleaning the reactor

Disadvantages

equipment required is likely to be new and expensive and needs complex process control devices

immobilisation is expensive

reactors are more complex than batch culture reactors

immobilised enzymes may be less active

substrate can block the column

contamination by micro-organisms is costly to rectify because the system must be closed down

Fig. 14 Comparing the costs of industrial production of an amino acid

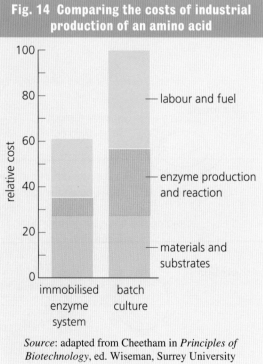

relative cost

labour and fuel

enzyme production and reaction

materials and substrates

immobilised enzyme system

batch culture

Source: adapted from Cheetham in *Principles of Biotechnology*, ed. Wiseman, Surrey University Press, 1983

Immobilised microbial cells

Processes using immobilised cells are a kind of 'half-way house' between fermentations that use microbial cells to produce enzymes and processes that use the immobilised enzymes. These processes immobilise whole cells while they produce the enzyme to catalyse another reaction at the same time. The methods of immobilisation are very similar to those for enzymes, and so are the advantages and disadvantages. Immobilised whole cells are not as specific in their reactions as pure enzymes but they are used in a number of important industrial processes such as the bioconversion of steroids, the production of amino acids, and the recovery of precious metals from dilute solutions. The uses of some particular species are shown in Table 4.

Bioconversion means using an enzyme to change one substance into another. It is often cheaper than a chemical conversion. Today, production of cortisone involves bioconversion using whole cells of *Rhizopus arrhizus* (Fig. 15). The process is enhanced

Table 4 Some uses of immobilised microbial cells		
Organism	Product type	Specific product
Bacillus sp.	antibiotic	bacitracin
Penicillium chrysogenum	antibiotic	penicillin
Escherichia coli	amino acid	L-tryptophan
Streptomyces fradiae	enzyme	protease
Lactobacillus delbrueckii	acid	lactic acid

by immobilising the cells. This is cheaper than isolating the relevant enzyme. Cortisone is a **steroid hormone** that can be given as an injection to arthritis sufferers like Anna's grandmother to reduce the swelling in their joints and relieve pain. Cortisone is also used in treating allergies, skin diseases, and leukaemia.

 16 Describe two developments in enzyme technology that you feel could have contributed to lowering the cost of steroid treatment for Anna's grandmother.

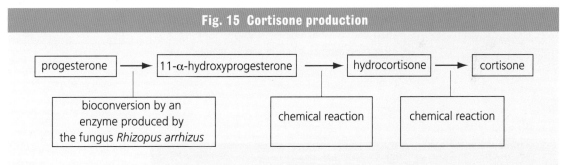

Fig. 15 Cortisone production

progesterone → 11-α-hydroxyprogesterone → hydrocortisone → cortisone

bioconversion by an enzyme produced by the fungus *Rhizopus arrhizus*

chemical reaction

chemical reaction

Key ideas

- The food processing industry, the detergents and cleaners industry, and the pharmaceutical industry all use enzymes.

- Industrial processes using enzymes are cleaner and cheaper than chemical processes.

- Industrial enzymes are usually extracellular and can be used in bulk as free enzymes.

- Enzymes can be used in immobilised form.

- Sometimes whole microbial cells are used in immobilised form.

Controlling microorganisms

" Who cares about bacteria in chickens? "

Which? magazine's 1994 survey not only found a very high proportion of the chickens in supermarkets to be contaminated, it also revealed another bacterium to be at least as much of a problem.

Salmonella was found in 36% of the raw chicken samples from the UK and a bacterium called Campylobacter was found in 41%. Like Salmonella poisoning, Campylobacter poisoning usually results in symptoms such as diarrhoea, stomach pain and fever. Nausea, chills, headaches, fatigue and vomiting also occur; in rare cases it can even result in death. Campylobacter causes more diarrhoeal disease in the UK than Salmonella.

There is no way for consumers to tell which chickens are uncontaminated, so until chicken production is cleaned up you should treat all chicken as suspect and follow these tips:
- never let raw chicken touch cooked food in the fridge, and never keep raw chicken on a shelf above foods you eat without cooking;
- after preparing chicken, wash your hands and utensils and chopping board (to avoid cross-contamination);
- cook chicken thoroughly until the juices run clear to ensure any bacteria are killed; never eat undercooked chicken.

Results from around Europe

Country	Salmonella %	Campylobacter %
Belgium	16	4
Denmark	51	36
France	25	53
Germany	26	22
Greece	4	0
Italy	24	13
Netherlands	23	45
Norway	0	1
Portugal	48	60
Republic of Ireland	13	29
Slovenia	11	47
Spain	8	26
Sweden	0	10
UK	36	41

Source: adapted from *Which?* magazine, October 1994

Bacterial resistance to an antibiotic occurs when a level of antibiotic that would normally kill the bacterium has no effect. Resistant bacteria that develop in animals can eventually spread to humans. There are many cases of food poisoning reported each year, and some are difficult to treat because the bacteria have become resistant to antibiotics.

Factory farming of chickens is unpleasant and messy. The animals are often kept in crowded conditions and infections spread rapidly reducing weight gain or even causing death. Antibiotics are often used to prevent this from happening but the prolonged use of antibiotics can encourage the development of antibiotic-resistant bacteria – a much more serious problem.

6.1 Learning objectives

After working through this chapter, you should be able to:

- **describe** the action of antibiotics and disinfectants;

- **explain** how to carry out a simple bioassay to determine the effectiveness of antibiotics and disinfectants;

- **list** a range of antibiotics and their sources;

- **describe** how microorganisms are screened for antimicrobial activity;

- **explain** the concepts of minimal inhibitory concentration and minimal lethal concentration;

- **describe** the use of multodiscs in assay techniques;

- **describe** the use of genetic and chemical manipulation in the quest for new antibiotics;

- **explain** why viruses are not inhibited by antibiotics;

- **describe** methods of growing viruses and the actions of antiviral agents;

- **list** some possible sources of new antimicrobial agents.

6.2 Sterilisation, disinfection and antiseptics

For thousands of years people have understood something of microorganisms. Fermented foods and drinks are described in some of the earliest examples of recorded history. Ancient Greeks used sulphur to fumigate rooms and Hebrew law insisted that clothes from leprosy victims should be burnt. The history of microbial control is as long as the history of biotechnology itself. The control of microorganisms is as vital today as it always has been. Microorganisms must be kept under control so that:

- food can be safely prepared in restaurants and homes;
- the spread of diseases in hospitals can be prevented;
- operations do not allow infection to occur;
- contamination does not occur in biotechnological procedures.

The processes and techniques used today to control microbes vary a great deal but can be divided into those that treat:

- inanimate objects;
- living tissues.

Sterilisation kills or removes all microorganisms, including spores, and can be done by physical means, for example heat or radiation, or by chemical means using a sterilant such as alcohol or chlorine compounds. Sterilisation can only be used on inanimate objects because it damages all living tissue (Chapter 11, p. 146).

Disinfection reduces the number of

Early writings give clear advice about the use of disinfectants for embalming bodies. The mummy inside this gilded case is that of Henutmehyt who lived in Thebes about 1300 BC.

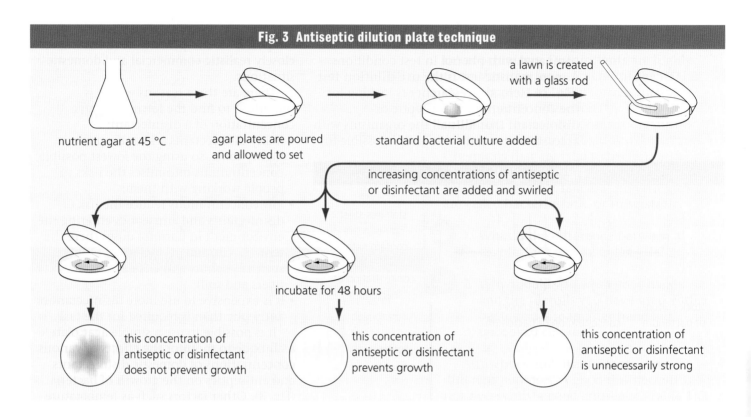

Fig. 3 Antiseptic dilution plate technique

nutrient agar at 45 °C

agar plates are poured and allowed to set

standard bacterial culture added

a lawn is created with a glass rod

increasing concentrations of antiseptic or disinfectant are added and swirled

incubate for 48 hours

this concentration of antiseptic or disinfectant does not prevent growth

this concentration of antiseptic or disinfectant prevents growth

this concentration of antiseptic or disinfectant is unnecessarily strong

6.3 Chemotherapy

A major problem with disinfectants and antiseptics is that they affect all microorganisms alike and may damage human tissue as well. Even the mildest antiseptics can be harmful if swallowed. In order to treat infections inside the body, a chemical must interfere with the microorganisms but not damage the host. Such agents are called **chemotherapeutic agents** (Table 3). Antibiotics are chemotherapeutic agents that are produced most commonly by bacteria and fungi.

The development of chemotherapy owes much to the work of the German physician Paul Ehrlich (1854–1915). Ehrlich attempted to develop a toxic dye molecule that would bind to pathogenic organisms and destroy them, but leave host tissues unharmed. By 1910, Ehrlich and a Japanese scientist called Sahachiro Hata had tested many compounds containing arsenic and found that one (arsphenamine) was active against the bacterium that causes syphilis.

Unfortunately, bacteria can become antibiotic resistant. Resistant bacteria are not caused by the antibiotic, it is just that when a resistant organism occurs, it is able to grow and reproduce successfully despite the presence of the antibiotic (Chapter 11, p. 150).

Table 3 Some important chemotherapeutic agents

Chemotherapeutic agent	Effect	Notes
cephalosporins	bactericidal	broad range some allergic responses
penicillins	bactericidal	narrow range some allergic responses
sulphonamides	bacteriostatic	broad range some allergic responses
tetracyclines	bacteriostatic	broad range some gastro-intestinal problems
trimethoprim	bactericidal	broad range some allergic responses

Source: adapted from Prescott, Harley and Klein, *Microbiology*, Wm. C. Brown, 1993

In 1935, Gerhard Domagk discovered that the leather dye prontosil red was active against some bacteria but non-toxic for animals. It was later discovered that prontosil red is converted in the human body to sulphanilamide – the forerunner of a family of important agents called the sulphonamides.

Antibiotic agents have been isolated from sharkskin and the skin of frogs.

Q6 What is the crucial difference between a disinfectant and a chemotherapeutic agent such as prontosil red?

New antibiotics

Screening programmes in many countries have detected around 8000 different antibiotics from microorganisms. A further 3000 active substances have been detected in algae, lichens, higher plants and animals. The search continues and approximately 300 new substances are added to the list each year. However, only a few hundred are in commercial production and it takes many years of research, development and testing before a new antibiotic is ready for use (Fig. 4).

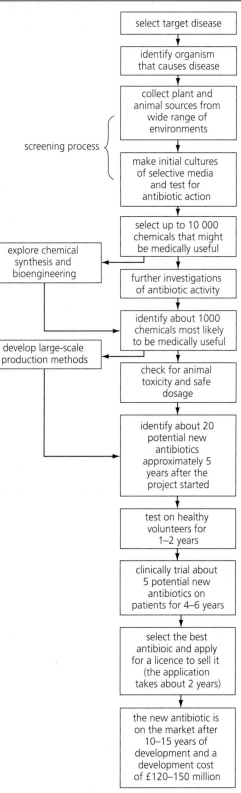

Fig. 4 Developing a new antibiotic

select target disease

↓

identify organism that causes disease

↓

collect plant and animal sources from wide range of environments

↓

make initial cultures of selective media and test for antibiotic action

screening process

↓

select up to 10 000 chemicals that might be medically useful

↓

further investigations of antibiotic activity

explore chemical synthesis and bioengineering

↓

identify about 1000 chemicals most likely to be medically useful

develop large-scale production methods

↓

check for animal toxicity and safe dosage

↓

identify about 20 potential new antibiotics approximately 5 years after the project started

↓

test on healthy volunteers for 1–2 years

↓

clinically trial about 5 potential new antibiotics on patients for 4–6 years

↓

select the best antibioic and apply for a licence to sell it (the application takes about 2 years)

↓

the new antibiotic is on the market after 10–15 years of development and a development cost of £120–150 million

An antibiotic must have selective toxicity: it must kill or inhibit the unwanted bacteria and fungi, but cause as little damage to the host as possible. The dose of the antibiotic needed to kill or inhibit bacteria is called the **therapeutic dose**. The level that causes damage to the host is called the **toxic dose**. The most effective antibiotics all have a high toxic dose and a low therapeutic dose. The ratio of these two factors is called the **therapeutic index**. An effective antibiotic has a high therapeutic index. Different antibiotics are effective against different types of microorganism. Some are only effective against a few types of bacterium and are called **narrow spectrum antibiotics**. Others kill or inhibit a wide range of bacteria and are called **broad** or **wide spectrum antibiotics**. The **minimal inhibitory concentration** (MIC) of an antibiotic is the lowest concentration that prevents growth of a specific bacterium. The **minimal lethal concentration** (MLC) is the lowest concentration that kills a specific bacterium. Most antibiotic chemicals fail animal toxicity tests. The few that do not will all have medical, research or agricultural uses.

During the screening process a large number of possible antibiotic-producing microorganisms are isolated from the environment. The initial test applied to these microbes aims to discover whether or not the organism produces a chemical that inhibits the growth of a standard range of bacteria. This is done by the **cross-streak method** (Fig. 5).

Bacteria which show some antibiotic activity are studied further to see if the substances they produce are more effective than existing substances. This involves more detailed tests.

7 a What is the difference between the MIC and MLC of a particular substance?
b Why is it important to know both?

Dilution tests can be carried out using either broths or agar plates (Fig. 6). The principles are the same in both cases, and are very similar to those of the dilution tests for disinfectants and antiseptics.

A **disc diffusion test** is a relatively simple way to determine antibiotic effectiveness. However, there are several factors that affect the spread of the antibiotic through the agar (Fig. 7). Some results from a disc diffusion test are given in Table 4.

Fig. 5 Cross-streak method

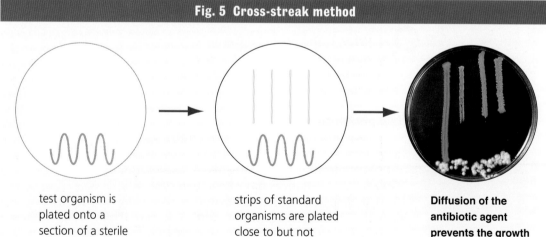

test organism is plated onto a section of a sterile nutrient agar plate

strips of standard organisms are plated close to but not touching the test organisms

Diffusion of the antibiotic agent prevents the growth of sensitive bacteria (streaks 2, 3 and 4), resistant organisms grow (streak 1).

Table 4 Some disc diffusion test results			
Antibiotic	Diameter of zone of clearing/mm		
	Resistant	Intermediate	Susceptible
penicillin G	< 11	12–21	> 22
streptomycin	< 11	12–14	> 15
chloramphenicol	< 12	13–17	> 18
erythromycin	< 13	14–17	> 18
sulphonamides	< 12	13–16	> 17
tetracyclines	< 14	15–18	> 19

8 The diameter of the zone of clearing around an antibiotic disc is mainly due to the effectiveness with which it kills the bacterium, but other factors also influence the size of the zone. What are they?

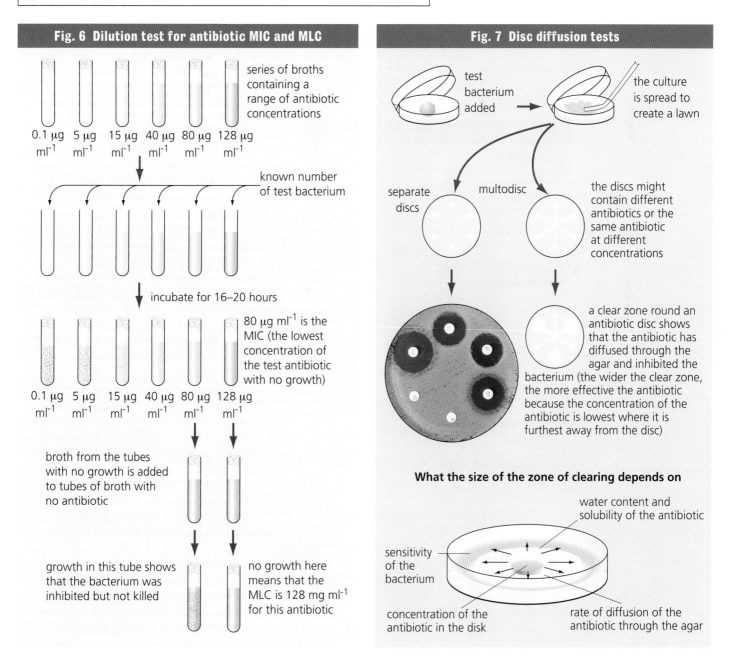

Fig. 6 Dilution test for antibiotic MIC and MLC

series of broths containing a range of antibiotic concentrations

0.1 µg ml⁻¹ 5 µg ml⁻¹ 15 µg ml⁻¹ 40 µg ml⁻¹ 80 µg ml⁻¹ 128 µg ml⁻¹

known number of test bacterium

incubate for 16–20 hours

80 µg ml⁻¹ is the MIC (the lowest concentration of the test antibiotic with no growth)

0.1 µg ml⁻¹ 5 µg ml⁻¹ 15 µg ml⁻¹ 40 µg ml⁻¹ 80 µg ml⁻¹ 128 µg ml⁻¹

broth from the tubes with no growth is added to tubes of broth with no antibiotic

growth in this tube shows that the bacterium was inhibited but not killed

no growth here means that the MLC is 128 mg ml⁻¹ for this antibiotic

Fig. 7 Disc diffusion tests

test bacterium added

the culture is spread to create a lawn

separate discs

multodisc

the discs might contain different antibiotics or the same antibiotic at different concentrations

a clear zone round an antibiotic disc shows that the antibiotic has diffused through the agar and inhibited the bacterium (the wider the clear zone, the more effective the antibiotic because the concentration of the antibiotic is lowest where it is furthest away from the disc)

What the size of the zone of clearing depends on

water content and solubility of the antibiotic

sensitivity of the bacterium

concentration of the antibiotic in the disk

rate of diffusion of the antibiotic through the agar

Chemical manipulation

Screening occasionally finds new types of antibiotics, but existing types can be improved using chemical or genetic methods. Most chemical manipulation is on antibiotics containing a β-lactam ring, such as the penicillins and cephalosporins.

Of the naturally occurring penicillins only penicillin G is therapeutically useful. The basic penicillin G structure can be modified biosynthetically by substituting the R group, or side chain, with other substances called side chain precursors (Fig. 8). Side chain precursors can be added to the broth during penicillin fermentation and the penicillins that are produced are called biosynthetic penicillins. It is also possible to modify penicillin G molecules directly using the enzyme penicillin acylase to remove the R group and then adding back a suitable side chain (Fig. 8). Penicillins produced this way are called semi-synthetic penicillins. In all cases, the β-lactam ring is made by microbial fermentations and the side chain is modified afterwards.

Genetic manipulation

Developments in genetic engineering could increase antibiotic yields. For a number of years scientists have treated bacteria with chemicals or radiation in an effort to create mutants that produce new or modified antibiotics. This process is called **mutagenesis**. In most cases, the mutants produce less useful antibiotic than the parents but occasionally higher yielding strains do result. The production of the antibiotics in cells involves many metabolic stages and these stages are controlled by many different genes. It is difficult to determine how these genes will be modified by mutagenesis.

It is now possible to place copies of antibiotic-producing genes into bacterial cells as plasmids. Even so, the metabolic pathway producing an antibiotic may involve up to 30 enzymes, each with its own gene. An early approach was to identify the key enzyme step and then try to transfer this gene in the hope that this would remove a 'bottleneck' in the production process.

It has recently been discovered that all of the genes for antibiotic production are close together on the DNA, and the gene for resistance to the antibiotic is usually also found within this cluster. This means that cloning the resistance gene also clones most of the genes for antibiotic production. This knowledge has led to a large increase in the production of the antibiotic actinorhodin by *Streptomyces coelicolor*.

9a What is mutagenesis?
b Genetic manipulation has resulted in increased yields of some antibiotics, but chemical manipulation is more effective for producing modified ones. Why?

Fig. 8 Structure of some penicillins

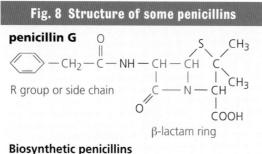

penicillin G

R group or side chain

β-lactam ring

Biosynthetic penicillins

penicillin V

this R group gives penicillin V more resistance to acid attack so it is suitable for oral use

penicillin O

$CH_2=CH-CH_2-S-CH_2-C-$

this R group makes penicillin O less allergenic

Semi-synthetic penicillins

ampicillin

this R group gives carbenicillin a broad spectrum of activity

carbenicillin

this R group gives ampicillin a broad spectrum of activity and makes it acid stable

Key ideas

- Sterilisation kills all microorganisms and spores; disinfection reduces the number of organisms and spores. Sterilisation and disinfection are used to keep inanimate objects and environments clean and reduce the risk of infection.

- Antiseptics kill or inhibit microorganisms and can be used on living tissue – but only on the outside.

- The effectiveness of disinfectants and antiseptics can be measured by the phenol coefficient test and the use-dilution test.

- The lowest effective does of antiseptic and disinfectants should be used to minimise risks to workers and the environment and to reduce cost.

- Chemotherapeutic agents kill or inhibit microorganisms but do not damage the host tissue.

- Chemotherapeutic agents produced by bacteria or fungi are called antibiotics.

- New antibiotics are searched for by screening. Antibiotics can be modified by chemical manipulation of the molecule. Genetic manipulation of the producing organism has been more successful in increasing yields of enzymes than in producing new antibiotics or even increasing the yield of antibiotics.

- The MIC of an antibiotic is the lowest concentration that prevents growth of a specific bacterium. The MLC is the lowest concentration that kills a specific bacterium.

- Antibiotic effectiveness can be measured using disc dilution tests.

6.4 The virus problem

Chickens suffers from virus infections too, and the risk of virus infection is much higher in the crowded conditions of intensive farming. Fowl plague, or avian influenza, is caused by viruses in the influenza A group. Infected chickens suffer breathing problems and almost always die. Another example is Newcastle disease which causes a range of symptoms including coughing, walking backwards and paralysis. Again, the mortality rate is high.

Viruses enter the host cell and use host cell constituents and enzymes to make new virus particles. Since viruses do not have the same biochemistry as other microorganisms, antibiotics that are effective against bacteria and fungi have no effect on viruses. For example, penicillins work by preventing cross-links forming in peptidoglycan cell walls. As viruses do not have a peptidoglycan cell wall they are not inhibited by penicillins. In addition, as viruses use host cell processes, any substance that interferes with such processes in an attempt to kill the virus, will inevitably damage the host. However, a number of substances that inhibit virus-specific enzymes have recently been developed. Examples include amantadine (used to prevent influenza A) and acyclovir (used to treat herpes).

Although viruses are not affected by antibiotics, patients who have a viral infection such as influenza are often prescribed antibiotics in order to prevent the occurrence of a secondary, bacterial infection.

10 a Why are viruses not affected by antibiotics?

b Do you think doctors prescribing antibiotics to people who have a virus disease is sensible? Can you think of a better approach?

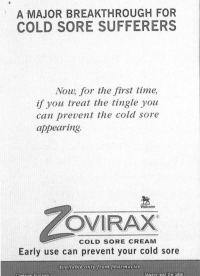
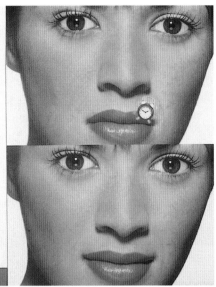

The herpes 'cold sore' can
now be prevented from
appearing.

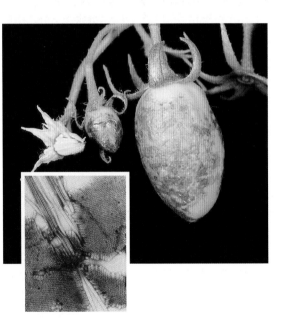

These tomatoes have been
damaged by the tobacco
mosaic virus and the potato
virus. Tobacco mosaic virus
attacks valuable food crops
such as tomatoes, lettuces
and raspberries; the virus
particles are long cylinders,
shown here in LS and TS.

Growing viruses in the laboratory
In order to examine the effects of antiviral
substances, it is essential to be able to
culture viruses in the laboratory. This is
difficult because viruses only grow and
reproduce inside living host cells. A virus
particle, or virion, consists of one or more
DNA or RNA molecules in a covering of
protein. Some viruses have extra layers of
lipids, carbohydrates and additional
proteins. Viruses can exist outside cells but
they cannot reproduce unless they enter a
host cell. For this reason viruses cannot be
cultured by simply adding them to a
nutrient medium.

For many years the standard way to
cultivate viruses has been to inoculate a
suitable host animal or inject the viruses
into fertilised chicken eggs. The most
common sites for egg inoculation are the
allantoic cavity and the chorioallantoic
membrane (Fig. 9).

More recently, viruses have been grown
in glass bottles or petri dishes on a single
layer of cells. This is possible because
suitable growth media have been developed
and there are antibiotics to prevent the
growth of bacteria and fungi that would
damage the cells.

Bacteriophages, or bacteria-infecting
viruses, are relatively easy to culture. They
are either inoculated into broth cultures of
suitable bacteria or added to bacteria which
have been allowed to grow as a continuous
thin layer (or lawn) on agar. In both cases,
the bacteriophages reproduce rapidly and
lyse the bacterial cells. On bacterial lawns,
small clear spaces called **plaques** indicate
bacteriophage reproduction.

Plant viruses can be cultured in a
number of ways. The most common are
plant tissue culture and whole plant
inoculation. It is relatively simple to rub a
mixture of virus and abrasive onto leaves.
The virions quickly enter the plasma

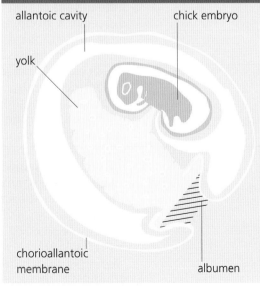

Fig. 9 Virus culture in chicken eggs

allantoic cavity   chick embryo

yolk

chorioallantoic
membrane   albumen

membranes of damaged leaf cells and then infect the cells themselves. Evidence for infections include large areas of dead cells, altered leaf shape and colour changes.

Viruses are of great importance in biotechnology for a number of reasons:
- the development of antiviral substances is of particular commercial and medical interest e.g. in the search for cures for AIDS;
- viruses, especially the bacteriophages, can be very damaging in industrial processes if they infect stock or working cultures;
- bacteriophages transport genetic material between bacteria (this makes them essential in genetic manipulation).

11 Why must viruses be cultured inside living cells?

6.5 New approaches

Microbiologists are looking for new antibiotics from unusual sources, including the slime moulds (*Myxobacteria*) sometimes seen on rotting vegetation. In addition, genetic engineering and chemical modifications may extend the range of antibiotics available. However, unless the use of antibiotics is more strictly controlled, for example in animal feed and meat preservation, the development of bacteria resistant to these newer antibiotics may be just a matter of time.

The problem of resistance
There is no doubt that the careless use of antibiotics over the past 40–50 years has contributed to the problem of bacterial resistance to antibiotics (Chapter 11, p. 150). Antibiotics have been overused and misused in treating human infections, and have also been widely used in intensive farming. There are two routes for tackling the problem of bacterial infections in chickens. One is to keep chickens in better conditions and use disinfectants more widely so as to reduce the likelihood of infection. The other is to continue to supply antibiotics in the chicken feed. But commercial values are influential here as well as scientific ones, and the second choice is the cheaper option.

12 Which do you think is the better solution: disinfectants on the outside, or antibiotics in the chicken feed? Why?

Key ideas

- It is more difficult to keep viruses under control than other microorganisms as they do not have the same biochemistry as other microorganisms and because they only reproduce inside a host cell.

- Viruses cannot be cultured on a nutrient medium, they must have a host cell.

- Viruses are traditionally cultured in a host such as fertilised chicken eggs. Today, tissue culture techniques have enabled the culture of viruses on single-cell layers in bottles and petri dishes.

- Bacteriophages are a group of viruses that infect bacteria. They are easy to culture because they grow on bacterial lawns. Bacteriophages can carry genetic material from a resistant bacterium to a non-resistant bacterium that then becomes resistant.

- Overuse of antibiotics for 40–50 years has led to a situation where bacterial resistance to antibiotics is a problem.

- Even if we find new antibiotics, resistance to them will develop unless we use them more sparingly and responsibly.

Diseases you can't catch

In the past, people thought of health as the lack of disease – there was more emphasis on illness than on well-being. A more modern holistic view of health includes physical, mental, emotional, social, spiritual, sexual, and environmental factors. Health promotion is more about promoting health than preventing illness. Health promotion recognises that each individual should be able to develop skills for living, such as decision-making, assertiveness, and problem-solving, and should also have a positive self-image. In western society, this is a new idea.

Until the early twentieth century, diseases were mainly of the type that you could 'catch'. But many of these infectious or communicable diseases are now much less common. In their place are diseases that attack people whose lifestyle is not healthy. You can take steps to protect yourself from quite a few of these diseases by maintaining a holistically healthy attitude, and changing behaviour thought to be damaging to health such as smoking, eating an unhealthy diet, and taking too little exercise. You will also improve your sense of well-being.

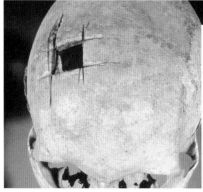

Holistic health is better than cure – especially when the cure is to drill a hole into the skull. Trepanning, as it is called, seems to have been practised from the Stone Age up to the present day and it frequently causes the death of the patient.

7.1 Learning objectives

After working through this chapter, you should be able to:

- **explain** the terms aetiology and epidemiology;

- **explain** the classification of disease into communicable and non-communicable diseases;

- **describe** the role of screening in detecting the early stages of disease;

- **describe** the role of biochemical tests, X-rays, endoscopy, ultrasound and genetic techniques in detecting disease;

- **explain** the aetiology, symptoms and epidemiology of a range of non-communicable diseases including atheroma, stroke, chronic bronchitis, emphysema, cancer, Down's syndrome and cystic fibrosis;

- **understand** the role of health-related behaviour in reducing a person's risk of disease.

7.2 Aetiology

The **aetiology** of a disease is a description of the characteristic cause(s) of that disease. Aetiological agents include:
- infective agents;
- chemicals;
- ionising radiation;
- physical agents;
- genetic abnormalities.

   Diseases caused by infective agents are communicable (Chapter 8). All other aetiological agents produce non-communicable diseases (Fig. 1).

1 What is aetiology?

2 Using Figure 2, what were the two main death-causing diseases in 1990?

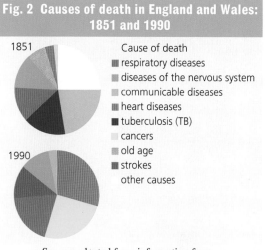

Fig. 2 Causes of death in England and Wales: 1851 and 1990

1851

1990

Cause of death
- ■ respiratory diseases
- ■ diseases of the nervous system
- ■ communicable diseases
- ■ heart diseases
- ■ tuberculosis (TB)
- cancers
- □ old age
- ■ strokes
-   other causes

Source: adapted from information from the Registrar-General 1855 and 1992

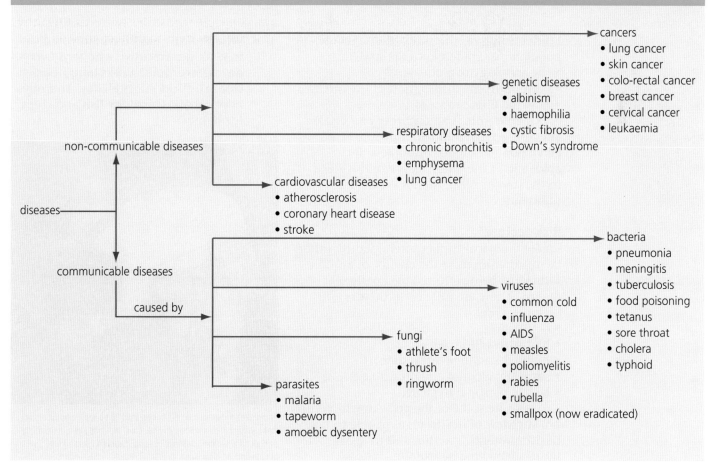

Fig. 1 Communicable and non-communicable disease

diseases

non-communicable diseases
- cancers
  - lung cancer
  - skin cancer
  - colo-rectal cancer
  - breast cancer
  - cervical cancer
  - leukaemia
- genetic diseases
  - albinism
  - haemophilia
  - cystic fibrosis
  - Down's syndrome
- respiratory diseases
  - chronic bronchitis
  - emphysema
  - lung cancer
- cardiovascular diseases
  - atherosclerosis
  - coronary heart disease
  - stroke

communicable diseases caused by
- bacteria
  - pneumonia
  - meningitis
  - tuberculosis
  - food poisoning
  - tetanus
  - sore throat
  - cholera
  - typhoid
- viruses
  - common cold
  - influenza
  - AIDS
  - measles
  - poliomyelitis
  - rabies
  - rubella
  - smallpox (now eradicated)
- fungi
  - athlete's foot
  - thrush
  - ringworm
- parasites
  - malaria
  - tapeworm
  - amoebic dysentery

CHURCH LANE
BLOOMSBURY

The change in the type of disease causing most deaths in 1851 and in 1990 is due to:
- the development of a public health policy that includes laws about handling food, water purification, sewage treatment, pollution and housing;
- the establishment of a National Health Service;
- health education and health promotion;
- developments in medicine, including vaccinations, new drugs, infection control and medical technology;
- improvements in nutrition and the general standard of living.

This is London in 1875. In the nineteenth century, city slums were overcrowded and had poor sanitation and contaminated water supplies.

7.3 Epidemiology

Epidemiology is the study of disease in populations. Epidemiologists study:
- the aetiology of a disease;
- patterns in the distribution of the disease;
- how the disease spreads.

An **epidemic** is an outbreak of a disease affecting a large number of people in a given population, for example a 'flu epidemic. If the outbreak is world-wide, as in the case of AIDS, then it is called a **pandemic**.

Risk factors
Epidemiological studies often identify other factors that increase the chance of an individual being affected by a particular disease. These are called **risk factors** and include:
- occupation;
- high-stress lifestyle;
- high-fat and high-sugar diet;
- smoking, alcohol and drug abuse;
- lack of personal hygiene.

These are some of the areas in which the holistic view of health urges people to take health-promoting action and to avoid health-damaging behaviour.

Q3 What holistic advice would you give to a young executive who jogs every day before work, works long hours, smokes, sucks mints all day, and buys pre-prepared meals or fish and chips for dinner?

There are a number of diseases that have well documented links with certain occupations. Coal miners are particularly at risk of pneumoconiosis, a lung disease caused by inhalation of coal dust.

Diagnosis

Diagnosis names a disease or condition in an individual patient. Correct diagnosis is essential before a doctor can choose the appropriate treatment. An early diagnosis enables early treatment. Diagnosis usually has three stages:

- talking to the patient, or a parent, about the **symptoms** (what the patient thinks indicates the disease);
- examination of the patient to observe the **clinical signs** (what the doctor can observe that indicates the disease);
- using diagnostic tests to further investigate the signs and symptoms.

After diagnosis the doctor prescribes a course of treatment based on:

- the needs of the patient;
- current medical knowledge;
- available resources.

Screening

Screening is looking for signs of disease when the patient may not be aware of any symptoms. It enables early diagnosis. Sometimes screening is random, for example, a doctor may decide to check the blood pressure of all adult patients who come to the surgery. Other screening programmes may be systematic, for example, the screening of schoolchildren for hearing or sight problems. Some screening is of self-selecting groups, for example, women who go for cervical smear tests.

4 Does screening fit in with a holistic attitude?

7.4 Screening and diagnostic tests

Doctors use a wide range of diagnostic techniques (Table 1).

Table 1 Diagnostic and screening techniques		
Chemical	Biological	Physical
biochemical tests	biopsies	X-rays
immunological tests	cytological examination	ultrasound
	culturing microorganisms	endoscopy
	genetic analysis	blood pressure
		eye tests
		hearing tests

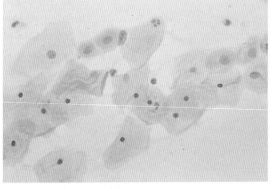
These are normal cervical cells.

Biochemical tests

Biochemical tests are carried out on body fluids such as blood and urine. For example, glucose in urine indicates diabetes. Testing urine for glucose is as quick and easy as dipping a plastic stick into a sample and looking for a colour change (Chapter 5, p. 66).

Immunological tests

These tests are a particular set of biochemical tests that involve the use of monoclonal antibodies (Chapter 11, p. 153).

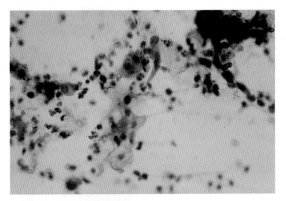
These cervical cells are from a tumour.

Biopsies

A **biopsy** is a sample of tissue taken from an organ. The sample is then sectioned so the cells can be examined under a microscope. Biopsies can be taken from an organ still in the body. It is used to detect certain forms of cancer, including liver and breast cancer.

Cytological examination

This usually refers to the microscopic examination of a few cells that have been removed from the body to see if there is any sign of them being or becoming cancer cells. An example is the cervical smear that women are advised to have every 3 years to detect any abnormal cells before they develop into cancer of the cervix.

Cervical screening has greatly reduced the number of cases of cervical cancer and the number of deaths from this disease. As soon as the first signs are found, treatment can begin, and with earlier treatment almost 90% of patients now survive for at least 5 years following diagnosis.

5 How does screening help reduce the number of women who die from cervical cancer?

Microorganisms can often be identified from the medium on which they grow.

Culturing microorganisms

Microbiologists in hospital pathology departments culture microorganisms from samples of blood, faeces, urine, epithelial tissue or mucus. Any microbes present are identified so as to confirm the diagnosis. Many infectious diseases are diagnosed in this way. At the same time, cultures are grown to test which antibiotics are most effective against them (Chapters 6, 11).

Genetic analysis

Amniocentesis is the method of collecting fetal cells for genetic analysis. It is done when there is a risk of the baby having a genetic disorder such as Down's syndrome.

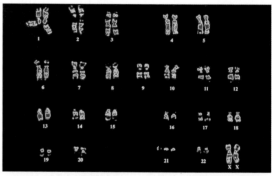

Chromosomes in a dividing cell can be photographed and then sorted into matching pairs. These arrangements are called *karyotypes*. This is the karyotype of a Down's syndrome female.

6 How can you tell if an unborn baby has Down's syndrome?

X-rays

X-rays show damage to bones and can detect abnormalities in soft tissue, for example, certain types of cancer can be detected this way. However, as X-rays are a form of ionising radiation and can damage DNA, care has to be taken. In particular, women's ovaries are always protected from X-rays, and pregnant women are not usually X-rayed. The **radiographer** – the person who takes X-rays – always works from behind a screen to avoid over-exposure to the radiation.

7 Why are women's ovaries protected from X-rays?

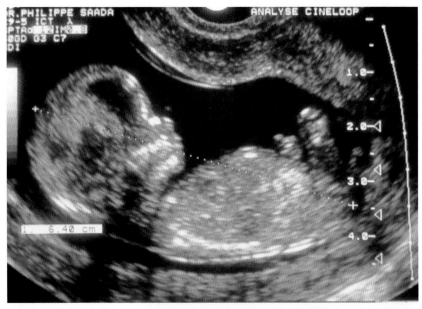

It is safe to monitor fetal development with ultrasound. This fetus is 12 weeks old.

Ultrasound

Ultrasound scanning directs very high frequency sound waves into the area being investigated, and converts the reflected sound into visual images. Unlike X-rays, ultrasound does not damage DNA.

8 Why is ultrasound used to monitor fetal development but X-rays are not?

Endoscopy

An **endoscope** is an instrument for looking inside the body, for example, to look for tumours or ulcers in the stomach.

Blood pressure measurement

Blood pressure is measured using a sphygmomanometer. High levels may be indicative of stress (Chapter 12, p. 170).

Sight and hearing tests

These tests involve checking whether or not an individual can read letters on a board or hear a whisper at a specified distance. Visual and aural problems can arise from a number of causes.

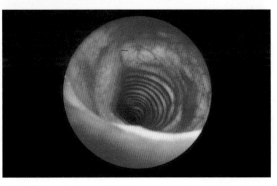

This is an endoscopic image of a normal human trachea.

Key ideas

- Aetiology is a list of causes of a disease.

- Diseases are either communicable or non-communicable. In the nineteenth century, most disease-related deaths were from communicable disease; in the twentieth century most such deaths are from non-communicable disease.

- Epidemiology is the study of the aetiology and distribution of a disease, and the means by which it is spread. Epidemiology also identifies risk factors. These do not cause disease but affect the likelihood of getting a disease.

- Diagnosis names a disease in a patient. Screening helps to enable early diagnosis.

- Chemical tests are usually carried out on body fluids and look for specific chemicals that indicate particular diseases.

- Biological tests involve microscopically examining cells (from biopsies or cytological samples) or culturing microorganisms taken from body tissues.

- Physical tests are those that employ X-rays or ultrasound, and the tests for blood pressure, hearing and vision.

7.5 Cardiovascular diseases

Maintaining the health of the **cardiovascular system** is very much a holistic concern. It is an area in which people can do a great deal to improve and maintain their health by eating a low-fat diet, not smoking, reducing stress and taking exercise.

Atherosclerosis

Atherosclerosis is an arterial disease caused by the build up of fatty deposits, known as **atheroma**, on the inner lining (Fig. 3).

It is likely that the artery lining has been damaged in some way before an atheroma develops (Fig. 4). A dangerous complication is the formation of a **thrombus** (stationary blood clot), or an **embolism** (mobile clot). A thrombus restricts the flow of blood, an embolism is carried round the body by the blood, but may eventually lodge somewhere and restrict blood flow.

9 **What can you do to reduce the risk of developing atheroma?**

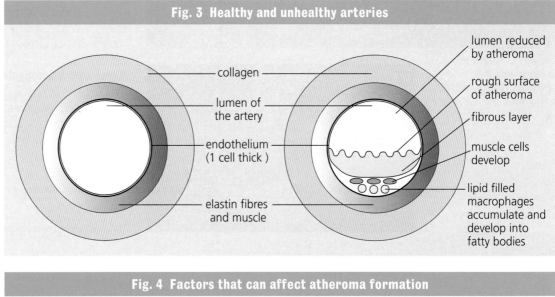

Fig. 3 Healthy and unhealthy arteries

- collagen
- lumen of the artery
- endothelium (1 cell thick)
- elastin fibres and muscle
- lumen reduced by atheroma
- rough surface of atheroma
- fibrous layer
- muscle cells develop
- lipid filled macrophages accumulate and develop into fatty bodies

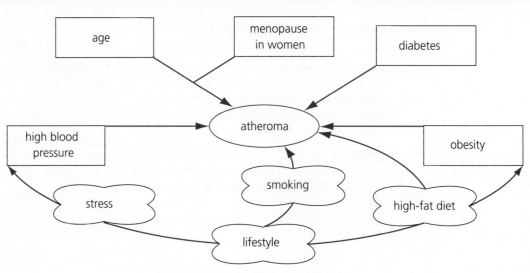

Fig. 4 Factors that can affect atheroma formation

- age
- menopause in women
- diabetes
- high blood pressure
- atheroma
- obesity
- stress
- smoking
- high-fat diet
- lifestyle

Coronary heart disease

Atheroma in coronary arteries is called coronary heart disease (CHD). If a thrombus forms in a coronary artery, an area of cardiac muscle is partially starved of oxygen. This causes severe pain in the chest, neck and arms – a condition called angina. Without treatment, the clot may eventually block the artery and completely deprive the cardiac muscle of oxygen. This causes a **myocardial infarction** (heart attack) because the cardiac muscle cannot contract. This can kill, although many heart attack patients survive if they are treated quickly. Heart attacks are also caused by embolisms that form somewhere else and travel to a coronary artery.

Aneurysm

When an atheroma forms, the artery wall is weakened because elastic tissue is lost. The wall swells into a balloon called an **aneurysm** that may burst and cause internal bleeding. Aneurysms can only be treated by surgery.

10 a How might a blood clot forming in an artery in the leg eventually cause a heart attack?
  b What is this type of blood clot called?

Cerebrovascular accident

A thrombus or embolism can block the blood flow to the brain. If this happens, a **cerebrovascular accident** occurs, that is, the patient suffers a stroke. This is more common in older people, but it can happen at any age.

A stroke can seriously damage or kill cells in brain tissue and, because of the way the brain is organised, the effects of this are often confined to one side of the body. Effects range from slight to severe paralysis and in many cases are permanent, but many people do make a good recovery. Speech is often affected.

7.6 Respiratory diseases

Respiratory health is another area in which people can do much for themselves. Smoking is a major cause of respiratory disease, although other factors include air pollution and certain occupations where irritant particles are likely to be inhaled.

11 In the 1950s there was legislation to severely reduce air pollution in the UK. Do you think this has had any effect on the respiratory health of people in the 1990s?

This is Kraków (Poland), where many years of acid air pollution have damaged buildings and health. Conditions are improving now, and the yellow building shows that restoration can be achieved for buildings. But lung cancer, asthma and chronic bronchitis are still more frequent than elsewhere in Poland.

Chronic bronchitis

A person is said to have chronic bronchitis if they have had a **productive cough** (where phlegm is coughed up) which has lasted for at least 3 months during 2 successive years with no obvious cause. People with chronic bronchitis quickly get out of breath.

Normally, cilia in the bronchial tubes beat rhythmically to produce a constant upward flow of mucus from the bronchi to the back of the throat where it is swallowed. The healthy mucus flow traps dust particles, microbes and other irritants, so they do not reach the alveoli. Smoking and air pollution paralyse the cilia so the mucus builds up into clumps that are coughed up. The lining of the bronchial tubes becomes irritated and inflamed. Without the mucus trap, irritants and microorganisms cause further irritation, inflammation, and infection.

Smoking damages the walls of small bronchioles and alveoli and causes the growth of fibrous tissue around the bronchioles, narrowing the air passageway. This makes it harder to breathe.

12a What damage does smoking do to the bronchi and alveoli?
  b What is the effect of this damage?

Emphysema

In emphysema, the walls of the alveoli are broken down so less surface area is available for the exchange of gases (Fig. 5). Emphysema is commonest in middle-aged male smokers, although it is also a linked to a number of occupations, such as coal mining.

Smokers with emphysema or chronic bronchitis are advised to give up smoking and to avoid environments with atmospheric pollutants. Vaccination is sometimes used to prevent complications such as the development of infections like pneumonia.

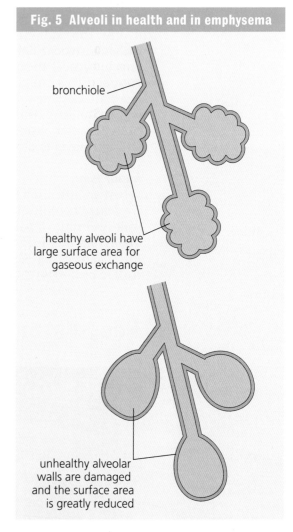

Fig. 5 Alveoli in health and in emphysema

bronchiole

healthy alveoli have large surface area for gaseous exchange

unhealthy alveolar walls are damaged and the surface area is greatly reduced

7.7 Cancer

A tumour or a **neoplasm** is a mass of cells that are undergoing repeated cell division regardless of the body's need of new cells for growth and repair. A **benign tumour** is one that forms a harmless lump. A **malignant tumour** is one whose cells are spread round the body by the blood and lymphatic systems to develop new tumours in other areas. **Cancer** is a range of diseases in which uncontrolled cell growth forms a malignant tumour. The spreading of tumour cells round the body is called **metastasis**.

13 How do malignant tumours spread?

Cancer may develop anywhere in the body, and roughly 25% of the UK population will have cancer at some point in their lives. The occurrence of different cancers is not the same in men and women (Table 2). Around 50% of cancer patients survive for at least 5 years after diagnosis.

Carcinogens

Carcinogens are factors that transform a normal cell into a cancer cell (Fig. 6).

14 Study Figure 6. Why are cancer cells often attacked by the body's immune system?

Table 2 Commonest forms of cancer	
Male	Female
lung	breast
skin	colo-rectal
colo-rectal	skin
prostate	lung
bladder	ovary
stomach	stomach
pancreas	cervix
lymphoma	uterus
oesophagus	pancreas
leukaemia	lymphoma

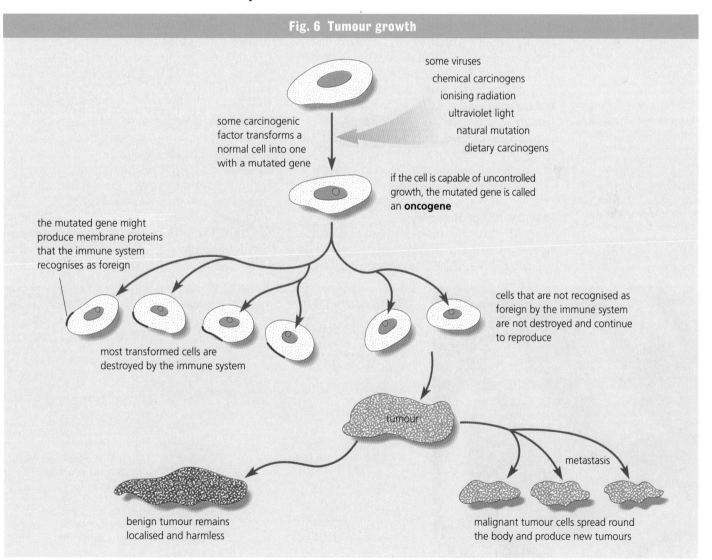

Fig. 6 Tumour growth

some viruses
chemical carcinogens
ionising radiation
ultraviolet light
natural mutation
dietary carcinogens

some carcinogenic factor transforms a normal cell into one with a mutated gene

if the cell is capable of uncontrolled growth, the mutated gene is called an **oncogene**

the mutated gene might produce membrane proteins that the immune system recognises as foreign

most transformed cells are destroyed by the immune system

cells that are not recognised as foreign by the immune system are not destroyed and continue to reproduce

tumour

metastasis

benign tumour remains localised and harmless

malignant tumour cells spread round the body and produce new tumours

Chemical carcinogens

Many different chemicals are known to be carcinogenic, for example, asbestos, benzene, and some components of cigarette smoke. Polycyclic aromatic hydrocarbons are a group of chemicals found in cigarette tar, and thought to be the main carcinogens involved in lung cancer in smokers.

Lung cancer usually develops in the epithelium lining the bronchioles. A cancer of the epithelium is known as a **carcinoma**. Lung cancer is often linked with chronic bronchitis and emphysema. In the early stages, there are often no noticeable symptoms, and the tumour often does not show up on X-rays. Later on, tumours block the air passageways making breathing difficult. Metastasis is common in lung cancer. Severe coughing, chest pains, fever, loss of weight and general weakness are all symptoms of the later stages. Only about 16% of lung carcinomas are diagnosed before metastasis and less than 45% of these patients survive. Less than 1% of patients diagnosed after metastasis survive.

Heavy smokers are 20 times more likely to suffer from lung cancer than non-smokers. Stopping smoking reduces the chance of developing lung cancer, and eventually the risk falls to the level for non-smokers. How long this takes, depends on how many cigarettes a day were smoked.

15 What are the main carcinogens causing lung cancer?

Ionising radiation

Ionising radiation includes X-rays, gamma (γ) rays and alpha (α) and beta (β) particles. All can damage DNA, causing mutations that might lead to cancer. In the UK, naturally occurring radiation is less than half the internationally prescribed safe upper limit and comes from a mixture of sources (Fig. 7).

This is one of the areas where taking a holistic approach is more difficult. For instance, there is considerable controversy about whether or not there are links between certain types of cancer, such as leukaemia, and nuclear power stations. Less controversial are the links between cancer and single, large, possibly short-lived doses of radiation like nuclear accidents.

Leukaemia is uncontrolled cell growth but in this case there is no tumour because the cells are white blood cells (leukocytes). Cells in the bone marrow may be damaged by ionising radiation, although exposure to benzene (a hydrocarbon found in some petrols) and a virus are other possible causes. The rapid increase in leukocyte production is accompanied by a reduction in red cell and platelet production. This means that leukaemia sufferers are often pale and tired as less oxygen is able to reach their cells. Leukaemic white cells do not function properly, so the immune system cannot defend the body from bacterial infections. There are several types of leukaemia and treatment is more successful for some than for others. Treatment usually involves drugs to reduce cell division in the bone marrow, and radiation therapy.

Fig. 7 Sources of ionising radiation in the UK

13% is radiation from artificial sources
- medical X-rays
- nuclear power stations
- industry

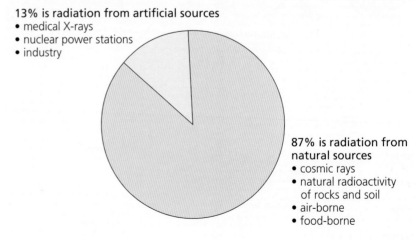

87% is radiation from natural sources
- cosmic rays
- natural radioactivity of rocks and soil
- air-borne
- food-borne

16 a Why is there no tumour in leukaemia?

b Why are bacterial infections particularly dangerous to leukaemia sufferers?

Ultraviolet light

Sunbathing is not part of a holistic lifestyle. Ultraviolet light (UVL) is a component of sunlight, and is believed to be the chief cause of skin cancer. Skin cancer occurs mainly in people who have light skin and live in very sunny climates or who visit such places for holidays. Melanin, a skin pigment, absorbs UVL so it does not damage cells in the basal layers of the epidermis. UVL can cause mutations in these cells such that malignant skin tumours arise. Protective creams with 'sun screens' reduce the effect of UVL, but in areas of strong sunlight, extra care should be taken. Treatment of skin cancer before any significant metastasis has a success rate of over 90%, but the success rate of treatment after metastasis is less than 15%.

17 How is skin cancer commonly caused?

Dietary carcinogens

Diet is an aspect of lifestyle that we can control. Our diet may contain carcinogens and substances with less direct links to cancer. Nitrates (in drinking water and in

Skin cancer incidence has increased markedly since the 1950s. This is partly due to the increase in sunbathing and 'beach-life' in the 1960s and 1970s and the increase in foreign holidays to sunny resorts.

meat products like bacon and corned beef) are converted by the body to nitrosamine. Nitrosamine is linked to the occurrence of stomach and other cancers. A high fat intake is thought to be linked to the occurrence of a number of cancers including breast cancer. On the positive side, dietary fibre has a role in reducing the risk of cancers such as colo-rectal cancer. Insoluble dietary fibre speeds up the passage of food through the colon, and so reduces the time for possible carcinogens to be in contact with the intestine wall.

One in ten women will develop breast cancer, usually after the age of 35. There are also a small number of cases in men. Besides restricting fat intake, monthly self-examination is recommended because early treatment has a high success rate. There are other causes of such lumps, so if one is found it is important to go to a doctor for a professional diagnosis (this may mean having a biopsy). Treatment is by chemotherapy, radiation, surgery, including **mastectomy** (removal of the breast), and hormone therapy.

18 What actions would a holistic attitude to breast cancer recommend?

Colo-rectal cancer seems to have a genetic factor but there is also considerable evidence that diet plays a significant role. Individuals who are overweight run a greater risk of developing colo-rectal cancer than those of average weight. Colo-rectal cancer can arise in any part of the lower intestine. Blood-stained faeces are an early sign, but a biopsy is necessary to confirm the diagnosis. Treatment is usually a combination of radiation therapy and surgery to remove the cancerous parts – this operation is called a **colostomy**. Sometimes, so much of the colon has to be removed that the faeces cannot pass out through the rectum and anus, and the patient needs a collecting bag attached outside the body to receive waste.

19 How does a high-fibre diet help reduce the risk of colo-rectal cancer?

Viruses

Retroviruses are thought to cause a number of cancers (Fig. 8).

It is thought that the *Herpes simplex* virus, which can be transmitted by sexual intercourse, may also be responsible for cervical cancer. It is not a retrovirus. Diagnosis is by cytological examination.

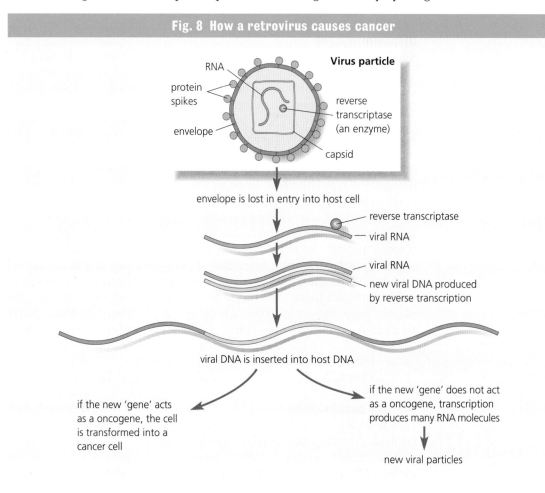

Fig. 8 How a retrovirus causes cancer

Virus particle

RNA
protein spikes
envelope
reverse transcriptase (an enzyme)
capsid

envelope is lost in entry into host cell

reverse transcriptase
viral RNA

viral RNA
new viral DNA produced by reverse transcription

viral DNA is inserted into host DNA

if the new 'gene' acts as a oncogene, the cell is transformed into a cancer cell

if the new 'gene' does not act as a oncogene, transcription produces many RNA molecules

new viral particles

7.8 Genetic diseases

About 2% of the UK population are affected by a genetic disease. Genetic diseases include cystic fibrosis, haemophilia, Down's syndrome and sickle cell anaemia. This is an area that provides a lot of difficulties for the holistic model of health. There is little anyone can do to affect the development of a genetic condition. However, the Human Genome Project is an international research programme to work out the DNA sequences of 50 000–100 000 genes in human chromosomes. The project aims to provide information for the possible treatment of genetic diseases. Genetic diseases can be divided into three groups:
- chromosome diseases;
- single gene disorders;
- multifactorial diseases (diseases involving several genes and diseases involving environmental and genetic factors).

Chromosome diseases
Chromosome defects may involve:
- changes in chromosome number;
- rearrangement of genes;
- loss or duplication of chromosome parts.

Aneuploidy is the addition or removal of all or part of a chromosome from a gamete. The individual who develops from such a gamete either has an irregular chromosome number or has chromosomes with extra parts or parts missing. Down's syndrome is the result of aneuploidy. In this case, the individual has three copies of chromosome 21. This triple chromosome condition is called **trisomy**, and it usually arises because chromosome 21 does not separate properly during meiosis in females, so the ovum has 24 chromosomes instead of the usual 23. The chance of this occurring increases as a woman gets older, which is why more Down's syndrome babies are born to older mothers (Table 3). Down's syndrome can be diagnosed by amniocentesis.

Greater risks of leukaemia and heart abnormality are associated with the condition. If a Down's syndrome mother and a genetically normal father have a baby, the chances of the offspring having Down's syndrome are 50:50.

Almost 7.5% of all conceptions involve chromosome aberrations, but most of these result in a spontaneous miscarriage early in the pregnancy because the defect prevents the fetus from developing. Only about 0.6% of live births have some chromosomal defect.

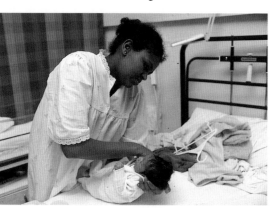

Table 3 Age and the occurrence of trisomy	
Age of woman	Risk of trisomy of chromosome 21
20–30	1:1500
30–35	1:750
35–40	1:600
40–45	1:300
45+	1:60

20 Why is an amniocentesis test recommended for pregnant women over forty?

Single gene disorders

Over 3000 single gene disorders have been identified, and 1% of the population are affected in some way. Each gene carries information coding for the production of a polypeptide or protein molecule. Many of these molecules are enzyme molecules, although some are structural proteins (like membrane proteins), and some are functional polypeptides (like those in haemoglobin). If the DNA sequence in a gene is changed, the protein or polypeptide that the gene produces will not contain the correct sequence of amino acids and will be the wrong shape to function properly. For instance, an enzyme may no longer fit with its substrate, or a haemoglobin molecule may have reduced oxygen-carrying capacity. There are three ways in which the DNA sequence may get changed (Fig. 9).

Fig. 9 Changing a gene

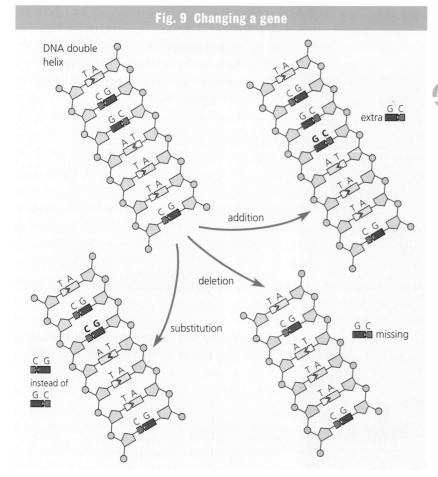

DNA double helix

addition

deletion

substitution

extra G|C

G C missing

C G instead of G C

95

The disorders that result from single gene mutation can be grouped into three categories:

- **autosomal dominant disorders** where the mutant gene is dominant to the normal gene
- **autosomal recessive disorders** where the mutant gene is recessive to the normal gene
- **heterosome disorders** or X-linked disorders.

21 How can a gene mutation resulting in the insertion of an incorrect amino acid into a polypeptide affect the functioning of an enzyme?

The distinction between autosomal dominant and recessive disorders is:

- if a **heterozygous** individual can function normally, the disorder is only seen in **homozygous** individuals and is recessive;
- if a heterozygous individual cannot function normally, the disorder is dominant; homozygous individuals usually miscarry.

Cystic fibrosis (CF) is an autosomal recessive disorder that causes a change in a membrane protein called the cystic fibrosis transmembrane regulator (CFTR). This protein controls the entry of chloride ions into cells. The frequency of heterozygous individuals (carriers) is somewhere between 2% and 5% of the population and the frequency of homozygous CF patients is between 0.2% and 0.3%. People with CF produce abnormally large amounts of mucus from the epithelia of internal organs such as the lungs and pancreas. The over-production of lung mucus causes serious breathing problems and an inability to clear the airways of fluid. This leads to chest infections because microorganisms get trapped in the lungs. Daily physiotherapy is needed to clear the lungs of mucus. There is also congestion due to mucus in other organs, and a high proportion of CF patients die before they are 30. Research is going on into the possibility of treating CF with gene therapy (Fig. 10).

22 Using Figure 10, what properties of liposomes enable them to be the vector for introducing therapeutic DNA into cells?

Heterosome or X-linked disorders are conditions due to a defective gene on an X chromosome. The defective gene can be either dominant or recessive, but most are recessive. As the heterozygous state is more common, very few women have X-linked disorders. (They would have to have the recessive gene on both X chromosomes.) But the number of women who carry such conditions is much higher. Colour-blindness and haemophilia are X-linked conditions (*Biology Core*, Chapter 10).

23 Why are X-linked genetic disorders more rare in women than in men?

Johnny and Edgar Winter have albinism (they have no melanin). This autosomal recessive condition is due to the absence of the enzyme tyrosinase, so the metabolic pathway that converts tyrosine to melanin is blocked.

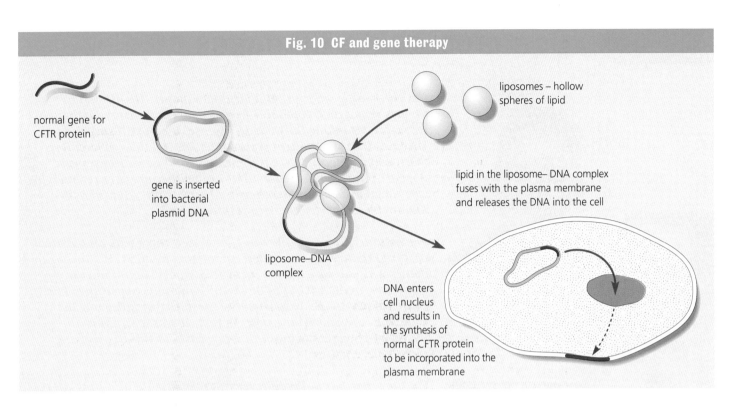

Fig. 10 CF and gene therapy

normal gene for CFTR protein

gene is inserted into bacterial plasmid DNA

liposome–DNA complex

liposomes – hollow spheres of lipid

lipid in the liposome– DNA complex fuses with the plasma membrane and releases the DNA into the cell

DNA enters cell nucleus and results in the synthesis of normal CFTR protein to be incorporated into the plasma membrane

Multifactorial diseases

Multifactorial diseases involving several genes are called **polygenic**. Diabetes mellitus is an example. There are also multifactorial diseases that involve a genetic factor but which do not appear unless certain environmental conditions occur. For example, some individuals cannot metabolise the amino acid phenylalanine, but this is not apparent until the individual is exposed to a large amount of phenylalanine. Then the amino acid builds up in the blood. However, a high blood concentration of phenylalanine affects the development of the central nervous system. Therapy is to adopt a low-phenylalanine diet.

A holistic attitude to health means maintaining behaviour and conditions thought to be good for health. It is thought that the chances of succumbing to many non-communicable diseases can be substantially reduced in this way. But a large number of these diseases are genetic and this is where holistic ideas can lead into controversial areas.

Key ideas

- The risk of cardiovascular disease can be kept low by healthy diet and lifestyle.

- The risk of respiratory disease can be kept low by not smoking and not going into environments with air pollution.

- Cancer is the unrestricted growth of cells that leave the original tumour and spread round the body (metastasise) to start new tumours. Cancer may be caused by chemicals (both edible and non-edible), ionising radiation, ultraviolet light, and some viruses. Treatment for cancer is more likely to be successful if the condition is diagnosed before metastasis.

- Genetic disorders can be divided into chromosome disorders, single gene disorders and multifactorial diseases.

Communicable diseases

I'm the health reporter on a local newspaper. Health issues always make good copy, so I'm never short of a story. Although we've fought a long battle with disease, it can still surprise us. Diseases that we thought were under control, like tuberculosis (TB), can suddenly make a comeback, and new diseases can appear. Sometimes diseases that are neither new nor re-emerging can surprise us by sudden localised outbreaks. And there'll always be a reporter there to record the event.

For instance, in early 1994 in Gloucester, there was an outbreak of a frightening disease called necrotising fasciitis. It causes rapid death of tissue which then turns to a stodgy, liquid mass. Patients can die within 24 hours of symptoms appearing. The national newspapers reported the 'flesh-eating killer bug' as though it was something new. In fact, it was a strain of the bacterium Streptococcus and a few cases of this disease are reported every year.

On the other hand, Ebola fever is a new disease and so is AIDS. Human immuno-deficiency virus (HIV), the virus which causes AIDS was identified in the 1980s. There's been lots of news coverage of AIDS and the fight against it. However, there are many, many other stories – all of them interesting and a lot of them surprising.

Ebola fever is usually fatal. It has killed thousands of people in Africa since 1976.

Coloured transmission electron micrograph of an Ebola virus. This virus was identified in the early 1990s.

8.1 Learning objectives

After working through this chapter, you should be able to:

- **describe** the ways a communicable disease spreads;
- **describe** ways to prevent the spread of communicable diseases;
- **explain** how the transmission of a pathogen can give rise to a disease;
- **describe** the transmission and symptoms of food poisoning caused by *Salmonella*;
- **describe** how situation, infectivity, invasiveness and pathogenicity affect the ability of a bacterium to produce disease;
- **explain** how viruses cause disease;
- **describe** the course of infection in influenza;
- **explain** why viruses are difficult to treat with drugs;
- **describe** the course of infection and the symptoms of athlete's foot.

8.2 Defences against infection

The body has defence mechanisms to prevent most potential infections developing (Chapter 9, p. 116). An infection only occurs if an infecting microorganism gets past the body's defences, or the defences break down.

The defence mechanisms include:
- the **normal flora of the body**;
- the epidermis;
- the **epithelial tissue**;
- lysozyme.

Normal flora of the body

People often link the word 'bacteria' to disease, but not all bacteria are harmful to us. The surfaces of the human body, such as the skin and the lining of the respiratory and digestive systems, are covered in bacteria, viruses and fungi that do not harm us. They are called the normal flora of the body. These organisms often protect us against infection caused by more harmful species, by competing more successfully for available nutrients. Some even produce substances which inhibit the growth of harmful organisms.

Epidermis

Skin cells from the outer layers of the epidermis are constantly being shed and replaced by new cells. This acts as a defence mechanism because shed cells take the bacteria with them.

Epithelial tissue

The surfaces of organs exposed to the outside world (respiratory system, digestive system, urinary system) act as physical barriers to microbe attack. These surfaces are covered with epithelial tissue (Fig. 1). Cells in epithelial tissue are tightly packed and sit on a layer of fibrous material called the **basement membrane**. The epithelial cells in the upper parts of the respiratory system have **cilia** on their outside surface. Cilia trap microorganisms and other particles. The cilia also beat to create a current of moving mucus up the bronchioles and trachea taking trapped microbes towards the throat. Swallowing carries the microbes to the stomach, where they are killed by stomach acid.

Coloured transmission electron micrograph of a group of *Staphylococcus aureus*. This bacterium is commonly found on healthy skin. It has been estimated that there are more bacterial cells on the skin of a healthy person than there are people alive in the world (nearly 5 billion in 1995).

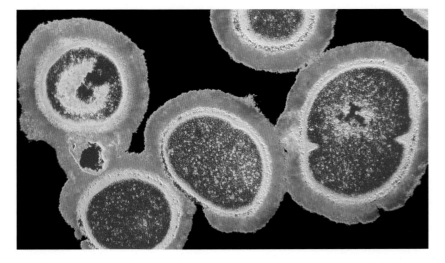

Fig. 1 Epithelial cells

Epithelial cells and the basement membrane

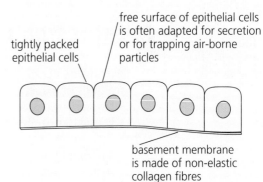

tightly packed epithelial cells

free surface of epithelial cells is often adapted for secretion or for trapping air-borne particles

basement membrane is made of non-elastic collagen fibres

Ciliated cells in the respiratory epithelium

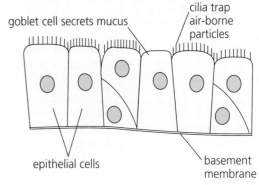

goblet cell secrets mucus

cilia trap air-borne particles

epithelial cells

basement membrane

Lysozyme

Tears and saliva contain lysozyme, an enzyme that kills bacteria.

Q 1 Why is the body's normal flora useful?

What is infection?

An infection occurs when an organism manages to get past the body's defence mechanisms. Microorganisms that cause disease are called pathogens and the transfer of pathogens from one individual to another is called **transmission**. If the pathogen begins to multiply in its new host, that person will be infected, but might not show signs of the disease immediately. This is why infection is not the same thing as having a disease.

There are three types of pathogen that cause infection:
- bacteria;
- viruses;
- fungi.

It is possible for an infected, but otherwise apparently healthy individual, to infect another person. The person passing on the infection is called a **carrier**. The bacterium that causes TB is thought to be carried by about 1.9 billion people at any one time, but most of these carriers will never develop the disease. Only a small percentage (about 20 million people) actually develop TB, so there is an immense disease reservoir carried by people who are unaware that they are infected. This is partly why TB was able to surprise us by suddenly reappearing.

Sometimes the infectious organism living in or on the carrier is going through an incubation period before the appearance of the disease. During the incubation period the microorganism may be multiplying until it reaches sufficient numbers to cause illness.

Q 2 What is the difference between infection and disease?

8.3 Infection routes

Pathogens can infect an individual in a number of ways. These include:
- by air;
- by contaminated water;
- by contaminated food;
- by direct contact (including sexual intercourse);
- by insect bites.

Air-borne infection

There are many diseases that are air-borne (Table 1). When an infected person coughs, sneezes, talks, or breathes, microorganisms are passed into the atmosphere in tiny droplets of saliva, mucus and water. Large droplets tend to travel only one or two metres before reaching the ground, but smaller droplets can remain suspended in the air for long periods. Even droplets that land on the ground dry out fairly quickly and expose the microorganisms to air currents that can circulate pathogen-laden

Table 1 Common air-borne diseases	
Viral diseases	Bacterial diseases
influenza ('flu)	tuberculosis
common cold	'strep' throat (sore throat caused by *Streptococcus* spp.
rubella	

air around a room. In unventilated, crowded buildings the air may carry a large number of pathogens.

But ventilation can cause problems too. Fresh air entering a building can contain pathogens and sometimes the pipes in ventilation systems become reservoirs of pathogenic microorganisms. This can lead to **sick building syndrome**. In 1994, the Inland Revenue closed one of its Merseyside offices because over half of its 2000 staff had suffered repeated bouts of 'flu and other air-born diseases over a five-year period. It was cheaper to close the office and move the workers, than to 'cure' the building by completely replacing the ventilation ducts.

3 **The air in hospital microbiology labs is often slightly below atmospheric pressure. How does this reduce the risk of infectious organisms spreading from the laboratory to other parts of the hospital?**

The air in hospital operating theatres is often slightly above atmospheric pressure, to prevent air from other areas getting in. Staff wear masks to filter out pathogens from breath, and the patient is covered with sterile cloths to prevent air-borne infection.

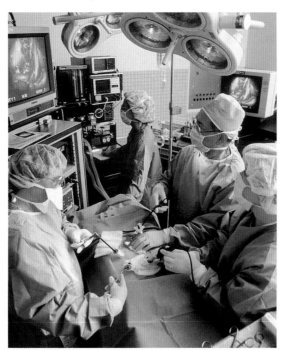

Reservoirs in the UK are often used recreationally.

Water-borne infection

Diarrhoea affects over 1 billion people a year and kills over 5 million, mainly children. Almost all of the deaths are in developing countries. Although diseases such as cholera can cause diarrhoea, the main cause is the bacterium *Escherichia coli* in water contaminated with human faeces. *E. coli* is present in faeces because it is part of the normal flora of the large intestine, but a few strains are pathogenic. The pathogenic strains cause the secretion of large amounts of fluid into the digestive tract resulting in diarrhoea. The body loses salts at the same time as it loses water.

People suffering from severe diarrhoea are often given **oral rehydration therapy** (ORT). They drink a solution of salts and sugars to replace some of the substances the body is losing. Many lives, especially those of children in developing countries, are saved by this technique. However, the disease will recur if poor sanitation is not improved and contaminated water supplies are not cleaned.

In the UK, water is stored in reservoirs. When the water leaves the reservoir it is specially treated to be suitable for drinking (Fig. 2). In addition, sewage is treated to prevent pathogens entering the water supply or from contaminating the environment in other ways. In areas where it is difficult to connect a house or other building to the sewerage system, waste water is fed into septic tanks that allow the water to soak away into the ground. The National Rivers Authority only allows these soakaways in areas where there is no chance of contamination reaching the water supply.

4 **How does ORT help patients suffering from diarrhoea?**

Fig. 2 The water treatment process

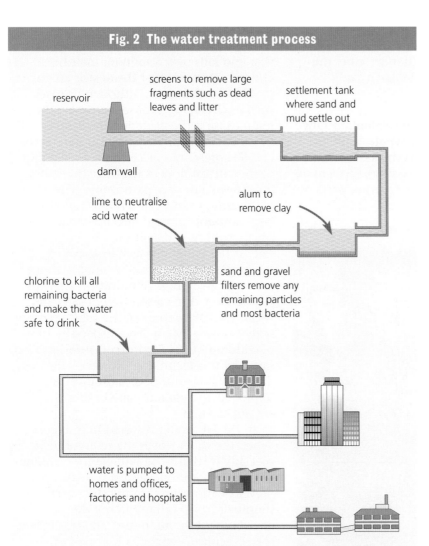

reservoir

dam wall

screens to remove large fragments such as dead leaves and litter

settlement tank where sand and mud settle out

lime to neutralise acid water

alum to remove clay

chlorine to kill all remaining bacteria and make the water safe to drink

sand and gravel filters remove any remaining particles and most bacteria

water is pumped to homes and offices, factories and hospitals

Production of food on a large scale must be carried out in hygienic conditions. The women inspecting these crisps are wearing the correct overalls and hats to prevent contamination.

Some dos and don'ts about food

Don't buy food outside its sell-by date (*microbial growth might have begun*).
Don't refreeze frozen food that has thawed out (*microbial growth might have occurred as food thawed*).

Do put perishable food in the fridge (*cold restricts microbial growth*).
Do wash vegetables thoroughly (*to remove soil microbes*).
Do keep your food preparation area clean (*to reduce the risk of contaminating food*).
Do wash your hands before handling food (*to prevent faecal and other contamination*).
Do keep hot food hot and cold food cold until eaten (*to prevent microbial growth occurring as food reaches a moderate temperature*).
Do be certain that you reheat thoroughly if you reheat food (*to kill microbes that might have started to grow*).

Food-borne infection

Many foods provide a good breeding ground for microorganisms. Food-borne infections usually arise when one or more of the guidelines above is not followed. All are aimed at restricting microbial growth on food. Bacterial diseases spread by contaminated food include *Salmonella* food poisoning, botulism, enteritis, cholera and typhoid.

Salmonella food poisoning is spread when the bacterium is transmitted by food contaminated with the faeces of a carrier. The carrier may be human or animal (p. 106). The symptoms of *Salmonella* food poisoning include stomach pain, nausea, vomiting, diarrhoea, chills, headaches fatigue and fever (Chapter 6, p. 170).

Direct contact infection

When a person with a cold blows their nose, some virus particles will end up on their hands instead of in the tissue. If they shake hands with someone who then brings *their* hand into contact with *their* nose, the virus could infect the second person. Washing your hands reduces the risk of this person-to-person infection.

Sexual intercourse can also spread infection. Bacterial diseases such as syphilis and gonorrhoea and viral diseases like genital herpes can be passed on by sexual contact. For HIV to pass from one person to another, body fluid containing the virus must pass from one person to another and the virus must get into the recipient's blood stream (Chapter 10, p.137). Using condoms helps reduce the risk of infection.

5 a Why should you wash your hands before preparing a family meal?
b Why is it especially important to wash your hands when you have a cold and a runny nose?

Insect-borne infection

Insects transmit a number of infectious diseases, the most important of which is malaria. Malaria is caused by a small parasitic **protozoan** (single-celled animal) that is transmitted from the blood stream of an infected individual to a recipient by a mosquito. The malarial parasite belongs to the genus *Plasmodium* and the mosquito is the Anopheles mosquito (Fig. 3). Malaria is another disease that has surprised us. After programmes to eradicate the disease from certain areas by interrupting the mosquito life cycle, it has suddenly reappeared because people stopped taking the precautions to keep it away too soon.

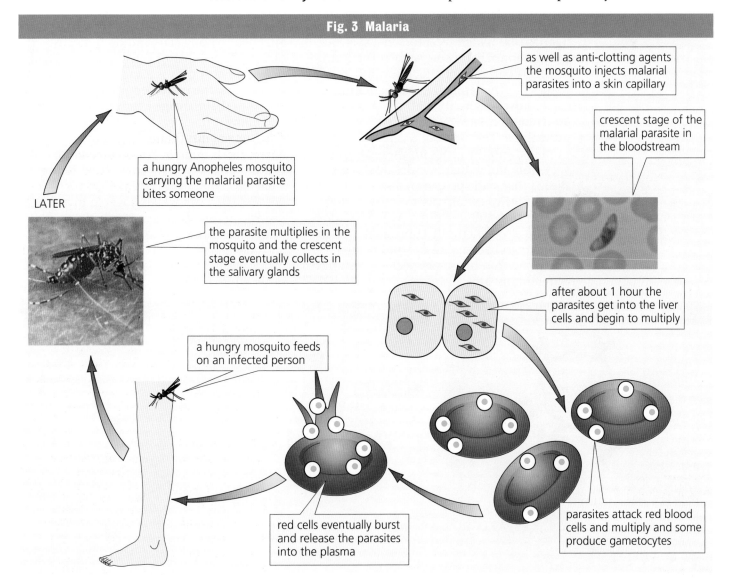

Fig. 3 Malaria

as well as anti-clotting agents the mosquito injects malarial parasites into a skin capillary

crescent stage of the malarial parasite in the bloodstream

a hungry Anopheles mosquito carrying the malarial parasite bites someone

LATER

the parasite multiplies in the mosquito and the crescent stage eventually collects in the salivary glands

after about 1 hour the parasites get into the liver cells and begin to multiply

a hungry mosquito feeds on an infected person

red cells eventually burst and release the parasites into the plasma

parasites attack red blood cells and multiply and some produce gametocytes

8.4 How an infection takes hold

After infection, a pathogen must do three things to produce a disease:
- attach itself to cells in the host;
- penetrate the host cells;
- colonise the host tissue.

Attachment

Most infections begin when pathogens attach to epithelial cells in the digestive, respiratory or urino-genital system. Microorganisms are able to attach to host cells because molecules known as **ligands** in the microbial cell wall or outer viral coat bind with receptor molecules in the host cell membrane (Fig. 4). Bacteria with ligands that match receptors in a specific human epithelial tissue, such as the lining of the throat, cannot attach to similar tissues in other animals. This matching is called **host specificity**, and the process of attachment is known as **specific adherence**. The host cell receptors contain proteins, and the genes for these receptors vary from individual to individual. This means that some people are more susceptible to certain diseases than others. Microbial ligands are often polysaccharides and are also genetically controlled. Genetic diversity in bacteria means that related strains (within the same species) often have different disease-causing properties.

Some bacteria have a sticky layer to their cell wall. This is known as a glycocalyx and is made up of a mixture of sugars and proteins. The glycocalyx helps the bacterium to stick to a host cell.

6a What is specific adherence?
b Why might your sore throat caused by *Streptococcus* sp. be passed on to one member of your family but not to another?

Entry

Attachment alone is not enough to cause a disease. Many of the body's normal flora are attached to body cells and do not cause disease. The ability of the microorganism to penetrate host cells is also important. In some cases, the pathogen produces enzymes that damage host cell membranes, and allow it to enter. In other cases, the host cell engulfs the pathogen by **endocytosis** (Fig. 5). Phagocytic white cells engulf bacteria and try to destroy them but some bacteria can survive this attack because their cell wall is covered in a protective capsule. Once inside the phagocyte, bacteria that survive can then reproduce freely. Since the bacteria are inside a cell, they are cannot be attacked by other white blood cells.

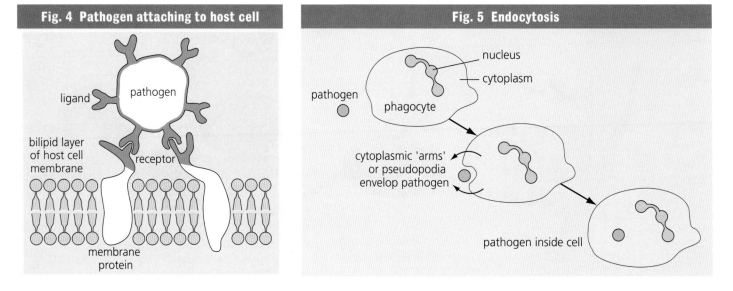

Fig. 4 Pathogen attaching to host cell

ligand
pathogen
bilipid layer of host cell membrane
receptor
membrane protein

Fig. 5 Endocytosis

pathogen
nucleus
cytoplasm
phagocyte
cytoplasmic 'arms' or pseudopodia envelop pathogen
pathogen inside cell

Colonisation

After attachment and entry, the pathogen multiplies and colonises the tissue. The host's immune system (Chapter 10) will attempt to fight off the invading microorganism but sometimes the pathogen can overcome this defence and the disease becomes established. The immune system may still eventually win, but only after the individual has suffered the symptoms of the disease. Antibiotics and other drugs can help. For instance, while antibiotics attack the invading microorganism, paracetamol can alleviate mild pain and lower body temperature which often rises during infections.

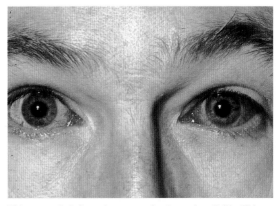

This person's inflamed eyes are due to conjunctivitis. This condition can be caused by bacteria that attack the conjunctiva, the single-cell layer that covers the front of the eyes.

 7 What two ways can a pathogen enter a cell?

Key ideas

- The body has several defence mechanisms against infection. These include the normal flora of the body, the epidermis, the epithelial tissue, and lysozyme.

- Microorganisms that cause disease are called pathogens. Pathogens can be transferred from one person to another (transmission). If a pathogen gets past the body's defence mechanism, that person is carrying an infection.

- Not everyone carrying and infection will develop the disease.

- Transmission routes may be via the air, contaminated water, contaminated food, direct contact between people, and insects.

- After infection, a pathogen will cause disease if it can attach to host cells, penetrate host cells, then colonise host tissue.

- Attachment is by ligands and is host specific. Entry may be by endocytosis or by damage to the host cell membranes. Colonisation occurs if the microorganism is able to multiply and attack more host cells.

8.5 Bacterial infections

There are many bacterial infections in humans (Table 2). Once bacteria have colonised host tissue, the next step is to either directly damage cells or produce toxins. Toxins released from the bacteria as they grow are known as **exotoxins**. Other bacteria do not release their toxins until the bacterial cell dies and the cell wall disintegrates. These toxins are called **endotoxins**.

The ability of bacteria to cause disease relies on:
- situation;
- **infectivity** (how easily a bacterium can cause an infection);
- **invasiveness** (how easily a bacterium or its toxin spreads within the body);
- **pathogenicity** (how toxic the toxin is; most bacterial diseases are due to the toxins produced).

Table 2 Bacterial infections in humans

Region affected	Disease	Bacterium
respiratory system ear, nose and throat	sore throat (pharyngitis) tonsillitis	*Streptococcus pyogenes*
	laryngitis sinusitis otitis media	*Streptococcus aureus*
	pneumonia	*Streptococcus pneumoniae*
	whooping cough	*Bordetella pertussis*
	diphtheria	*Corynebacterium diphtheriae*
	tuberculosis	*Mycobacterium tuberculosis*
digestive system	food poisoning	*Staphylococcus aureus* *Escherichia coli* *Clostridium perfringens* *Salmonella* spp.
	botulism	*Clostridium botulinum*
	salmonellosis	*Salmonella* spp.
	cholera	*Vibrio cholerae*
	typhoid	*Salmonella typhi*
skin	boils	*Staphylococcus aureus*
conjunctiva	conjunctivitis	*Haemophilus influenza* *Streptococcus pneumoniae*
meninges (membranes surrounding the brain and spinal cord)	meningitis	*Haemophilus influenza* *Neisseria meningitides*
nervous system and skin	leprosy	*Mycobacterium leprae*
sexual organs	syphilis gonorrhoea	*Treponema pallidum* *Neisseria gonorrhoeae*
nervous system	tetanus	*Clostridium tetani*

8 What is the difference between an endotoxin and exotoxin?

Situation

Bacteria that get into an area of the body that is normally sterile can cause infection. Bacteria in the normal body flora might reach sterile internal tissues through a wound. The tetanus bacterium *Clostridium tetani*, which lives in soil, can get into the body through broken skin or cuts. Doctors often give anti-tetanus injections following injuries with a risk of tetanus infection.

If people know that their job exposes them to the risk of tetanus infection, they can be vaccinated against it. The vaccine contains tetanus toxin, which stimulates the body's immune system and provides protection for up to 10 years. Unprotected individuals suffering a puncture wound are injected with anti-tetanus antibody, which remains active for only a few months. Vaccination is discussed in Chapter 9.

Infectivity

Often very large numbers of an organism must be present before an infection results. The normal body flora contains a huge variety of different species and no one type of microorganism is present in very large numbers. But if a person is taking antibiotics, much of the normal flora will be destroyed and organisms resistant to the antibiotic will remain. In the absence of competition, these resistant strains will multiply, and could reach levels high enough to cause an infection.

Salmonella enteritidis is a bacterium causing *Salmonella* food poisoning that does not come from chickens. It does not have a high infectivity and needs to be present in large numbers for the disease to occur. If it is eaten, usually through food contaminated by human faeces, it multiplies in the intestine and eventually reaches a concentration high enough to cause symptoms such as enteritis and diarrhoea. There are over 1800 different species of *Salmonella*, but only about 10 cause food poisoning.

Typhoid fever is also caused by a species of *Salmonella*, but in this case the disease occurs when only a small number of bacteria are present. This organism is highly infective and people become ill within hours of infection.

Invasiveness

Invasive bacteria are able to penetrate cells and break into blood and lymph vessels so the pathogens are carried to other organs. Toxins can also spread around the body through the blood and lymph systems and may damage tissues far away from the initial site of infection.

The first bacterial exotoxin to be discovered was produced by the bacterium that causes diphtheria. This toxin works by preventing protein synthesis in host cells, and a single molecule is sufficient to kill a cell. Unlike many toxins, diphtheria toxin has its main effect in the area of the infection, which is the upper respiratory tract.

The toxin produced by *Clostridium tetani* travels round the body and inhibits the neurones which relax muscles. The result is that muscles contract and are then unable to relax – this condition is called spastic paralysis. If spastic paralysis occurs in the intercostal muscles, breathing becomes very difficult and the person may die of asphyxiation.

Pathogenicity

The toxicity of the bacterial toxin is very important in determining how dangerous the infection is. Some toxins are mild and do not produce serious illness. Others, such as the diphtheria toxin, are highly toxic and cause life-threatening disease.

9 Why do bacteria that belong to the body's normal flora sometimes cause disease?

8.6 Virus infections

Many common virus diseases are serious:
- poliomyelitis;
- viral hepatitis;
- rabies (hydrophobia in humans);
- herpes simplex infections;
- AIDS;
- influenza;
- measles and german measles (rubella);
- smallpox;
- mumps;
- viral pneumonia;
- glandular fever.

Influenza

Influenza is very common in the UK. It is sometimes mistaken for the common cold, though there are differences in symptoms between the two diseases (Table 3).

The 'flu virus usually affects tissues in the upper respiratory tract, although it can reach the lungs. Secondary infections sometimes occur when other bacteria and viruses take advantage of the weakened state of the infected tissues. This can be fatal for the old and very young. 'Flu epidemics occur annually, particularly in winter, and in some years these reach very serious levels. Recent major epidemics occurred in 1993 and 1976.

10 a What is a secondary infection?
b Why are secondary infections common during periods of viral infection?

In 1918 influenza gave us a very nasty surprise. That year saw the end of the First World War and the outbreak of the worst 'flu epidemic ever. Over 22 million people worldwide had the disease and more people died from 'flu than had been killed during the First World War.

11 Why is influenza dangerous for the very old and the very young?

Table 3 The common cold and influenza		
	Common cold	Influenza
Caused by	rhinoviruses	influenza virus
Symptoms	sore throat	sore throat
	headache	headache
	sneezing	fever
	runny nose	shivering
	chesty cough	tiredness
		aching joints and muscles
		dry cough
Transmission	droplet infection	droplet infection
	direct contact	direct contact
Secondary infections	bacterial infection of the upper respiratory tract	viral and bacterial pneumonia
Period of illness	3–5 days	up to 7 days

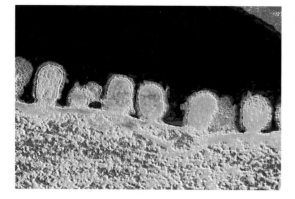

The influenza virus usually spreads from person to person, although animals such as pigs, ducks and poultry can also carry it. The usual infection route is through droplets in human breath, and through mucus. Once inside a new host, the virus particles invade the epithelial tissues of the nose, throat and sometimes the bronchi (Fig. 6). Ligands in the outer coat of the virus combine with a receptor in the host cell membrane so that the virus binds to

the epithelial cell membrane. Since ligands bind to specific receptors, most viruses only affect one species although some viruses can affect a small number of related species.

The influenza virus exists in a number of forms, usually called Type A, B and C. Most influenza outbreaks are of Type A. A person who has suffered from influenza becomes immune to that virus and will not suffer further attacks. However, mutations to the virus can mean that the body fails to recognise the pathogen next time, and the disease returns. Type B is less common than Type A but causes worldwide epidemics (pandemics) about every 5 years. Type C is much rarer, and does not seem to cause such wide-spread outbreaks.

Doctors often recommend vaccination against influenza, particularly for the elderly. The problem is that vaccines can only be developed against individual strains of the virus. Pharmaceutical companies need to prepare large quantities of the vaccine to match the particular strain

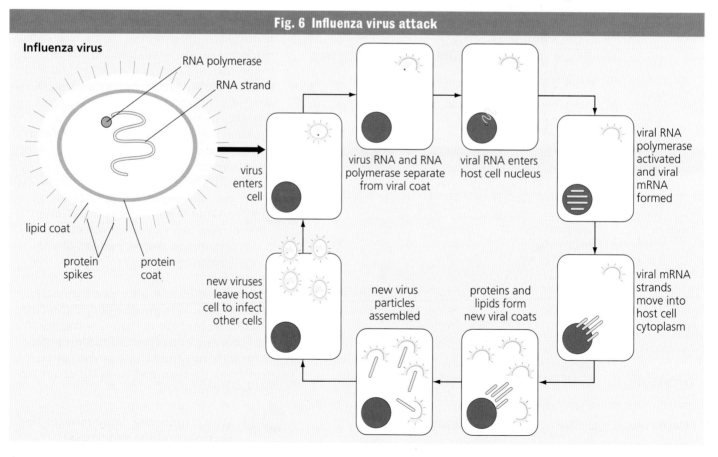

Fig. 6 Influenza virus attack

Influenza virus

RNA polymerase

RNA strand

lipid coat

protein spikes

protein coat

virus enters cell

virus RNA and RNA polymerase separate from viral coat

viral RNA enters host cell nucleus

viral RNA polymerase activated and viral mRNA formed

viral mRNA strands move into host cell cytoplasm

proteins and lipids form new viral coats

new virus particles assembled

new viruses leave host cell to infect other cells

common that year. But another vaccination will be necessary next year to fight the new viral strain that will have developed. Vaccines are usually injected but recent research with liposomes shows that it is possible to produce a vaccine that can be inhaled (Fig. 7).

12 Why doesn't vaccination against influenza give lifelong protection against the disease?

Viral damage to the host

Viruses cause disease by disrupting the host cell and turning it into a virus-making machine. After a period of virus production, the cell dies, and its cell membrane disintegrates by a process called lysis. The heavy mucus produced during a cold or 'flu is largely made up of lysed cells. More seriously, the poliomyelitis virus damages the cell bodies of nerve cells attached to muscles (motor neurones). In good health, muscles contract and relax according to the messages they receive through the motor neurones (Fig. 8). Damage to these nerve cells results in paralysis because the muscles no longer receive the appropriate messages.

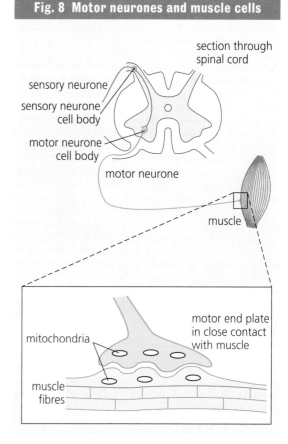

Fig. 8 Motor neurones and muscle cells

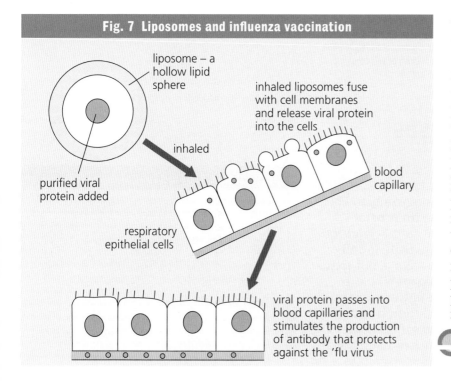

Fig. 7 Liposomes and influenza vaccination

Sometimes damage to the body is caused by the substances from broken-down infected cells entering the blood stream. For example, some of these substances seem to make capillaries 'leak' fluid into the tissues at a rate faster than it can be reabsorbed by other capillaries and lymph vessels. This net loss of fluid causes a drop in blood volume and 'waterlogging' of the tissues. The lowered blood volume reduces blood pressure, which can fall to a level that is fatal in diseases such as smallpox. In viral pneumonia, fluid collects in the lungs. This reduces the area for gaseous exchange as the alveoli fill with liquid. The patient cannot breathe properly, so the heart does not get enough oxygen and cannot work properly. If the heart eventually stops, the patient dies. Secondary bacterial infections increase the risk of death.

13 What are the two ways viruses can cause damage to their host?

Fighting viruses

Viruses move into host cells and rely on them to produce new viral DNA or RNA and proteins. In other words, viruses do not have their own cell metabolism. This means that antibiotics (which disrupt metabolism) cannot be used to fight viruses. Many virus diseases have no remedy because the viruses are inside the host cell and can't be damaged without damaging the host. Treatment is often aimed at reducing the symptoms so the patient feels better even though the number of viruses is not reduced. For example, cold and 'flu patients may be prescribed pain-killing drugs such as paracetamol or aspirin to relieve some of the aches and pains and to help lower body temperature.

However, there are a few antiviral drugs. Some inhibit the production of viral DNA or RNA, by altering the host cell's DNA. Others prevent the enzymes essential for the production of new virus particles from working. A third group of antiviral drugs prevent the virus particles from entering cells in the first place, but since most viral diseases do not produce symptoms until the virus has colonised many host cells, these drugs have little effect.

14 Why is it difficult to find new antiviral drugs?

Poliomyelitis used to be very common in the UK. These children were among the first to be vaccinated against the disease at the start of a national programme to reduce the number of cases. Nowadays, all children are vaccinated against polio and it is very rare in the UK.

8.7 Fungal diseases

There are only about 50 fungal diseases or **mycoses**. The most well known are probably athlete's foot, ringworm and thrush (a yeast infection). In general, fungal diseases affect the outer regions of the body such as the skin, nails and the lining of the mouth and vagina, but some can affect the internal organs (Table 4).

Fungi that cause skin diseases are called dermatophytes. All spore-forming fungi can cause respiratory problems if the spores are inhaled. Care is needed when handling any fungus.

Table 4 Some fungal diseases	
Type of infection	Name of infection
skin mycoses	athlete's foot
	ringworm
epithelial mycoses (affect the lining of mouth and vagina)	thrush (candidiasis)
	aspergillosis
systemic mycoses (affect organ systems)	candidiasis
	histoplasmosis
	conidiomycosis

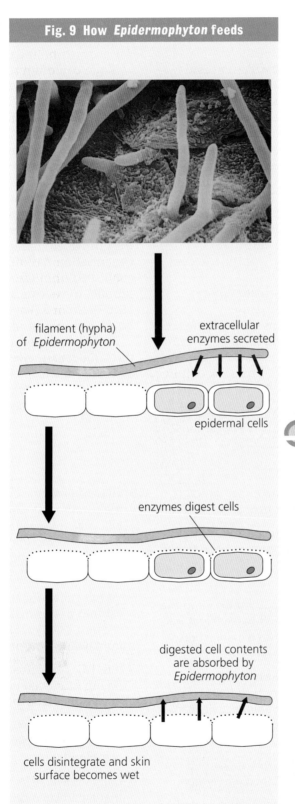

Fig. 9 How *Epidermophyton* feeds

filament (hypha) of *Epidermophyton*

extracellular enzymes secreted

epidermal cells

enzymes digest cells

digested cell contents are absorbed by *Epidermophyton*

cells disintegrate and skin surface becomes wet

Athlete's foot

Athlete's foot is caused by the fungus *Epidermophyton*. It is a contagious skin disease, which attacks damp areas of the body, like the skin in between the toes. Fungal spores from an infected person can be passed on to others via wet floors and puddles at communal baths and swimming pools. This is why most modern swimming pools make sure that people walk through an antiseptic footbath on their way to and from the pool. The fungus feeds on dead epidermal cells (Fig. 9). The area around the initial infection becomes red and itchy. As the fungus spreads outwards, the infected area becomes white and feels wet. The outer edge of the area contains fungus capable of producing more spores and so infecting new areas of skin. Special cream and powder are available without prescription to treat athlete's foot. Fungal diseases are quite difficult to clear and the treatment should be continued for 2 weeks after visible signs of the mycosis have disappeared.

15 Why is it important to dry between your toes?

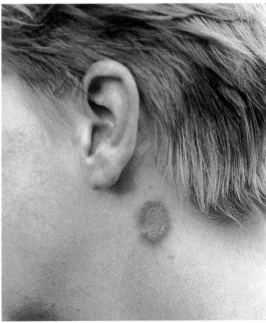

Ringworm commonly affects the scalp (the skin under hair on the head) but can also affect other skin areas. It is caused by a fungus.

8.8 Germ theory of disease

In the nineteenth century, Pasteur and Koch worked on understanding the relationship between disease and microorganisms (Chapter 1). Koch summed up the conditions for proving that a particular organism causes a particular disease in a list known as Koch's postulates.

1 The organism thought to be causing the disease should always be present in animals suffering from the disease and be absent from healthy ones.
2 The organism must be cultivated in pure culture outside the body of the infected animal.
3 The culture, when inoculated into healthy animals should cause characteristic symptoms of the disease.
4 The organism should be re-isolated from the experimental animals and be cultured again in the laboratory. This new culture should be the same as the original one.

Koch could not have imagined that one day not only could we prove that a particular organism caused a particular disease and be able to vaccinate against it, but we would also be able to eradicate the organism and the disease from the world. This is the case with smallpox.

Smallpox was once one of the most dreaded diseases in the world because most sufferers died very painfully, and those who survived were scarred for life. Smallpox is the only disease that the World Health Organisation has officially declared to be eradicated from the world. Even the last supplies of vaccine and stock culture have been destroyed. There should never again be an outbreak of smallpox to surprise us.

How long will it be before we can say the same for the necrotising fasciitis described at the beginning of this chapter? Or AIDS?

Key ideas

- Bacterial disease is due to either direct damage to host cells or toxins.

- Exotoxins are released from bacterial cells during cell growth; endotoxins are released when the bacterial cell dies. Some toxins are more toxic than others.

- The situation of bacteria is important in the disease-causing process. If bacteria get into an area that is normally sterile, infection results.

- Bacteria with low infectivity need to be present in high numbers in order to cause disease. Bacteria with high infectivity can cause disease when only a small number of bacteria are present.

- Invasive bacteria and toxins are carried round the body in the blood and lymph.

- Secondary infections occur when bacteria and viruses infect tissue already weakened by illness.

- Influenza and the common cold are among the commonest viral diseases in the UK. Influenza is usually spread from person to person and vaccination against the disease only gives protection against the specific strain expected that year.

- Viruses cause disease by turning the host cell into a virus-making machine. Eventually the host cell dies. Sometimes the products from lysed cells cause damage in the host.

- It is difficult to attack viruses because they do not have their own cell metabolism and are always inside the host cells.

- There are only about 50 fungal diseases of which athlete's foot is one of the most common.

- Koch's postulates must be satisfied to prove that a particular organism causes a particular disease.

Preventing infection

I'm Chris, and I'm a hurdler. The rewards for success in sport are great, but so are the costs. I start my day by training at 6.00 a.m. every morning. After school I train again then get an early night, so I'm fresh for tomorrow. It's a tough schedule and its difficult to fit everything in. But that's not all. Training and competing put great strains on my body in terms of physiology and 'wear and tear'. Recently I was competing in a club-level event, to qualify for a county-level championship when I fell and landed on my knee. It was a bit like Michelle Freeman's accident in 1993! I gashed my knee and needed hospital treatment. Fortunately there were no broken bones, or sprained joints, but I did need stitches.

Michelle Freeman fell into the path of Julie Bauman at the 1993 World Indoor Games in Toronto.

9.1 Learning objectives

After working through this chapter, you should be able to:

- **describe** the mechanisms for blood clotting and wound healing;

- **explain** how the body produces an inflammation reaction;

- **describe** non-specific immune mechanisms, including barrier mechanisms;

- **describe** how phagocytes ingest foreign material;

- **list** the different parts of the body's immune system;

- **explain** the role of T lymphocytes and B lymphocytes in the immune response;

- **explain** the significance of antigens in the immune response;

- **describe** how antibody structure is related to function;

- **explain** the difference between a primary and a secondary response to infection;

- **explain** why humans suffer from some diseases only once, but can suffer from others (such as influenza) several times;

- **explain** the role of vaccination in disease prevention;

- **describe** the active immunisation schedule for children in the UK;

- **describe** the method of production and administration technique for a range of vaccines including whooping cough, rubella, diphtheria, influenza, hepatitis B.

9.2 The body's reaction to injury

At the local Accident and Emergency Department, the doctor noticed that the area around the wound was red, swollen and hot. Chris said it was painful to touch. In addition, she had a high temperature. The doctor carefully cleaned out the wound again, and applied adhesive stitches. The body would do the rest.

Wound healing follows a regular sequence of events:
- blood clots seal the wound;
- localised inflammation occurs;
- the number of white blood cells in the damaged area increases;
- new epidermal cells are formed;
- collagen is formed in the dermis;
- granulated tissue forms if the wound is very deep.

Blood clotting

As the skin is damaged, blood vessels are broken and bleeding occurs. This triggers blood clotting (Fig. 1). Blood clots to prevent the loss of body fluids and help prevent the entry of pathogens.

Inflammation

Following injury, inflammation of the damaged area occurs (Fig. 2). Eventually, clots form to seal the injured area from the inside and prevent bacteria moving into undamaged tissue.

Fig. 1 Blood clotting

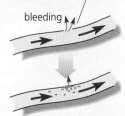

damaged blood vessel

bleeding

Immediate rapid response
platelets stick to collagen fibres in damaged blood vessel walls and form a plug to restrict the flow of blood out of the wound

blood vessel contracts to restrict blood flow out of wound

After about 20 seconds
blood clotting starts with a series of chemical reactions in the blood that produce a 'prothrombin activator'

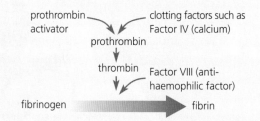

prothrombin activator → clotting factors such as Factor IV (calcium)

prothrombin

thrombin → Factor VIII (anti-haemophilic factor)

fibrinogen → fibrin

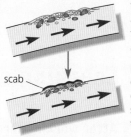

scab

fibrin is an insoluble protein and forms long threads that trap blood cells and platelets and plasma

plasma forms a gel and the clot contracts closing damaged vessels; on the outer surface, the clot may harden to form a scab

Fig. 2 Inflammation and fever

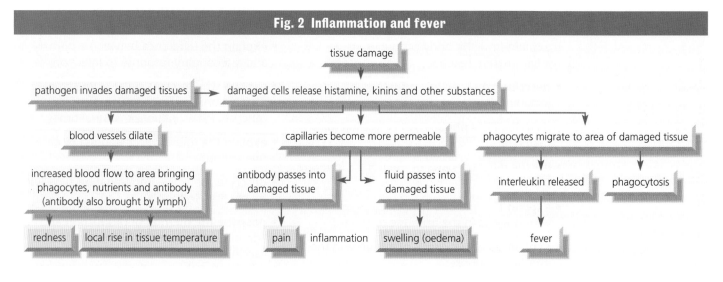

tissue damage

pathogen invades damaged tissues → damaged cells release histamine, kinins and other substances

blood vessels dilate

capillaries become more permeable

phagocytes migrate to area of damaged tissue

increased blood flow to area bringing phagocytes, nutrients and antibody (antibody also brought by lymph)

antibody passes into damaged tissue

fluid passes into damaged tissue

interleukin released

phagocytosis

redness | local rise in tissue temperature

pain | inflammation | swelling (oedema)

fever

Increased number of white blood cells

Stored white blood cells are released from bone marrow. The mechanism that causes this is not fully understood, but is thought to be triggered by a chemical released by the damaged tissues.

Some white blood cells produce a substance called interleukin. Interleukin alters the body's 'thermostat' (which is located in the hypothalamus in the brain) so as to produce a rise in body temperature. In severe cases, this results in a fever. High body temperature has a detrimental effect on viral metabolism.

The white cells invade the damaged tissue and ingest bacteria, viruses and dead cells. The process of ingestion is called **phagocytosis**, and the white cells that carry it out are called **phagocytes**. Phagocytes leave capillaries at sites of inflammation, by a process similar to the movement of an amoeba. A white liquid called pus forms; it is made up of tissue fluid and dead white cells. This may build up under the developing scab, and may ooze out if the scab is broken.

New epidermal cells

Cell division increases in the damaged area, to close up the damaged tissue beneath the developing scab. Once the cells have multiplied in sufficient numbers to cover the wound, they then form layers of epidermal cells to replace the stratified skin that has been destroyed by the injury. When the area has been repaired, cell division returns to its normal level.

New collagen fibres

Behind the newly developing epidermis, the cells of the dermis produce extra collagen fibres that help to build up new tissue behind the wound.

Granulated tissue

If the original wound was very deep, **granulated tissue** develops during the healing process. This is a type of temporary connective tissue that has a rich blood supply and is highly resistant to infection. It also contains more collagen than other tissues. After the wound has healed, granulised tissue remains as scar tissue. It lacks hair follicles and nerve endings, and looks different from epidermal tissue.

Thankfully for Chris, the stitches did their job; the damaged skin on her knee healed up completely and left no lasting scar.

Q 1 Why was the area around Chris's wound swollen and hot?

Q 2a Why was Chris's body temperature higher than normal?
b Why might this be useful?

Wound healing is one of the body's mechanisms to restrict entry of bacteria into the body. The tissues of the body provide an ideal growth medium for bacteria – warm, moist, oxygenated and with a good supply of nutrients. The body has a number of other mechanisms to protect itself from invasion by microorganisms (Fig. 3). These mechanisms can be divided into two groups:
• non-specific defence mechanisms;
• specific defence mechanisms.

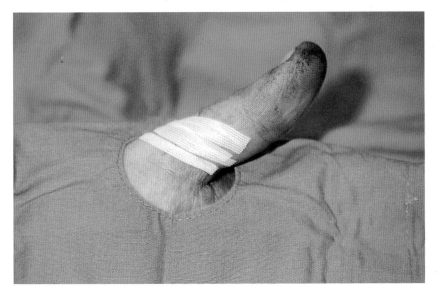

When a wound is particularly deep or long, doctors use stitches, either threads or small adhesive plasters, to hold the wound edges together. This helps the healing process by effectively reducing the size of the area that needs to be covered with new tissue. If a wound is very big, skin grafts from elsewhere on the body may be needed.

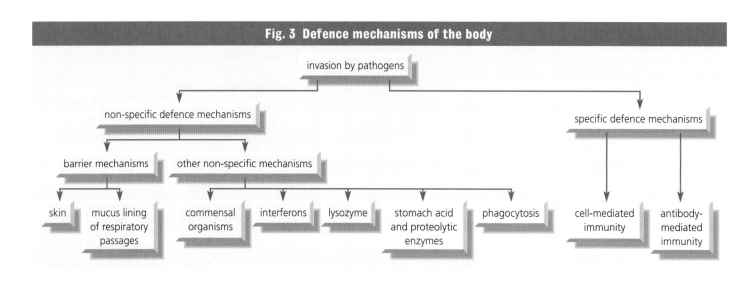

Fig. 3 Defence mechanisms of the body

invasion by pathogens

→ non-specific defence mechanisms

→ specific defence mechanisms

non-specific defence mechanisms:
- barrier mechanisms
  - skin
  - mucus lining of respiratory passages
- other non-specific mechanisms
  - commensal organisms
  - interferons
  - lysozyme
  - stomach acid and proteolytic enzymes
  - phagocytosis

specific defence mechanisms:
- cell-mediated immunity
- antibody-mediated immunity

9.3 Non-specific defence mechanisms

Fig. 4 Structure of human skin

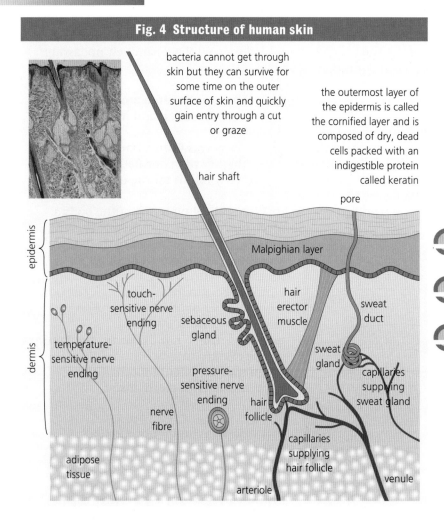

bacteria cannot get through skin but they can survive for some time on the outer surface of skin and quickly gain entry through a cut or graze

the outermost layer of the epidermis is called the cornified layer and is composed of dry, dead cells packed with an indigestible protein called keratin

hair shaft

pore

epidermis

Malpighian layer

dermis

touch-sensitive nerve ending

sebaceous gland

hair erector muscle

sweat duct

temperature-sensitive nerve ending

pressure-sensitive nerve ending

sweat gland

capillaries supplying sweat gland

nerve fibre

hair follicle

capillaries supplying hair follicle

adipose tissue

arteriole

venule

The environment is literally alive with bacteria. They are present on all surfaces, including the food we eat, dust particles that we breathe in, and in droplets produced when we breathe out, cough or sneeze.

So how is it that we are not continually affected by this vast army of microbes, some of which are able to cause serious illness? How do we stop them getting inside our tissues? The body has a number of non-specific ways to prevent this from happening (Fig. 3).

3 Why is it important to prevent bacteria from entering the body's tissues?

4 What are the sources of bacteria that could cause infections?

5 What are the two types of defence mechanism that the body has to prevent infection by microorganisms?

Skin

One of the main barriers to microorganisms is the skin (Fig. 4). It is generally impenetrable and is toughened by collagen and keratin. Skin also secretes sweat and sebum which contain substances able to destroy bacteria.

Mucus lining of respiratory passages

Mucus-covered cilia line much of the respiratory tract and trap air-borne pathogens. Mucus contains lysozyme, an enzyme that destroys Gram-negative bacteria. The beating of the cilia carries the mucus and any trapped pathogens towards the throat and swallowing carries them into the stomach where they can be attacked by the stomach acid and enzymes.

Commensal bacteria

On the skin live a group of bacteria called **commensals**. Commensals compete much more successfully than pathogens for the small amount of nutrients available on the outside of the skin. Commensals are also found in the mouth, the respiratory tract, the vagina, and the digestive system, where they have a similar protective effect on the body. Certain drugs, known as wide spectrum antibiotics destroy the natural microbial inhabitants of the gut (the gut flora), and therefore remove some of the protection they provide against infection by pathogens.

6 a What does lysozyme do?
  b How do commensal bacteria help to protect us against pathogenic organisms?

When Chris fell over the hurdle, not only did she pick up bacteria from the track surface, but bacteria already present on her skin found a way into her body. The processes involved in the initial inflammation reaction prevented the spread of a bacterial infection beyond the wound.

Interferons

Lymphocytes respond to viral infection by producing proteins called **interferons**. Interferons stimulate other blood cells to produce a range of antiviral proteins that stop cells invaded by viruses from manufacturing substances necessary for viral reproduction. Interferons also stimulate certain types of lymphocyte to identify and destroy body cells that have been infected by viruses. Recently, it has become possible, using genetic engineering techniques, to incorporate the human gene for interferon production into the DNA of the bacterium *Escherichia coli*. This has allowed mass production of a potentially life-saving drug. Some recent research has shown that interferon may help in the treatment of cancer, although the hopes following its discovery in 1957 have not yet been fully realised.

Other non-specific mechanisms

Surfaces other than the skin also come into contact with the outside world and are vulnerable to invasion by air and food-borne bacteria. Many of these surfaces are moist, provide bacteria with a source of food, and unlike skin, are not toughened with collagen and keratin. The eyes, and the digestive and urinogenital systems are vulnerable to microbial attack but each has a defence mechanism (Table 1).

7 a How do interferons help to protect us?
  b Why might someone taking antibiotics be more vulnerable than usual to infection by fungi?

Table 1 Defence mechanisms		
Surface	Defence mechanism	Mode of action
eyes	lysozyme	lysozyme in tears destroys Gram-negative bacteria
digestive system	lysozyme	lysozyme in saliva destroys Gram-negative bacteria
	stomach acid and enzymes	stomach acid and proteolytic enzymes attack bacteria
	commensals	commensals compete for nutrients
vagina	commensals	commensals living on the vaginal walls produce an acid secretion that inhibits microbial growth, particularly that of fungi
urinary system	lysozyme	urine contains lysozyme to destroy Gram-negative bacteria in the bladder and urethra

Key ideas

- Wound healing follows a regular pattern: blood clotting is followed by inflammation and increased numbers of white blood cells migrating to the area; new epidermal tissue develops then new collagen is laid down. If the wound is deep, granulated tissue is formed.

- Blood clots at the surface of a wound prevent external bacteria from getting into the healing wound. Internal clots prevent any bacteria in the would from getting into other parts of the body.

- Inflammation involves a series of events in which the body fights invading pathogens.

- Many of the extra white blood cells are macrophages and ingest bacteria and viruses.

- The new epidermal tissue covers the wounded area.

- Wound healing is a mechanism for preventing infection. Other non-specific defence mechanisms include barrier and non-barrier methods.

- The skin and mucus lining of the respiratory passages are physical barriers that microorganisms find difficult to pass.

- Non-barrier methods include: commensal organisms that compete with pathogens for nutrients; interferons that stop viral reproduction; lysozyme – an enzyme that destroys Gram-negative bacteria; stomach acid and proteolytic enzymes that digest bacteria; and phagocytosis of microorganisms.

9.4 Specific immune responses

The immune system

Unlike the respiratory or digestive system, the immune system is not a series of closely connected organs. It is made up of a number of seemingly unconnected sections, including white blood cells found in blood and lymph vessels, and in tissue fluid. The main organs of the immune system are the thymus, spleen and lymph nodes (Fig. 5).

Lymph is formed when excess tissue fluid drains from the tissues into tubes called lymph (or lymphatic) vessels. Eventually, this fluid is returned to the bloodstream, but along the way, it passes through many structures called lymph nodes.

Immunity is the body's ability to identify and react to foreign materials. The body's immune system is based on the activity of various types of white blood cell or **leucocyte**. The main types are **macrophages** and **lymphocytes**. Macrophages are phagocytic, but are also involved in the immune response. Some

lymphocytes attack pathogens directly; these lymphocytes are called **T cells** (or T **lymphocytes**). Some lymphocytes produce **antibodies**, special proteins that can kill invading pathogens; these lymphocytes are called **B lymphocytes** (or **B cells**). There are two types of immune response:

- **cell-mediated immunity** (when T lymphocytes attack pathogens directly);
- **antibody-mediated immunity** (when B lymphocytes produce antibodies to kill invading pathogens).

An immune response is triggered when the body detects the presence of foreign material. A substance that causes an immune response is termed an **antigen**, or **immunogen**. Antigens are large molecules, usually located in the outer cell membrane or cell wall of an invading organism.

Antigens are usually proteins or polysaccharides or **glycoproteins** (combinations of proteins and polysaccharides). Specific immune responses are aimed at particular types of antigen.

Fig. 5 Organs of the immune system

Lymph nodes filter the lymph. The nodes contain a concentration of phagocytes that ingest pathogens present in the lymph. In this way they help prevent infection in one part of the body getting into general circulation. The nodes also contain T and B lymphocytes.

tonsils
Lymph nodes in the tonsils help protect the respiratory system

lymph nodes

thymus
The thymus is at its largest during fetal development. It reduces in size throughout childhood, reaching its smallest size in adults. It activates T lymphocytes.

spleen
The spleen has phagocytes to filter the blood in a way similar to the lymph nodes filtering lymph.

appendix
Lymphoid tissue in the appendix helps to protect the digestive system.

lymph nodes

Cross section through a lymph node

afferent lymph vessels bring lymph into the node

lymph node sinuses – spaces where phagocytes collect and phagocytosis occurs

germinal centre

valves

efferent lymph vessels carry lymph away from the node

Macrophages

The macrophages ingest foreign cells and viruses. This results in some of the antigen molecules becoming embedded in the macrophage cell membrane and this alerts both T lymphocytes and B lymphocytes to the fact that the body has been invaded by a particular pathogen.

T lymphocytes

T lymphocytes develop from **stem cells** in the bone marrow, and then pass to the thymus gland, where they are changed to make them active in the immune response. This activation process is said to make the cells **competent**. T lymphocytes are mainly found in the lymphatic system. Embedded in their cell membranes are proteins called **T cell receptors**. There are millions of types of T cell, each with a different type of T cell receptor, because each T cell can only recognise and respond to one type of antigen.

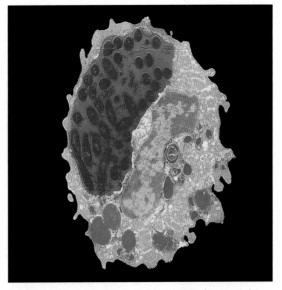

Coloured transmission electron micrograph of a macrophage in human lung. The macrophage has a dumbbell-shaped nucleus (orange and green) and has engulfed many cells of *Legionella pneumophilia*, the bacterium that causes Legionnaires' disease. The bacteria (red) are all in a cell vacuole (dark blue).

B lymphocytes

B lymphocytes, like T cells, are derived from stem cells in the bone marrow. However, whereas T cells are activated in the thymus gland, we do not know what activates B cells in mammals. In birds, they are activated by the organ called the bursa (hence the name B cells). The plasma membrane of each B cell has protein molecules that are specific for a particular antigen. These proteins are called antibodies and are released into the lymph. Each B cell has a single antibody. When the antibody matches a particular antigen, the B cell is said to be competent.

8 What is the main function of the macrophages?

Cell-mediated immunity

T cells can detect bacteria but not isolated viruses. When a virus infects a cell, it forces the cell to make viral protein. Some viral protein gets into the cell membrane of the host cell, and is recognised as foreign by certain T cells (Fig. 6).

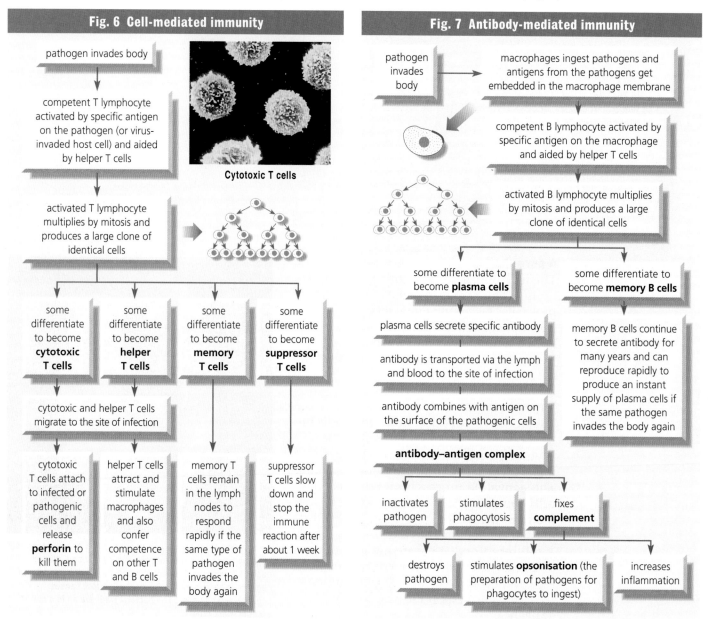

Fig. 6 Cell-mediated immunity

pathogen invades body

↓

competent T lymphocyte activated by specific antigen on the pathogen (or virus-invaded host cell) and aided by helper T cells

↓

activated T lymphocyte multiplies by mitosis and produces a large clone of identical cells

Cytotoxic T cells

some differentiate to become **cytotoxic T cells** | some differentiate to become **helper T cells** | some differentiate to become **memory T cells** | some differentiate to become **suppressor T cells**

cytotoxic and helper T cells migrate to the site of infection

cytotoxic T cells attach to infected or pathogenic cells and release **perforin** to kill them | helper T cells attract and stimulate macrophages and also confer competence on other T and B cells | memory T cells remain in the lymph nodes to respond rapidly if the same type of pathogen invades the body again | suppressor T cells slow down and stop the immune reaction after about 1 week

Fig. 7 Antibody-mediated immunity

pathogen invades body → macrophages ingest pathogens and antigens from the pathogens get embedded in the macrophage membrane

↓

competent B lymphocyte activated by specific antigen on the macrophage and aided by helper T cells

↓

activated B lymphocyte multiplies by mitosis and produces a large clone of identical cells

some differentiate to become **plasma cells** | some differentiate to become **memory B cells**

plasma cells secrete specific antibody

antibody is transported via the lymph and blood to the site of infection

antibody combines with antigen on the surface of the pathogenic cells

antibody–antigen complex

memory B cells continue to secrete antibody for many years and can reproduce rapidly to produce an instant supply of plasma cells if the same pathogen invades the body again

inactivates pathogen | stimulates phagocytosis | fixes **complement**

destroys pathogen | stimulates **opsonisation** (the preparation of pathogens for phagocytes to ingest) | increases inflammation

Antibody-mediated immunity

After infection, a macrophage with antigen embedded in its membrane causes a competent helper T cell to interact with the appropriate competent B cell (Fig. 7).

The increased activity in lymph nodes during times of infection results in a characteristic swelling of lymphatic tissue near the area of infection. A viral or bacterial infection of the upper pharynx (a sore throat), often results in swollen tonsils because the lymph nodes in the tonsils are where the B cells are producing antibodies.

9 What are the main differences between cell-mediated and antibody mediated immunity?

Key ideas

- The immune system is made up of the thymus, spleen, lymph nodes, white blood cells and the blood and lymph vessels.

- Lymph is excess tissue fluid that drains into the lymph vessels and is eventually returned to the bloodstream after passing through lymph nodes.

- Lymph nodes contain macrophages waiting to ingest foreign material in the lymph – they filter the lymph.

- The spleen filters the blood.

- Lymphoid tissues protect the digestive system (the appendix) and the respiratory system (the tonsils).

- A substance that causes an immune response is called an antigen or an immunogen.

- There are two types of immune response, cell-mediated immunity and antibody-mediated immunity.

- Cell-mediated immunity depends on killer or cytotoxic T cells directly attacking pathogens.

- Antibody-mediated immunity depends on B cells producing specific antibodies to destroy pathogens.

- Helper T cells and macrophages alert both T and B cells to the presence of a pathogen. The alerted cells multiply rapidly to produce clones of cells. Some of the cells are memory cells that enable the body to recognise the pathogen very quickly if it attacks again.

- Antigens are usually large molecules – proteins, polysaccharides or glycoproteins.

9.5 Antibody structure and function

Antibodies are proteins found in plasma, tissue fluid and milk (Fig. 8). They are called **immunoglobulins**.

The variable region of the antibody is the part that combines with the antigen. There is a three-dimensional fit between the amino acid chain in the antibody and the antigen. The fit between the two molecules is similar to that between an enzyme and its substrate, although not so precise.

There are five different types of immunoglobulin molecule in humans. The differences are in the constant region of the amino acid chains. The five types are known as IgG, IgM, IgA, IgD and IgE. IgG is usually referred to as gamma-globulin (γ-globulin), and is the most abundant globulin found in blood. IgA is found in many of the body's secretions such as tears and mucus.

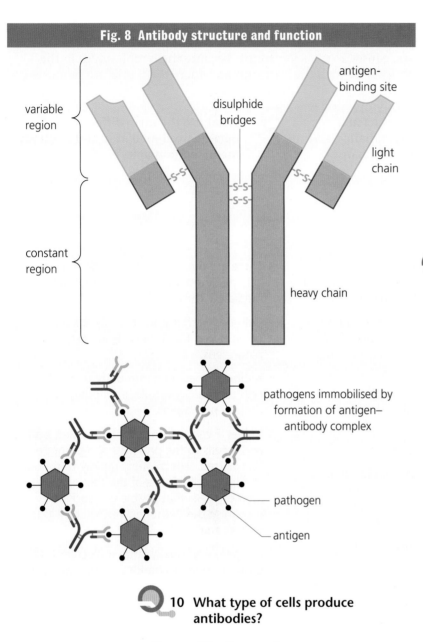

Fig. 8 Antibody structure and function

variable region

disulphide bridges

antigen-binding site

light chain

constant region

heavy chain

pathogens immobilised by formation of antigen–antibody complex

pathogen

antigen

10 What type of cells produce antibodies?

How antibodies work

Antibodies have two active sites, each of which can combine with a separate antigen molecule. This allows a number of antibody molecules to combine with a number of antigen molecules to form a lattice-like structure called an **antibody–antigen complex** (Figs 7 and 8). The antibody–antigen complex immobilises virus particles so they cannot latch onto host cells. The interlocking of antibody and antigen could render a toxic antigen harmless if its active region was blocked by

an antibody molecule. Phagocytes can more easily track down and ingest pathogens if they are immobilised in an antibody–antigen complex. The antibody–antigen complex also stimulates the activation of a number of plasma proteins. This leads to a substance called complement binding with the complex and destroying the pathogens. Sometimes, some of the proteins cover the outer membrane of the pathogens so phagocytes can ingest them more easily. The preparation of pathogens for phagocytes to ingest is called opsonisation.

11 Why do antibodies have two active sites on each molecule?

The **primary response** is what happens the first time an individual comes into contact with a particular antigen. It takes 3–14 days after infection for the body to produce antibody. This period between infection and the onset of antibody production is the **latent period**. After the latent period, the amount of antibody in the blood rises rapidly and then begins to fall. During the immune response, memory cells are produced. These are clones of the lymphocytes that fought off the pathogen, and they remain in the body as a long-term defence against a second or subsequent infection by the bacterium or virus.

The **secondary response** is what happens if a second infection occurs. A much smaller amount of antigen will induce the secondary response. The response is much more rapid than the primary response and more antibody is produced. The speed of the secondary response means that the pathogen is destroyed before it fully infects the body and causes the symptoms of a disease. The individual has acquired immunity to the disease (Fig. 9).

12 a Which has the longer latent period, the primary response or the secondary response?
b Why is the secondary response both faster and greater than the primary response?

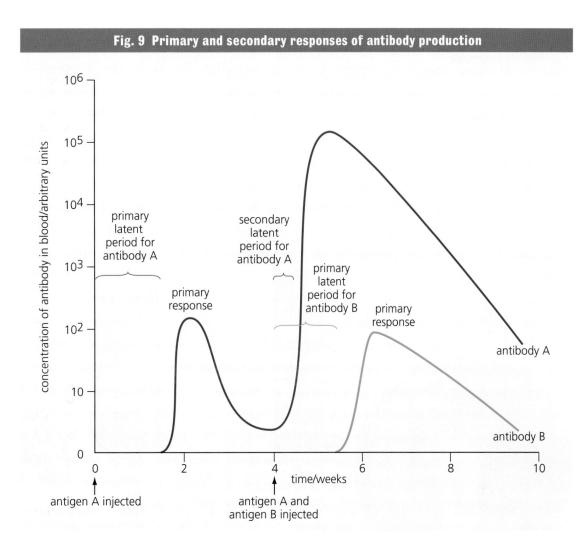

Fig. 9 Primary and secondary responses of antibody production

So why do we suffer from many colds and bouts of 'flu in our lives? Doesn't this contradict the description of primary and secondary responses outlined above? The problem with the viruses causing these two very common diseases is that they occur in many forms. Each form contains a different antigen. Each one, therefore, causes its own primary response. In addition, new mutations constantly arise, so the body can never learn to recognise the virus.

Influenza outbreaks occur every year in Britain, and they sometimes reach epidemic proportions. In 1989 influenza is thought to have killed 25 000 people. When a new epidemic seem likely, high-risk individuals are identified and contacted, so that they can be offered vaccination. These are the people who are most likely to develop serious complications that could lead to death.

Three groups of influenza virus are recognised: type A, type B and type C. However, there are many different strains in each group. Influenza vaccines are prepared from highly purified inactivated viruses, grown in hen's egg albumen (Chapter 6, p. 80). GPs order the amount of vaccine they think they need, often a year in advance, and administer it in preparation for the oncoming winter. Most 'flu vaccines are cocktails of type A and type B antigens. Type C influenza virus is not often involved in UK outbreaks.

13 Why does an attack of influenza or the common cold not give immunity to these diseases?

9.6 Vaccination

When the body is exposed to a pathogen, an impressive array of defence mechanisms contribute to maintaining health. However, there are some bacteria and viruses that get past these mechanisms and cause disease. Of these pathogens, some are so active that the disease ends in death. Examples of such diseases are cholera, smallpox and diphtheria. Diseases such as these were the targets of public health programmes for proper sewage treatment and the development of safe water supplies, and for the many vaccinations now available.

The term vaccination comes from the Latin word *vaccinia* (cowpox), which is derived from *vacca* (cow). A vaccine contains antigen derived from pathogenic organisms. When injected into an individual, the antigen stimulates a primary response that leaves memory cells to generate the secondary response if the individual is subsequently infected by the relevant pathogen.

As adults we have immunity to most common diseases, apart from the common cold and influenza. This immunity is

Modern vaccination techniques stem from the work of four enlightened people.

Lady Mary Wortley Montague was the wife of the British Ambassador to Turkey in the early eighteenth century. In Turkey she discovered a technique called *variolation* and introduced it to Britain. In variolation, the doctor scratches the skin and introduces a small amount of smallpox material into the wound from the skin of an individual with a mild form of the disease. The procedure was not very safe – about 3% of patients died. Even so, the procedure became quite popular.

Edward Jenner, an eighteenth-century Gloucestershire physician, studied the role of cowpox in the development of immunity to smallpox.

Benjamin Jesty was a farmer in South West England in the eighteenth century. He also noticed that people who had had cowpox did not get smallpox. He used a variolation technique on his family, none of whom had had cowpox, and prevented them from getting smallpox during a severe smallpox outbreak in 1774.

Louis Pasteur, the nineteenth-century French scientist, demonstrated that heat-treated anthrax bacteria could be injected into sheep to give immunity to anthrax.

Table 2 Types of immunity		
Immunity type	How acquired	Duration
active natural immunity	immunity develops following natural exposure to antigen	memory cells develop to produce long-lasting immunity
active artificially induced immunity	immunity develops after immunisation with a vaccine	memory cells develop to produce long-lasting immunity
passive natural immunity	immunity develops through transfer of antibodies from mother to baby through the placenta and breast milk	no memory cells develop so the immunity is short-term and lasts only a few months
passive artificially induced immunity	immunity develops after injection with antibodies	no memory cells develop so the immunity is short-term and lasts only a few months

This girl is being vaccinated against rubella, a disease that can cause malformations in the developing baby if a woman gets it when she is pregnant.

usually acquired through either contact with the pathogen at an earlier age or vaccination. Both types of immunity are classed as **active immunity** (Table 2). In the 1990s, immunity against diseases such as polio, tuberculosis (TB) and diphtheria is likely to be the result of childhood vaccinations.

During the first few days of breast-feeding, the breasts produce a high-protein, low-fat liquid called collostrum. This contains many antibodies, and provides the young infant with immunity against a number of infectious diseases. Antibodies are also present in the milk that is produced after the collostrum. This is naturally induced immunity but no primary response takes place in the baby, because the infant

simply receives antibodies from another individual. This is called **passive immunity**. Artificially induced passive immunity arises when someone receives an injection containing antibody (as opposed to antigen). Whether naturally or artificially induced, passive immunity normally lasts for a few months (Table 2). The body does not produce its own antibody or memory cells, since both these processes require the presence of an antigen.

14 Why is passive immunity temporary?

Vaccination schedules for children

It is important that children receive the necessary vaccinations as they grow up to prevent large-scale outbreaks of disease. Artificially creating immunity is called **immunisation**. Table 3 shows the sequence of vaccinations for children living in the UK in the 1990s. Children who go through this schedule are likely to be protected throughout their life from some potentially lethal diseases, but it is not compulsory in the UK for children to have these vaccinations.

Table 3 Vaccination schedule for children		
Age	Immunisations	Method
2 months	diphtheria tetanus whooping cough (pertussis) combined injection 1 (DTP 1)	injection
	polio 1	oral
4 months	DTP 2	injection
	polio 2	oral
6 months	DTP 3	injection
	polio 3	oral
15–18 months	measles, mumps, rubella (MMR)	injection
4.5 years	DTP 4	injection
	polio booster	oral
11–13 years	rubella (girls)	injection
13 years	BCG (tuberculosis) unless there is evidence of immunity	injection
15 years	tetanus booster	injection
	polio booster	injection

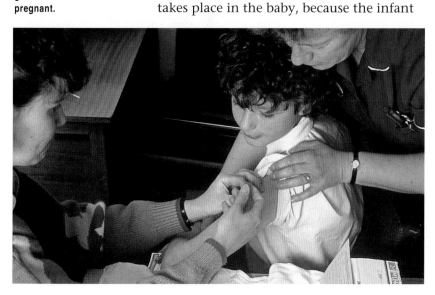

125

Sometimes, it may be felt that the original injection is not enough and booster vaccinations are needed. The possibility of a measles epidemic in 1994–95 was so high that a major publicity campaign was launched to ensure that all school-age children were immunised against the disease. School-age children can be very ill if they get measles; some cases are fatal. The symptoms are a high temperature, a rash, a cough, and sore eyes. Measles can also lead to pneumonia, and may result in blindness, deafness and brain damage. Possible side-effects of the measles vaccine include a mild fever or rash after about a week, but these should not last longer than 3–4 days. There is also a very small risk of brain damage. However, the dangers of measles greatly outweigh the dangers of the vaccine's side-effects.

Parents took a very different view over the whooping cough vaccine. In the 1980s and 1990s there was a widespread refusal to immunise children against whooping cough because the vaccine was thought to have possibly fatal side-effects. There was a rise in the occurrence of whooping cough but vaccination levels have gone up again.

Percentage cover

The proportion of individuals who must be immune to a disease in order to prevent an epidemic is called the **percentage cover**. Percentage cover varies from one disease to another. For instance, polio epidemics are prevented by 70% cover, but influenza requires 90–95% cover to stop epidemics. This high level is never reached, so there are frequent influenza epidemics.

Types of vaccine

There are many types of vaccine (Table 4). Vaccines can be produced from:
- killed pathogens;
- isolated antigens;
- attenuated strains;
- toxoids;
- genetically engineered antigens.

Some vaccines, e.g. the whooping cough vaccine, are made up of killed **virulent** pathogens. Because the cells are dead, they cannot cause the disease but when they are injected, the body reacts to the antigens present in the cell membranes and a primary response is induced. This sort of vaccine is used against influenza and whooping cough.

Some vaccines are made from antigen that has been isolated from the organism that produced it. The isolated antigen cannot cause the disease. Some influenza vaccines are of this type.

Sometimes, a less virulent strain of the pathogen is used. This is usually a mutated form that does not cause disease. Such a non-virulent form is called an **attenuated strain**. This sort of vaccine is used to combat rubella.

With many diseases, the illness is caused by the toxin produced by the pathogen. The toxin is often the antigen that induces the immune response. Some vaccines, such as the one for diphtheria, are made of altered or modified toxin molecules that cannot cause disease but do provoke the immune response. Such modified toxins are called **toxoids**.

Genetically engineered bacteria and yeasts are used to produce vaccines for the viral disease hepatitis B. The gene coding for the viral antigen (in this case, the virus coat protein) is cloned and inserted into bacterial or yeast cells. This enables large-scale production of the antigenic protein which is then purified for use as a vaccine against hepatitis B. When the antigen is injected, it stimulates the immune response and a long-lasting immunity is generated. Sometimes, a person may be in a very high risk situation, for example a baby born to a mother with hepatitis B. In such a case, temporary immunity against hepatitis B can

Table 4 Examples of different vaccines			
Disease	Type of vaccine	How given	Duration of effect
diphtheria	toxoid	into muscle	10 years
hepatitis B	purified and inactivated virus coat protein (antigen made by genetically engineered bacteria and yeasts)	into muscle	many years
influenza	killed virus or isolated antigen	into muscle	1–3 years
whooping cough	killed bacterial cells	into muscle	many years
rubella	live attenuated strain of virus	subcutaneous	permanent

be created by injecting *antibody*, and long-term immunity produced by injecting *antigen* at the same time.

Tetanus is caused by *Clostridium tetani* producing a deadly toxin. Spores of the bacterium are found almost everywhere, but are particularly common in soil and in dust. While Chris was in hospital, she was asked about her tetanus protection. As a young child. Chris received the usual series of vaccinations including a tetanus booster when she was 15. The effect of this tetanus 'jab' lasts about 10 years and a new booster is then needed. Few people keep their tetanus immunity up to date after the effect of their last school booster has worn off. So, whenever a patient comes in with an injury such as Chris had, or a wound caused by a gardening, or an industrial accident, it is vital to check up on the patient's tetanus immunity.

15 When is your next tetanus booster due?

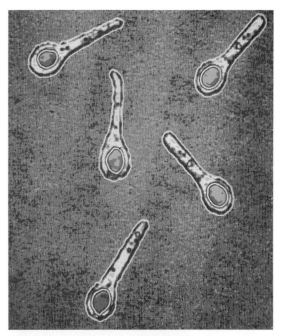

False colour transmission electron micrograph of *Clostridium tetani*. This is a Gram-positive spore-forming bacterium that lives in anaerobic conditions and causes tetanus if it gets into a deep wound.

Key ideas

- Antibodies are proteins called immunoglobulins. there are five types: IgG (γ-globulin), IgM, IgA, IgD, and IgE.

- Antibodies have two binding sites so they can each attach to two antigen molecules and produce a lattice-like structure that immobilises the pathogens.

- Binding an antibody to an antigen can also render a toxic antigen harmless by blocking its active site.

- Immobilised pathogens are easier for phagocytes to ingest.

- The primary response (antibody production after a first infection) takes 3–14 days. The secondary response (antibody production after a subsequent infection) is much faster.

- There are three groups of influenza virus – types A, B and C. Most 'flu vaccines are against types B and C.

- A vaccine is a preparation of antigen from a pathogen that will generate a primary response when injected into an individual, but will not cause the disease.

- Children in the UK are usually vaccinated against many diseases: diphtheria, tetanus, whooping cough, polio, measles, mumps, rubella, and tuberculosis.

- Vaccination and natural exposure produce long-term active immunity that relies on the production of antibody and memory cells.

- Passive immunity is the result of receiving antibody. It is short-lived.

Immune under-reacting

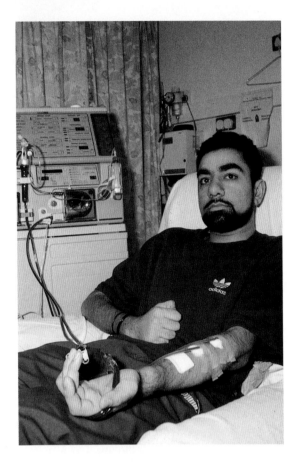

Mohammed has kidney failure and is waiting for a kidney transplant. Since none of his family have compatible tissues, he has to wait for an organ from a dead person. While he waits, he has to undergo dialysis, eat a special diet and give up sport and other physical activities. This seriously affects his ability to enjoy life. If he gets a transplant, Mohammed will gradually be able to enjoy a more 'normal' life.

However, kidneys for transplant are not very plentiful. They are only available when somebody dies and that person's relatives are willing for their kidneys to be used. And transplant operations are not straightforward: the donated kidney has to 'match' the recipient, and the recipient's immune system has to be suppressed to increase the chances of success for the transplant. Suppressing the immune system is dangerous for the patient. On the other hand, dialysis machines are expensive and although they keep people alive, the quality of life is not always good. Research scientists are working on alternatives such as genetically changed organs from pigs. The genetic change should help to reduce the risk of rejection by the recipient's tissues.

10.1 Learning objectives

After working through this chapter, you should be able to:

- **explain** the need for tissue compatibility for transplant operations;

- **describe** the causes of tissue rejection;

- **explain** the principles underlying the treatment of transplant patients;

- **construct** compatibility tables for ABO and rhesus blood groups;

- **describe** the cause of haemolytic disease of the newborn;

- **distinguish** between HIV infection and AIDS;

- **describe** the effects of HIV on the body's immune system;

- **describe** the mode of transmission and replication of HIV;

- **suggest** methods to reduce the spread of HIV and AIDS;

- **describe** the causes of auto-immune diseases;

- **describe** the symptoms and treatment for multiple sclerosis.

10.2 Organ transplants

Sometimes an organ is so damaged by disease that the only way to save the person's life is to replace it with a healthy organ from another individual. Taking an organ, such as a heart or a kidney, from one person and putting it into another, is called **transplantation**. Parts of organs (such as heart valves) and tissues (such as bone, cornea, skin, veins and cartilage) are also transplanted. Sometimes the transplant is to save a life, as in heart transplantation; on other occasions, the transplant is to enhance the quality of life, as when sight is made possible through a cornea transplant.

Transplant rejection

Transplanted organs can easily be rejected by the body's defence mechanisms. This is because the immune system can recognise cells that are from another individual. The recognition depends on immune responses to special protein molecules called antigens that are found in cell membranes (Chapter 9, p. 118). In humans, the most important antigens for transplant surgery are the HLA (human leucocyte antigen) group. The HLA group of proteins is determined by five different genes. Tissues with the matching HLA groups are said to be **compatible**. If the organ is incompatible, it will be rejected and attacked by the recipient's T cells and antibodies.

Transplants from one part of an individual to another are called **autografts**. In these cases, rejection is almost unknown because there is no difference between the HLA groups of tissues from different parts of the same body. Burn victims who have suffered severe damage to the skin on their faces are often given autografts of skin from another part of the body, such as the thigh.

 1 **Is a skin graft between identical twins likely to be successful?**

Compatibility

For Mohammed to have a kidney transplant, a compatible kidney has to be found. The first step is to find out Mohammed's **tissue type** or HLA group. The five genes that control an individual's HLA protein group exist in several forms – they are **multiple alleles**. This gives rise to a range of possible HLA protein types, so it is not likely that two individuals chosen at random will have the same or similar HLA groups.

2 **Why does rejection of transplanted organs occur?**

Not all transplants from donors are likely to be rejected. Bone and cornea can be transplanted from one individual to another with few, if any, problems caused by rejection. Both of these tissues are **non-vascular**, i.e. they are not served by blood vessels; they are not served by lymph vessels either. Since these tissues do not come into contact with blood or lymph, the cells of the transplants are not recognised as foreign by lymphocytes, so there is no immune response and rejection does not occur.

Tattoos are permanent marking of the skin. The only way to remove a tattoo is to remove the tattooed skin and replace it with a skin graft from another area of the body.

10.3 Preventing rejection

While Mohammed waits for a transplant operation, he can treated in a number of ways to help reduce the effect of any HLA incompatibility. Since only identical twins have the same HLA combinations, any likely donor would have some differences in HLA composition from Mohammed. The closer the tissue type, the lower the possibility of rejection.

Tissue typing

Although HLA proteins are found in the membrane of all cells, tissue typing is carried out using lymphocytes. The process takes about 6 hours and it must be done for each of the HLA proteins (Fig. 1). A freshly removed kidney can be stored for up to 48 hours while a recipient is identified and prepared for the operation.

3 Where are the HLA proteins found?

Matching donors and recipients

Most transplanted organs come from individuals who have died. These organs are called **cadaver organs** and their availability depends on the donor carrying a donor card, although permission from close relatives will still be sought. If a child has died, permission may be given by parents to use their child's organs for transplants.

A national register lists all patients who need transplants and donor details are entered on a national database. A hospital or group of hospitals has a transplant coordinator whose job is to match donated organs with these patients. As soon as Mohammed was told a suitable organ was available, he went straight into hospital to prepare for surgery.

Immunosuppression

Even when the tissue types of donor and recipient are closely matched there is still the possibility of tissue rejection. The donor who provided a kidney for Mohammed had a very close tissue type, so the chances of a successful transplant were good. In order to reduce the risk of rejection even further, Mohammed received treatment to suppress his immune system so his T lymphocytes

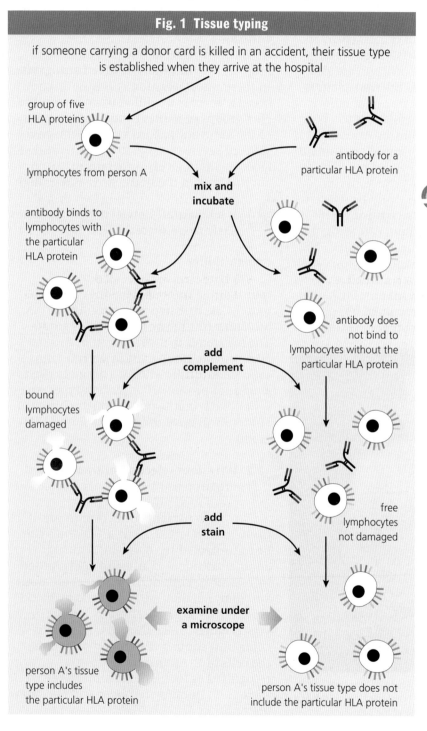

Fig. 1 Tissue typing

if someone carrying a donor card is killed in an accident, their tissue type is established when they arrive at the hospital

group of five HLA proteins

lymphocytes from person A

antibody for a particular HLA protein

mix and incubate

antibody binds to lymphocytes with the particular HLA protein

antibody does not bind to lymphocytes without the particular HLA protein

add complement

bound lymphocytes damaged

free lymphocytes not damaged

add stain

examine under a microscope

person A's tissue type includes the particular HLA protein

person A's tissue type does not include the particular HLA protein would not recognise the transplanted organ cells as foreign. The immune system is suppressed by treatments that reduce white blood cell activity. The main methods used are:

- **radiotherapy** – using X-rays to irradiate the bone marrow and other blood-producing areas to inhibit the production of leucocytes;
- **chemotherapy** – using drugs; drugs that suppress the immune system are called **immunosuppressant drugs**.

There is a big danger in suppressing the immune system because it also reduces the body's ability to fight infection. So, it is vital that Mohammed stays in sterile conditions. For instance, the air he breathes is filtered to remove any air-borne pathogens. Treatment to reduce tissue rejection can also increase the risk of tumour growth, since tumour cells are usually attacked by lymphocytes.

4 Why does irradiating bone marrow reduce the risk of a transplanted organ being rejected?

One of the most useful drugs for immunosuppression is cyclosporin A. It only affects T lymphocytes. This means that the patient's B lymphocytes are unaffected and are able to resist infection by antibody-mediated immunity (Chapter 9, p. 121).

Following the operation

Transplant surgery carries risks for many months after the operation. For instance, tissue rejection, infection following immunosuppressive therapy, and infection following the operation are all possible. High blood pressure (hypertension) is common in transplant cases and a transplanted kidney can easily be damaged by too high a blood pressure. Drugs can be used to keep blood pressure at a level that does not damage the new transplant. Rejection is still possible for a long time after the operation. Blood samples are taken to check for signs of imminent rejection, such as increased numbers of lymphocytes and the presence of antibodies to attack the transplant. Despite the problems, over 85% of kidney transplant patients survive for at least a year after their operation.

5 For several months after Mohammed's kidney transplant, his doctors monitor him to be sure that everything is going well. What would they do if they discovered Mohammed's blood pressure was going up?

Key ideas

- Damaged organs can often be replaced by healthy cadaver organs from donors who have died. This is called organ transplantation. Parts of organs and tissues can also be transplanted.

- Transplanted organs may be rejected by the recipient, but autografts and non-vascular tissues are rarely, if ever, rejected.

- Rejection is an immune response that occurs because the recipient's T lymphocytes recognise the new cells as foreign.

- Organs for transplant are tissue typed and only ones with a good match for the recipient's tissue type are used.

- Tissue type compatibility depends on a group of five proteins called the human leucocyte antigen (HLA) group.

- The risk of rejection can be further reduced by immunosuppression to reduce the number of the recipient's T lymphocytes. Immunosuppression can be achieved by radiotherapy or by drugs.

- A national register lists all patients needing transplants. Transplant coordinators match donors with patients.

- High blood pressure, infection, and rejection remain as possible problems for many months after the operation.

10.4 Blood groups

During his operation Mohammed was given a lot of blood. Just as it was necessary to match his tissue type with that of the kidney donor, it was also essential to make sure that the blood Mohammed received was matched with his own blood group. Blood groups are based on the presence or absence of certain antigens in the membranes of red blood cells. These antigens are proteins and glycoproteins. The two most important blood grouping systems are the ABO system and the rhesus (Rh) system (Fig. 2). We all have blood that is either group A, B, AB or O. In addition, we are all either Rh positive or Rh negative (we have the Rh antigen or we do not have the Rh antigen). So, a person's blood group is referred to as AB positive, or B negative and so on. Although grouping blood according to the ABO and rhesus systems is sufficient for most purposes, a complete classification involves over 20 separate factors.

ABO system

This system depends on two glycoprotein antigens called A and B in red blood cell membranes (Fig. 2). Careful cross-matching of donor and recipient blood is necessary (Table 1).

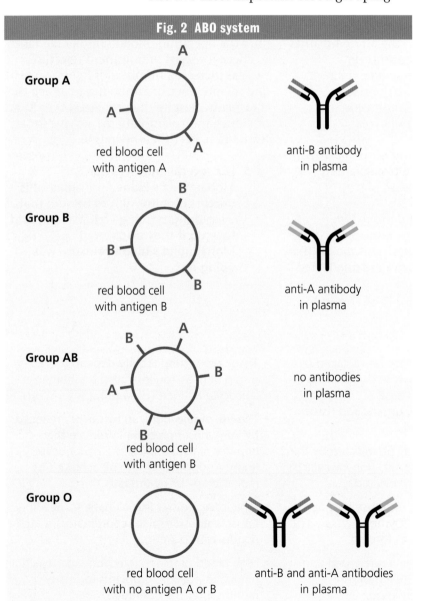

Fig. 2 ABO system

Group A
red blood cell with antigen A
anti-B antibody in plasma

Group B
red blood cell with antigen B
anti-A antibody in plasma

Group AB
red blood cell with antigen B
no antibodies in plasma

Group O
red blood cell with no antigen A or B
anti-B and anti-A antibodies in plasma

Table 1 ABO compatibility				
Donor blood group	Recipient blood group			
	A	B	AB	O
A	✓	✗	✓	✗
B	✗	✓	✓	✗
AB	✗	✗	✓	✗
O	✓	✓	✓	✓

✓ = recipient accepts transfused blood
✗ = recipient has transfusion reaction

A **transfusion reaction** occurs if blood of an unsuitable group is given to a patient. The donated blood **agglutinates** (the red cells clump together) in the recipient's blood vessels and donated red blood cells **haemolyse** (burst) releasing haemoglobin into the plasma. This can cause severe kidney damage and even lead to death. Blood group antigens are often called **agglutinogens**, and the antibodies are known as **agglutinins**. It is the binding of agglutinins to the matched agglutinogen that causes the red cells to agglutinate or clump together in a lattice-like structure held together by antigen–antibody complexes.

Q 6 The terms 'universal donor' and 'universal recipient' are sometimes used to refer to two blood groups in Table 1. Which is which – and why?

Q 7 Compile a table showing the antigen in red cell membranes and the antibody in plasma for each of the blood groups A, B, AB, and O.

Once blood has been donated, it must be kept sterile. This is a sterile environment for the production of blood products.

person would not have any harmful consequences (Table 2). Rh positive people do not produce the anti-D antibody in any circumstances.

Table 2 Rhesus compatibility		
Donor	Recipient	
	Rh +	Rh –
Rh +	✓	✗
Rh –	✓	✓

✓ = recipient accepts transfused blood
✗ = recipient has transfusion reaction

In practice, when blood is cross-matched for transfusion, both the ABO and Rh factors are matched.

Q 8 Given that the transfusion reaction is an immune response, why does a second 'dose' of Rh positive blood produce a rapid transfusion reaction in a Rh negative person?

Q 9 Draw up a compatibility table (in the style of Table 2) for blood groups. Use both the ABO and rhesus systems (A Rh +, A Rh –, etc.).

Rhesus factor

The rhesus factor is also called antigen D. It was discovered first in the rhesus monkey, but is found in human blood as well. About 75% of the population are Rh positive and have antigen D in their red cell membranes. A Rh negative person has neither antigen D nor the anti-rhesus antibody, anti-D.

Anti-D is only produced if Rh positive blood is introduced into the bloodstream of a Rh negative person. If this happens, there will be a gradual production of anti-D. This does not usually cause any problems the first time it happens. But if it happens again, a very rapid transfusion reaction occurs because the recipient's anti-D binds to the antigen D of the donated red cells and causes them to agglutinate.

Rh negative blood does not contain anti-D, so introducing Rh negative blood into the bloodstream of a Rh positive

Haemolytic disease of the newborn

The rhesus gene has two alleles. The dominant allele produces the factor, the recessive allele does not, so a Rh negative mother can have a Rh positive baby (Fig. 3).

The mother's bloodstream is quite separate from that of the fetus. In the placenta, substances such as oxygen and food diffuse from the mother's blood into the blood of the fetus and waste substances such as carbon dioxide and urea diffuse in the opposite direction. There is no direct contact between the mother's blood and that of her fetus. However, during the very late stages of pregnancy, mixing of maternal and fetal blood does sometimes happen. The strong muscular contractions of the uterus can damage placental membranes, and a small amount of blood from the fetus may get into the mother's circulation. This does not affect the baby

133

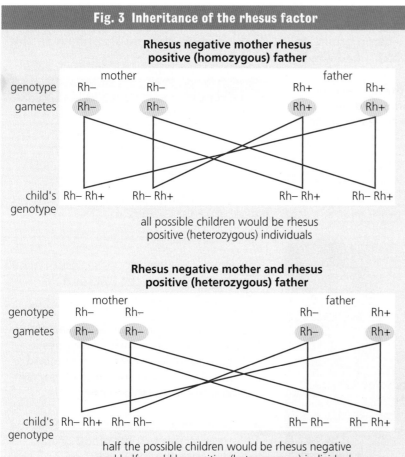

Fig. 3 Inheritance of the rhesus factor

Rhesus negative mother rhesus positive (homozygous) father

	mother			father	
genotype	Rh–	Rh–		Rh+	Rh+
gametes	Rh–	Rh–		Rh+	Rh+
child's genotype	Rh– Rh+	Rh– Rh+		Rh– Rh+	Rh– Rh+

all possible children would be rhesus positive (heterozygous) individuals

Rhesus negative mother and rhesus positive (heterozygous) father

	mother			father	
genotype	Rh–	Rh–		Rh–	Rh+
gametes	Rh–	Rh–		Rh–	Rh+
child's genotype	Rh– Rh+	Rh– Rh–		Rh– Rh–	Rh– Rh+

half the possible children would be rhesus negative and half would be positive (heterozygous) individuals

Blood supplies

For Mohammed to get a blood transfusion during his operation, the hospital had to have a supply of blood of the right type available. In the UK, the National Blood Transfusion Service (NBTS) provides this supply. The NBTS arranges donor sessions all over the country: in large cities the sessions may be held every day in special clinics; in many towns and cities, sessions are held several times a year in a convenient hall; in remote rural areas the sessions may be held in caravans that tour a number of villages. Blood donors usually give blood twice a year and anyone aged between 18 and 65 can go along to a donor session and volunteer to give blood. People who are HIV-positive, or who have had hepatitis or one of a number of other infectious diseases, are not allowed to donate because the infection may be passed on to patients receiving blood transfusions. Drug users are also not allowed to donate.

11 Look at the photograph. Why do you think you are not allowed to give blood if you are under 18 or over 65?

but the mother develops a small amount of anti-D.

If the mother gets pregnant again, and if the baby is again rhesus positive, there is a problem. Placental membranes are permeable to antibodies. In most cases, this is advantageous to the baby, since it provides short-term immunity to a number of antigens that the baby may come into contact with immediately after birth. However, anti-D antibody is not advantageous to a rhesus positive baby; it causes a number of problems such as anaemia and jaundice. The child is likely to be born prematurely and will need an immediate blood transfusion to replace all its blood. This condition is called haemolytic disease of the newborn.

10 Why does haemolytic disease of the newborn never affect a first baby?

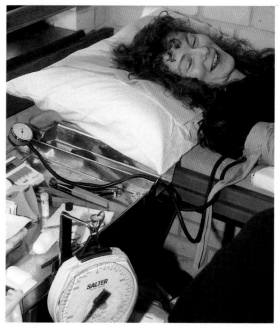

Giving blood is very straightforward. You must be in good health so you quickly make up the cells and plasma you have donated.

Key ideas

- Blood is usually grouped using the ABO and Rh systems. This is fine for most purposes but a full classification would include more than 20 factors.

- We all have blood that is either group A, B, AB, or O. This is because we all have either antigen A, or antigen B, or both antigens A and B, or neither in the membrane of our red blood cells.

- Those who have antigen A, have the antibody anti-B in their plasma; those with antigen B, have anti-A in their plasma. People with group AB have neither antibody, and those in group O have both.

- Giving blood of an incompatible ABO group to a patient will cause a transfusion reaction. The donated red blood cells clump together and burst.

- The A and B antigens are sometimes called agglutinogens and the antibodies are sometimes called agglutinins. The clumping of the cells is called agglutination.

- About 75% of people are Rh positive and have the rhesus antigen (antigen D). Rh negative people do not have either antigen D or the antibody, anti-D.

- Giving Rh positive blood to a Rh negative person causes a slow production of anti-D. If it happens again, the production of anti-D is very rapid and causes a transfusion reaction. Rh negative blood can be given to both Rh negative and Rh positive people.

- If a Rh negative mother has a Rh positive baby, she may produce a little anti-D in late pregnancy. If a second baby is Rh positive, it will have problems caused by the anti-D. The child may be premature and will need a complete transfusion to replace its blood. The condition is called haemolytic disease of the newborn.

- Blood supplies in the UK are donated free and are tested and distributed by the NBTS.

10.5 Acquired immune deficiency syndrome

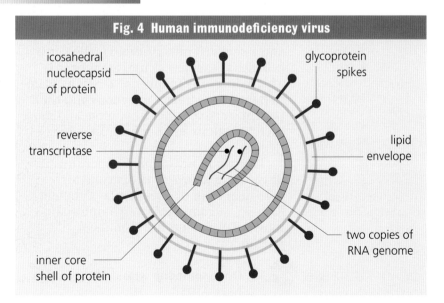

Fig. 4 Human immunodeficiency virus

icosahedral nucleocapsid of protein

reverse transcriptase

inner core shell of protein

glycoprotein spikes

lipid envelope

two copies of RNA genome

Patients like Mohammed undergo immunosuppression in order to increase their chance of life through a successful transplant operation. Even though it is a necessary part of life-saving transplant procedure, suppressing the immune system is a technique that involves serious risks. Acquired immune deficiency syndrome (AIDS) is a condition that shows very clearly how health deteriorates when the immune system breaks down and can no longer protect the body.

Most scientists believe AIDS is caused by the human immunodeficiency virus (HIV) (Fig. 4). However, it is important to remember that infection is not the same as having a disease. People who are infected with HIV produce antibody to combat the virus. If this antibody is detected in the blood, the individual is said to be **HIV-positive**. Being HIV-positive is not the same thing as having AIDS. An HIV-positive individual may show no signs other than the presence of antibody for many years. However, the virus attacks the immune system and the individual eventually suffers from a range of other secondary infections that the weakened immune system cannot fight off. Tumours (cancerous growths) also occur more easily, since a correctly functioning immune system has a role in destroying cancer cells.

How HIV causes AIDS

Infection with HIV is eventually followed by the onset of symptoms such as tiredness, fever, weight loss and diarrhoea. The person with these symptoms is said to have **AIDS-related complex** (ARC). Doctors and scientists do not know what percentage of people who are HIV-positive eventually show ARC, and developments in treatment have tended to delay the onset of ARC for 5–10 years after infection. Eventually, symptoms of one of the diseases known to be related to AIDS appear. Only then is the person said to be suffering from AIDS. The AIDS-related diseases are also called **opportunistic diseases** because they usually only affect people whose immune system is damaged. As the immune system continues to break down, the individual suffers from multiple opportunistic infections and/or tumours that eventually lead to death.

This all happens because HIV attacks the very cells that protect the body against infection. The HIV attaches to the cell membrane of a helper T cell, then viral RNA is released into the lymphocyte along with reverse transcriptase. Once inside the T cell, the viral RNA and enzyme produce viral DNA. The DNA enters the lymphocyte's nucleus and becomes incorporated into the resident DNA. The host T cell now contains a viral 'gene' coding for the production of viral proteins.

It may be a long time before the 'gene' is activated. Eventually, perhaps during an infection, the helper T cell's own DNA becomes active but the presence of the viral DNA means that viral proteins are produced and assembled into viruses. The helper T cell dies as the new viruses are released. This reduces the number of T cells available to fight off secondary infections and the patient starts to suffer from more and more such infections and opportunistic diseases (Fig. 5).

The two most common opportunistic diseases are Kaposi's sarcoma and a particular form of pneumonia. Although Kaposi's sarcoma looks very unpleasant, most AIDS patients die from the pneumonia.

Fig. 5 The immune response and HIV

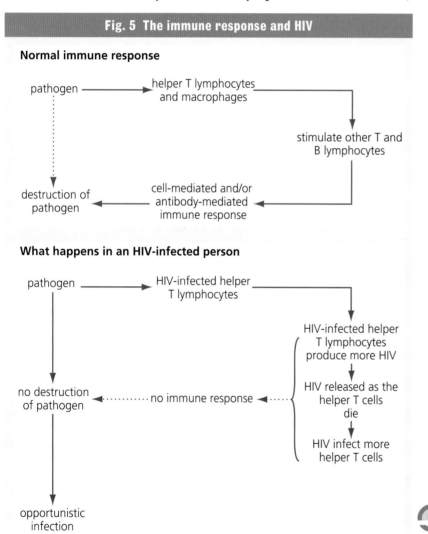

Normal immune response

What happens in an HIV-infected person

12 Does someone who is HIV-positive have AIDS?

Coloured scanning electron micrograph of newly assembled HIV (red) leaving a T lymphocyte (green). The T cell will die and the viruses will infect other T cells.

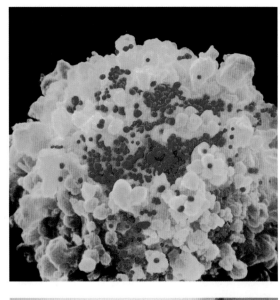

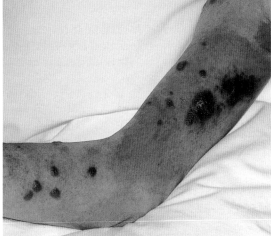

Kaposi's sarcoma is a rare form of cancer that causes these black tumours. It was known to affect some elderly people from Eastern Europe and the Mediterranean area, but the sudden rise in the number of cases among gay men in California during the late 1970s led to the recognition of HIV and AIDS.

Body fluids and HIV

Most HIV in an infected person is found in the T lymphocytes and only HIV in T lymphocytes seems to cause infection. There are plenty of T lymphocytes in blood, which is why blood is infectious. Semen also contains very high numbers of T lymphocytes so there is a build up of HIV in the semen of an infected man. Likewise, vaginal secretions contain high numbers of lymphocytes so the vaginal secretions of an infected woman are infectious.

There has been one documented case of HIV being transmitted through breast milk. This low figure is because it is difficult for the virus to gain entry to the recipient's bloodstream. Ingested milk travels from the mouth into the digestive system which is lined with epithelial tissue that, unless it is damaged, provides a barrier against entry to the bloodstream.

In urine and saliva, the virus has been found as isolated particles. These do not cause infection. There is no risk of infection for hospital staff, carers and other individuals who have normal daily contact with HIV-positive people. This is important. People who are HIV-positive and AIDS patients have endured much prejudice because of misconceptions about how the virus can be transmitted. In 1995 there was the ludicrous and deeply insulting case of American presidential guards wearing rubber gloves to greet a party of gay men at the White House. Not only did the guards appear to believe that the men were likely be suffering from AIDS simply because they were homosexual, they also seemed to believe that the infection could be passed on by shaking hands.

Transmission of HIV

HIV is only transmitted by the introduction of blood, semen or vaginal secretions from an infected individual into the bloodstream of another person. This can occur by:
- transfusion of infected blood;
- sharing needles;
- sexual activity.

HIV and blood transfusions

Between 1978 and 1984 many people did become infected with HIV through contaminated blood. In particular, a large number of haemophiliacs who need blood products such as Factor VIII to help with their blood clotting became infected. This happened before the link between blood and HIV infection was recognised and before screening tests for HIV antibody were developed. The donors themselves did not know they were infected. Since 1985, all blood donations in the UK are tested for HIV antibody and this has stopped HIV infection being passed on through blood products. People who are HIV-positive may not have any ill-effects for years, so they may not know they are infected. If a blood donor's blood is found to be HIV-positive, that person receives a letter from the NBTS. In the UK, nobody is paid for their blood, so no-one can gain financially by selling their blood.

Q 13 In some countries, including the USA, people are paid when they give blood. What sort of problems do you think this might cause?

HIV and needles

HIV-infected blood can get directly into the bloodstream if a needle (either a drug-user's hypodermic or a tattooist's specialised needle) is first used on someone who is HIV-positive and then used on an uninfected person. Blood cells from the first person remain in the needle and are transferred directly into the second person's bloodstream. Drug addicts who share needles are one of the main groups with a high risk of contracting AIDS.

Although the don't-share-the-works and new-needles-for-old schemes outraged people who thought the schemes encouraged drug abuse, they do seem to have had some effect in reducing the spread of HIV among drug users.

HIV and sex

The main way HIV gets into the body is through sexual activity and the transfer of infected semen and infected vaginal secretions. Kissing is not a high-risk activity but oral, vaginal and anal intercourse are all high-risk. It is not known whether cuts or abrasions in the mouth, vagina or anus are needed for the transmission of HIV. Both males and females can get infected by sex with an HIV-positive partner.

Preventing HIV infection

HIV transmission between drug users is prevented if they do not share needles. Many hospitals now operate a 'new-for-old' policy whereby they will give users clean new needles in exchange for their old ones.

Tattooing can also transmit HIV if needles are reused. Reputable tattooists should show their customers the new, sealed needles that will be used in producing the tattoo.

Q 14 Do you think giving drug addicts new needles in exchange for their old ones is a good way to combat the spread of HIV? Why?

Reducing the spread of HIV has been the subject of a number of campaigns throughout the world, and has given rise to the concept of 'safe sex' i.e. using a condom during sexual activity. Condoms cannot give 100% protection but they considerably reduce the chances of an exchange of body fluids.

Condoms are not just for vaginal intercourse. It is particularly important that a condom is used during anal intercourse. This prevents infected lymphocytes from semen entering the recipient's bloodstream through the small breaks in rectal tissue that anal intercourse frequently causes.

It is also particularly recommended that a condom should be used if either partner has genital herpes. Genital herpes causes a patch of tiny blisters to appear in the genital area; the blisters then burst and eventually heal up. These blisters are easily broken by friction and people of either sex should think of them as small breaks in the skin.

AIDS DON'T DIE OF IGNORANCE

[GAY OR STRAIGHT, MALE OR FEMALE, ANYONE CAN GET AIDS FROM SEXUAL INTERCOURSE.
SO THE MORE PARTNERS, THE GREATER THE RISK. PROTECT YOURSELF, USE A CONDOM.]

MORE O'FERRALL P.L.C. L.2007

World distribution of HIV and AIDS

In late 1994, the World Health Organisation estimated that about 14 million people around the world had been infected with HIV. By late 1994, there had been just over a million reported AIDS cases, but the estimated number of AIDS cases was 4.5 million. This looks as though 3.5 million cases of AIDS have not been recognised and reported.

15 If the estimates are correct, what percentage of HIV-positive individuals are known to have developed AIDS?

The number of casual sexual encounters in society is difficult to measure. There is evidence that when the contraceptive pill became widely available in the 1960s, the average number of sexual partners per person for people aged 18–30 increased. With the arrival of AIDS, there is now evidence that the average number of sexual partners for sexually active people in this age group has reduced.

10.6 Auto-immune diseases

In a healthy person, the immune system functions to prevent the body from being invaded by material that the system recognises as foreign. Foreign material may be cells in a transplanted organ or invading microbial pathogens. Sometimes we want to suppress the immune system – as in Mohammed's case so as to give transplant surgery an increased chance of success. This is a short-term strategy and does not harm the individual in the long run. Sometimes the system is suppressed by infection, as in the case of HIV, this is a long-term effect and eventually leads to death. There is a third set of circumstances in which the immune system is under-functioning – it is called auto-immunity.

The body can make lymphocytes that produce an immune response to its own antigens instead of to foreign ones. During embryonic development, potentially **auto-immune** or self-reactive lymphocytes are

usually removed by the thymus gland. However, it is possible that some of these lymphocytes escape this deletion process. In most cases, the action of these survivors is prevented by the presence of other lymphocytes called suppressor T cells. Suppressor T cells generally limit the length of time an immune response lasts, but they also prevent any immune response at all when auto-immune lymphocytes are stimulated.

In some individuals, deletion or suppression of auto-immune lymphocytes goes wrong. When this happens, auto-immune lymphocytes cause an immune response to the person's own antigens, and a condition known as **auto-immunity** results. There are many auto-immune diseases, among them are:
- multiple sclerosis;
- some forms of diabetes;
- rheumatoid arthritis.

Multiple sclerosis

In multiple sclerosis (MS), the patient's immune system progressively destroys the myelin sheaths that surround neurones (nerve cells). The myelin sheath is formed from cells called Schwann cells that wrap around the developing neurone (Fig. 6). The auto-immune response in MS is to the Schwann cells which the auto-immune T lymphocytes attack and kill. The resulting widespread demyelination of neurones in the brain and spinal cord leads to a number of neurological disorders. Among the first signs of MS are problems with the eyes and other sense organs, numbness, muscle fatigue and 'tingling nerves'. The disease tends to progress through alternating attacks of severe symptoms and periods of **remission** when the symptoms are less evident or missing altogether. Patients may eventually develop problems with coordination, and partial or complete paralysis of parts of the body may occur. The treatment for MS involves the use of drugs such as adrenocorticotrophic hormone (ACTH) and corticosteroids. Both these drugs can relieve some of the symptoms, but there is no known cure for the condition. About 70% of sufferers are able to lead a relatively normal life, but the other 30% have many progressive problems.

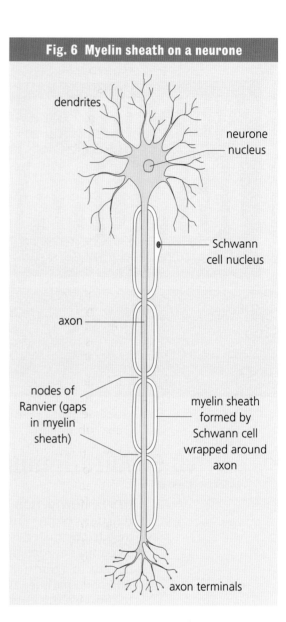

Fig. 6 Myelin sheath on a neurone

dendrites

neurone nucleus

Schwann cell nucleus

axon

nodes of Ranvier (gaps in myelin sheath)

myelin sheath formed by Schwann cell wrapped around axon

axon terminals

10.7 Which way forward?

Mohammed's transplant operation was a success. He was given a cadaver kidney that closely matched his tissue type and his immune system did not reject the transplant. The immunosuppressive therapy was eventually stopped and Mohammed is able to live a normal life.

Not all patients are so lucky. Even with the donor card scheme there are not as many organs available for transplant surgery as there are patients who need them. Not only are there many more patients than willing donors, just carrying a donor card is not enough. Whatever age you are, if your relatives object to the donation, your organs will not be used. And not all transplants succeed. The immune system is the 'enemy' of the transplant surgeon and can cause the new organ to be rejected. Research scientists are working to produce a steady supply of genetically changed organs that can be grown in pigs. These organs will be designed to have the HLA proteins that atransplant patient needs for a perfect match. So, when the organ is transplanted into the human patient, no rejection will occur.

17 a Do you think more publicity for the donor card scheme and greater efficiency in maintaining the database of donors would provide enough transplant organs?

b Do you think genetically changed organs grown in pigs are a suitable alternative? Why?

Key ideas

- AIDS is caused by HIV infection.

- HIV infects T lymphocytes – the cells that usually protect the body from infection. HIV replication and release kills the T cells. This means there are not enough T cells to fight infections and tumours.

- Infection with HIV is eventually followed by ARC and later by the onset of opportunistic diseases because the person does not have enough T cells.

- HIV is transmitted by infected lymphocytes in blood, semen, and vaginal secretions. Isolated HIV particles in urine and saliva are not infective.

- HIV infection can occur through infected blood transfusion, use of shared needles, and sex with an infected partner.

- Since 1985 all UK blood donations are HIV tested so blood transfusion in the UK is safe.

- In the campaign to limit the spread of HIV infection, drug users are encouraged to change their used needles for clean ones, and those who are sexually active are encouraged to practise safe sex.

- The immune system sometimes responds to the body's own antigens. This is called auto-immunity and is usually prevented by the thymus and suppressor T cells.

- Auto-immune diseases include MS, some forms of diabetes, and rheumatoid arthritis.

- In MS, auto-immune lymphocytes attack the Schwann cells. The resulting demyelination causes a range of neurological disorders. MS attacks alternate with symptom-free periods.

- MS is treated with ACTH and corticosteroids, but these drugs can only relieve the symptoms; there is no cure.

Targeting pathogens

This is a hospital in the Bosnian war zone in 1995.

Eighteenth-century surgical techniques look terrifying now, but surgeons did the best they could.

In the UK in the 1990s, we expect a lot from our hospitals. We expect a bed, highly trained professional staff, drugs for pain relief, and anaesthetics during operations. We take it for granted that the operating theatre and equipment are sterile and that blood is available for transfusion. We also expect our hospitals to have fully staffed and well equipped laboratories. But in today's war zones, conditions in which city hospitals have to cope with civilian casualties are very different. There are severe shortages of drugs, blood, anaesthetics, clean laundry, beds, supplies for laboratories and maybe even no water or electricity. It's almost like going back in time.

If you needed major surgery such as a leg amputation, in the early part of the nineteenth century, you had only a 50% chance of surviving the treatment. If you were lucky, you might have been given a sleeping draft like morphine or laudanum. More likely, you would have been aware of everything that was going on, down to the last sweep of the saw as it cut through your femur. It wouldn't have lasted long. Surgeons could amputate a limb in as little as 30 seconds because assistants couldn't hold patients down any longer.

11.1 Learning objectives

After working through this chapter, you should be able to:

- **explain** how people can use disinfectants and antiseptics to prevent infection;

- **recognise** situations where antibiotics can be useful;

- **justify** the selection of a particular antibiotic to treat a specific disease;

- **explain** how microorganisms can become resistant to antibiotics;

- **explain** how monoclonal antibodies are used in research on drug targeting;

- **explain** how ELISA techniques work.

11.2 Development of surgical practice

Today, we see three main problems in surgery:

- controlling pain;
- controlling blood loss and shock;
- controlling wound infection.

The development of surgical practice through the nineteenth and twentieth centuries has been the development of ways of dealing with these three problems.

1 Why was speed important in nineteenth-century amputations?

Controlling pain

In 1797 Sir Humphrey Davy discovered that nitrous oxide, or 'laughing gas', could deaden pain, but his report was not widely read and even though he suggested that the gas could be used during operations, surgeons did not use it. A chemical that can deaden pain is called an **anaesthetic**. Ether was the first anaesthetic and it was used first in the 1840s in America, over 40 years after Davy's discovery of nitrous oxide. Ether remained the main pain-killing substance until halothane was introduced in the 1950s.

As well as an anaesthetic, ether is also a muscle relaxant. This is a great help to surgeons, particularly in abdominal operations. The amount of ether necessary to make a patient unconscious is quite small, but much more is needed to produce muscle relaxation. After operations using ether, the patient often slept for many hours, or even days because the whole body was saturated with ether. It was not until the 1930s that an alternative muscle relaxant was discovered – tubocurarine.

2 What is an anaesthetic and what was the first anaesthetic to be regularly used during surgery?

Curare comes from S. America and is used by Amazonian Indians to coat arrow tips for hunting.

Curare paralyses the heart and intercostal muscles (the muscles needed for breathing) when injected into the body – including injection by arrow-tip. When taken by mouth it is harmless, so meat killed with curare can be eaten safely. In 1935, Harold King isolated the active ingredient in curare, and named it tubocurarine. This made it possible to produce standardised samples of the drug and its ability to cause muscle relaxation was investigated. From then on, much smaller amounts of ether could be used to anaesthetise a patient.

Today, along with tubocurarine, a range of new anaesthetics and muscle relaxants is used. The effects of a general anaesthetic do not last so long, and the patient suffers fewer side-effects.

3 Why were large doses of ether given to a patient before an operation?

Controlling blood loss and shock

In the early nineteenth century, patients usually lost a lot of blood during operations. If they didn't die from blood loss, they went into the condition called **shock**. This condition is due to loss of body fluids and drop in blood pressure. Today, this is prevented by better operating conditions and transfusion of blood and other fluids.

Surgeons tried to transfuse blood into patients in the 1500s. Unfortunately, they used lambs' blood which caused a transfusion reaction (Chapter 10, p. 132) and the patients died. In 1818, the first human blood donors were used and sometimes the transfusion was successful. The A, B, AB and O blood groups were discovered in 1900 and from then on, careful matching of the ABO groups removed most of the dangers of blood transfusion. At first, transfusions were made directly from donor to recipient. During the First World War, blood was donated by healthy individuals to give to the wounded. Anti-clotting agents such as sodium citrate were added so that bottles of blood could be kept for short periods, and then used when required.

4 What causes the medical condition called shock?

5 Why is sodium citrate added to blood stored for use at a later date?

Kenneth Williams, Sid James, Frankie Howerd and Bernard Bresslaw got too much laughing gas in the comedy film *Carry On Doctor*. Nitrous oxide did gain acceptance as an anaesthetic in dentistry, but it still wasn't funny to have a tooth out.

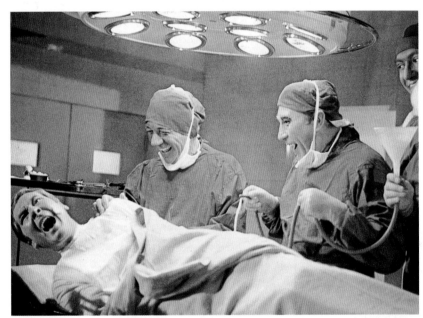

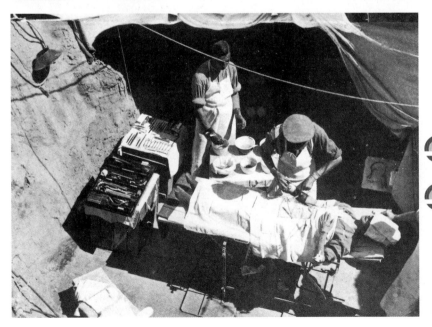

In the First World War, the Red Cross ran field hospitals and coordinated the first blood transfusion service.

Controlling infection

In the eighteenth and early nineteenth centuries, many surgeons were also barbers. The traditional red and white striped barber's pole is a reminder of this time – the colours represent blood and bone.

Surgeons then worked in unhygienic conditions. They would have an operating coat or apron but it was likely to be spattered with blood from previous operations. Although 'clean' surgical instruments would have been used, they would not have been sterile, so when an incision was made, microbes present on the blade would have entered the body along with any microbes on the skin. Microbes would also have been likely to get into the wound from the surgeon and the operating theatre. Human breath contains droplets of water in which there is a high concentration of bacteria and viruses, and surgeons then did not wear masks. Air is laden with air-borne microbes, and any that fell into a wound would have had an excellent place to grow.

The British surgeon Joseph Lister applied Pasteur's theories to wound infection. He believed that spraying carbolic acid over a wound during the operation would reduce the risk of post-operative infection. The carbolic acid killed the microbes and the number of infected wounds decreased dramatically. Instruments used in the operation were also soaked in carbolic acid to kill microbes.

It was late in the nineteenth century before there were any serious attempts to reduce infection in operations. By that time, the discovery and use of anaesthetics meant that surgeons were able to perform longer operations, and abdominal surgery had become quite common.

6 In nineteenth-century operations, the wound often became infected. How?

7 Why did Lister start to use carbolic acid spray during his operations?

During the latter years of the nineteenth century, Lister's carbolic acid spray was accepted and in 1889 rubber gloves were first used during an operation, initially to reduce skin irritation caused by the carbolic spray. Lister's ideas marked the beginning of the concept of **aseptic technique**. Good modern practice includes using special operating gowns, hats and masks, scrubbing all surfaces, and sterilising all instruments. Dressings, equipment, and fluids such as plasma, saline, and blood must also be sterile.

Hospital infections

Even today, 5–10% of hospital patients suffer an infection caught in hospital. The main causes of this are:

* post-operative wound infection;
* infections caused by air-borne microbes;
* self-infection, (microbes present on one part of the body infect another);
* infected food;
* infected equipment;
* infected blood transfusions.

Hospital infections are serious, and may even kill the patient, although this is rare in developed countries. Infected patients are a risk to other patients and staff. The chance of hospital infection is generally reduced by:

* sterilisation;
* disinfection.

8 How is post-operative wound infection kept to a minimum today?

11.3 Sterilisation

A piece of equipment is sterile if it is free from all **viable** (capable of reproducing) organisms such as bacteria, bacterial spores, viruses, fungi and fungal spores. Methods used to achieve sterility include:

- heat;
- ionising radiation;
- filtration;
- chemicals (gases and liquids).

Heat

Heat treatment is used for surgical instruments, dressings and certain heat-resistant drugs. Temperatures above 100 °C kill almost all bacteria and other microbes. Naked flames can be used on certain instruments, and burning or incineration destroys used dressings and other soiled materials.

Autoclaves heat water under pressure to more than 100 °C. This is known as **moist heat sterilisation** (flames provide **dry heat sterilisation**). However, some heat-resistant bacterial spores can survive even this treatment. Items to be autoclaved are cleaned first because if large quantities of bacteria are present, the process may leave some of the more heat-resistant strains relatively unaffected. Sterilisation is improved if air is sucked out of the autoclave chamber before high-pressure steam is added. The usual heating cycle is 15 minutes at 121 °C. This is sufficient to kill bacteria, and provide a margin for safety.

9 What is moist heat sterilisation?

Ionising radiation

Beta radiation (high-speed electrons) and gamma radiation (high-energy photons) are used to sterilise batches of single-use instruments, such as syringes and lancets. The articles are usually in sealed packages, and are not opened until use. Irradiation can also be used for certain vaccines, and some types of food. Ionising radiation disrupts the microbial DNA and so prevents the organism from reproducing.

Filtration

Some liquids, such as blood and serum, are damaged by heat. Electrostatic filters can be used for these materials. The filters are made of a nitrocellulose net with a pore size small enough to trap microbial particles, except for some tiny harmless viruses.

Chemical sterilisation

Certain plastic items, such as heart valves, used to be sterilised by toxic gases, but the process is potentially explosive and has been replaced by gamma radiation. Formaldehyde might be used as a disinfectant, for instance in cleaning an isolation room, but the fumes are very unpleasant and can irritate the mucous membranes of the respiratory system.

10 How does ionising radiation sterilise equipment?

A sterile supply department is vital to modern hospitals.

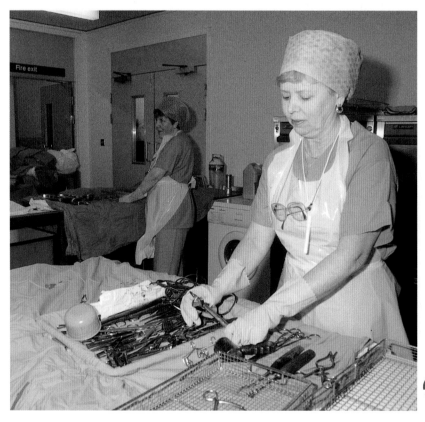

11.4 Disinfection

Disinfection does not kill bacterial spores. It is used in situations that do not require sterility, or where it is impractical to achieve sterility. For instance, bed pans, cooking utensils, hospital floors, walls and furniture do not need to be sterile. Immersion in boiling water kills most bacterial cells, but not all spores. This approach is called **moist heat disinfection** and is used in emergencies when it is not possible to employ moist heat sterilisation. Adding 2% sodium carbonate to the water increases the bactericidal effect.

'Sterilising fluids' do not create sterile conditions, and should be regarded as disinfectants. Disinfectant effectiveness is affected by:
- the porosity, texture or physical condition of the surface being disinfected;
- availability of moisture;
- temperature;
- pH;
- disinfectant concentration;
- quality of the diluting water (hardness);
- the number, type and condition of microbes on the surface being disinfected.

11 Do you think a porous surface would be more or less difficult to disinfect than a non-porous one? Why?

Antiseptics

Antiseptics are in effect, disinfectants for use on skin or wounds. Like disinfectants, antiseptics do not kill bacterial spores. Lister used carbolic acid (phenol) as an antiseptic, although when used on a hospital floor it would be classed as a disinfectant. Thorough scrubbing of hands is vital to reduce the risk of hospital workers transferring infection. However, even thorough washing with an antiseptic soap does not remove all microbes; those that live in ducts leading to sweat glands or in hair follicles are largely untouched and begin to recolonise open areas of the skin within 1–2 hours.

Most disinfectants act by damaging microbial cell components such as membrane lipids, DNA or proteins. The effectiveness of disinfectants can be evaluated by the phenol coefficient test, the use-dilution test and the antiseptic dilution plate technique (Chapter 6, pp. 72–74).

12 What is the difference between sterilisation and disinfection?

13 When is disinfection used rather than sterilisation?

Key ideas

- Good surgical practice has developed from ways of controlling pain, blood loss and shock, and wound infection.

- Pain in operations is controlled by anaesthetics.

- Blood loss and shock are controlled by the transfusion of blood and other fluids. Successful blood transfusion became possible after the A, B, AB and O blood groups were discovered in 1900.

- Wound infection is controlled by aseptic technique and sterilisation.

- Before Louis Pasteur, it was not realised that microbes caused infection. Joseph Lister first used carbolic acid as an antiseptic.

- The risk of infection in hospital is reduced by sterilisation and disinfection.

- Sterilisation kills or removes all microbial life, including spores.

- Disinfection kills microbial cells but not the spores.

- Antiseptics can be used on skin or wounds.

11.5 Antibiotics

Penicillin was the first antibiotic. Research on penicillin was pushed forward because of the Second World War, and it was first used to treat bacterial infections in soldiers in the early 1940s. Since then, antibiotics have been used to treat many infectious bacterial diseases. Many such infections that were once killers are now preventable by vaccine and treatable by chemotherapy. Chemotherapy is the use of chemical agents, including antibiotics, that are toxic to selected microorganisms but do not harm human cells. There are now about 50 antibiotics in common use – about 1% of those that have been successfully isolated from their microbial source. Some are effective against only a few types of bacterium and are called narrow spectrum antibiotics. Others kill or inhibit a wide range of bacteria and are called broad (wide) spectrum antibiotics. Some antibiotics have been chemically altered to make them more effective – these are termed semi-synthetic antibiotics (Chapter 6, p. 78). Antibiotic effectiveness can be determined by disc diffusion tests (Chapter 6, pp. 76–77).

Alexander Fleming discovered penicillin. A substance released from the *Penicillium* fungus at the centre of the petri dish kills bacterial colonies (grey) close to the fungus but colonies farther away (red) are still viable.

Action of antibiotics

Antibiotics can destroy or inhibit microorganisms by:
- inhibition of cell wall synthesis;
- inhibition of protein synthesis;
- inhibition of nucleic acid synthesis;
- cell membrane disruption;
- inhibition of cell metabolism.

Penicillin, ampicillin and the cephalosporins inhibit the enzymes that help to form the cross-links in the bacterial cell wall (Fig. 1). This leads to a breakdown of the wall and the leakage or **lysis** of the cell contents. Bacitracin interferes with the lipid that transports key cell wall components across the cell membrane.

Fig. 1 Penicillin action on bacterial cell walls

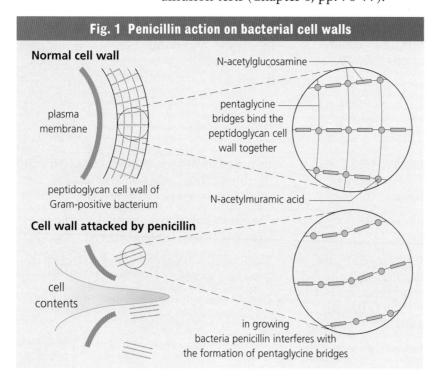

Normal cell wall

plasma membrane

peptidoglycan cell wall of Gram-positive bacterium

N-acetylglucosamine

pentaglycine bridges bind the peptidoglycan cell wall together

N-acetylmuramic acid

Cell wall attacked by penicillin

cell contents

in growing bacteria penicillin interferes with the formation of pentaglycine bridges

Streptomycin, gentamicin and the tetracyclines bind across bacterial ribosomes (Fig. 2). Bacterial cells are prokaryotic and the ribosomes are different from those in human cells which are eukaryotic (Chapter 1, p. 10), so protein synthesis in the host cells is not inhibited.

Fig. 2 Protein inhibition by antibiotics

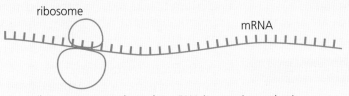

ribosomes move along the mRNA in protein synthesis

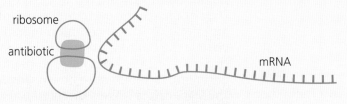

antibiotics such as streptomycin bind to ribosomes and prevent protein synthesis

Massive supplies of drugs such as antibiotics are needed to keep infection under control in war zones and natural disaster areas but convoys carrying food and medical aid cannot always get through border posts.

Nucleic acid in prokaryotic cells is similar to nucleic acid in eukaryotic cells so antibiotics that inhibit the synthesis of nucleic acid are not as specific as some others. However, ciprofloxacin interferes with prokaryotic DNA replication and transcription, and rifampicin blocks prokaryotic RNA synthesis by binding to RNA-polymerase.

Polymyxin B binds to the cell membrane and alters its structure making it more permeable, and leading to cell death.

Inhibition of prokaryotic cell metabolism is brought about by a number of antibiotics that act as **antimetabolites**. Antimetabolites inhibit key reactions in cells and result in a shortage of essential metabolites. For example, sulphonamides inhibit folic acid production in prokaryotic cells. As humans do not metabolise folic acid but must obtain it from food, sulphonamides have no detrimental effect on human metabolism.

14 Why are humans not affected by the actions of:
   a) penicillins?
   b) sulphonamides?

It is more difficult to treat fungal infections than bacterial infections. This is because fungi are eukaryotic organisms and their cell processes are very similar to those of human cells. This makes most antifungal agents very toxic for humans, but there are a few exceptions. Polyoxin D inhibits chitin synthase – an enzyme essential in fungal cell wall synthesis that human cells do not have. Another very useful antifungal agent is nystatin. It damages the fungal cell membrane so the cell contents leak out. It is used to treat skin infections.

Selecting a particular antibiotic to treat a specific disease means considering how the drug works, its side-effects, possible reactions with other drugs that the patient might be taking, whether or not the patient is pregnant, and so on.

15 Why is it easier to treat bacterial infections than it is to treat fungal infections?

Resistance to antibiotics

For as long as antibiotics have been used to treat bacterial infections, the bacteria have been fighting back. Not all bacteria are susceptible to all antibiotics. For example, it is pointless to treat an infection caused by Gram-negative bacteria with penicillin, because these bacteria have a thick outer envelope that prevents penicillin from entering the cell.

There are a number of different mechanisms by which bacteria are able to resist the action of antibiotics (Fig. 3).

Transmission of antibiotic resistance

There has also been a development of resistant strains among bacterial species that were generally susceptible to particular antibiotics. It is important to remember that resistant bacteria are not caused by antibiotics. An antibiotic-resistant organism develops and is able to grow and reproduce successfully despite the presence of the antibiotic. In other words, the resistant bacterium is selected. Bacteria become antibiotic-resistant when they obtain the genes for drug resistance. There are two ways this can happen:
• spontaneous mutation;
• transfer of genes for resistance from other bacteria.

Mutations in the bacterial chromosome do not occur very often but when they do, they can make the bacterium resistant to an antibiotic. The most common mutations change the binding site for an antibiotic (for example, the ribosomes) so that the antibiotic cannot bind. These changes in the DNA can be passed on by transduction and transformation (Fig. 4) and also by conjugation (Fig. 5). Many resistant mutants do not survive the normal defence mechanisms of the host, but some do. In a host that is being treated with an antibiotic, these surviving mutants are at a selective advantage because non-mutated bacteria are inhibited or killed by the antibiotic. The mutants can then grow and reproduce with much less competition for nutrients.

Besides the bacterial chromosome, bacteria can also contain genetic information on small circular pieces of DNA called plasmids. If a gene for antibiotic resistance is among the genetic information on a plasmid, it is called an **R plasmid**. Once a bacterial cell contains an R plasmid, the resistance gene on the plasmid can be transferred to other cells through conjugation (Fig. 5) and also by transformation and transduction (Fig. 4). Plasmids can cross species boundaries.

Fig. 3 Mechanisms of bacterial resistance to antibiotics

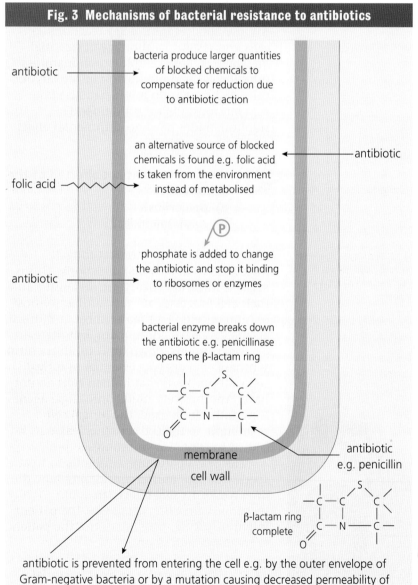

antibiotic → bacteria produce larger quantities of blocked chemicals to compensate for reduction due to antibiotic action

folic acid → an alternative source of blocked chemicals is found e.g. folic acid is taken from the environment instead of metabolised ← antibiotic

antibiotic → phosphate is added to change the antibiotic and stop it binding to ribosomes or enzymes

bacterial enzyme breaks down the antibiotic e.g. penicillinase opens the β-lactam ring

membrane

cell wall

antibiotic e.g. penicillin

β-lactam ring complete

antibiotic is prevented from entering the cell e.g. by the outer envelope of Gram-negative bacteria or by a mutation causing decreased permeability of the cell membrane in *Neisseria meningitidis*

Q 16 Why are resistance genes in plasmids more of a problem to medical staff than resistance genes on the bacterial chromosome?

Fig. 4 Transduction and transformation in bacteria

Transduction

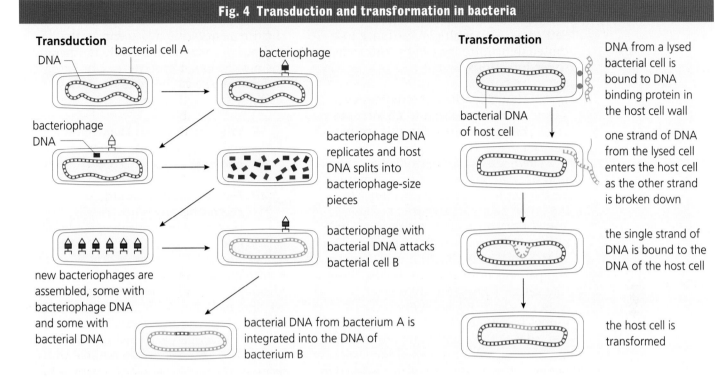

bacteriophage DNA replicates and host DNA splits into bacteriophage-size pieces

bacteriophage with bacterial DNA attacks bacterial cell B

new bacteriophages are assembled, some with bacteriophage DNA and some with bacterial DNA

bacterial DNA from bacterium A is integrated into the DNA of bacterium B

Transformation

DNA from a lysed bacterial cell is bound to DNA binding protein in the host cell wall

one strand of DNA from the lysed cell enters the host cell as the other strand is broken down

the single strand of DNA is bound to the DNA of the host cell

the host cell is transformed

Fig. 5 Conjugation in bacteria with a plasmid

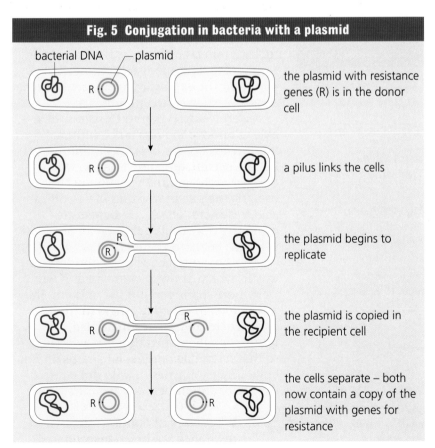

the plasmid with resistance genes (R) is in the donor cell

a pilus links the cells

the plasmid begins to replicate

the plasmid is copied in the recipient cell

the cells separate – both now contain a copy of the plasmid with genes for resistance

Resistant infections and super-infections

Many diseases that were once thought to be under control are now making a reappearance. This is because the pathogenic bacteria now have genetic changes that allow them to survive antibiotic attack. The widespread and sometimes indiscriminate use of antibiotics for 40–50 years has provided an environment for the growth of resistant bacteria.

Hospitals are a focus for bacteria. People going in for treatment often have infectious diseases, and take the bacteria into hospital with them. Sometimes these bacteria include resistant strains that are at a selective advantage in hospitals because the generally high concentration of antibiotics allows the resistant strains to multiply as the rest fall victim to the effects of the drugs. Today, a major reservoir of genetically altered resistant strains is found in hospitals. This reservoir of resistant bacteria carries a pool of resistance genes in bacterial plasmids. A single plasmid can contain genes for resistance to more than one antibiotic. This means that resistance to several antibiotics can spread rapidly through the bacterial population. Pathogens with multiple resistance have caused difficult-to-treat infections called **super-infections** (Fig. 6).

17 How does the indiscriminate use of an antibiotic lead to an increase in bacteria resistant to this antibiotic?

Where resistance seems likely, doctors now use combinations of two or more antibiotics to reduce the possibility of infectious bacteria surviving. Before antibiotics, tuberculosis (TB) was a very serious disease for which there was no cure. Then antibiotics brought it under control and patients recovered. But the bacterium that causes TB has now developed resistance and TB has re-emerged as a serious infectious disease in western countries. A three-antibiotic drug regime has been used against it with some success, but even this approach has not worked in all cases. In an outbreak of TB in the US between 1990 and 1992, over 140 patients had a strain of TB which was resistant to the three-antibiotic treatment. In the absence of suitable anti-TB chemotherapy, the pre-antibiotic procedure of isolating TB sufferers in special hospital wards has started to be used again.

18 Why are hospitals likely to be a source of antibiotic-resistant bacteria?

19 Even multiple-antibiotic chemotherapy is not always successful in controlling bacterial infection. Why not?

Fighting resistance

Although the search for new drugs is on-going (Chapter 6, p. 75), merely looking for or designing new antibiotics is not enough to combat resistance. As fast as we develop a new antibiotic, resistance follows on through the combination of mutations and cross-species transfer of resistant genes. So, what other approaches to combat resistance are possible? Plasmid-based research is looking for ways to:
- eliminate R plasmids from bacteria;
- prevent the expression of the resistance genes carried by the plasmids.

Ascorbic acid (vitamin C) seems to be able to remove the resistance without killing the bacteria. It is important not to kill the bacteria because doing so would encourage the natural selection of those bacteria capable of resisting the ascorbic acid treatment. Other researchers are exploring how to stop the spread of plasmids between bacteria.

Another approach is to reconsider the way in which antibiotics are used. If we were more sparing in our use of them, they would remain effective longer in those cases where they are really needed. International co-operation is needed here so that reservoirs of resistant strains do not build up in countries that do not control the use of antibiotics.

20 What ways of fighting bacterial resistance are being investigated?

Fig. 6 How bacteria can become resistant to more than one antibiotic

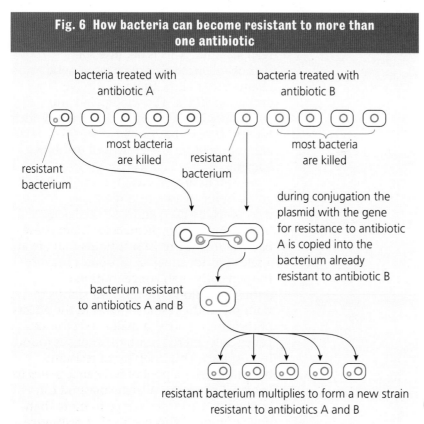

bacteria treated with antibiotic A

bacteria treated with antibiotic B

most bacteria are killed

resistant bacterium

most bacteria are killed

resistant bacterium

resistant bacterium

during conjugation the plasmid with the gene for resistance to antibiotic A is copied into the bacterium already resistant to antibiotic B

bacterium resistant to antibiotics A and B

resistant bacterium multiplies to form a new strain resistant to antibiotics A and B

11.6 Monoclonal antibodies

Specific antibodies are produced by competent B lymphocytes in response to the presence of an antigen (Chapter 9, p. 120). During an infection, competent B lymphocytes undergo repeated mitosis (or cloning) to produce an array of cells capable of producing the particular antibody needed. Antibodies produced in this way, and specific to only one antigen, are termed **monoclonal antibodies**.

Monoclonal antibodies are causing a revolution in diagnosis. Techniques using monoclonal antibodies are frequently quick and easy to perform, and do not need large and expensive apparatus. This means that such antibodies and the tests that employ them are well suited to use in difficult and adverse conditions such as war zones.

Growing monoclonal antibodies

Monoclonal antibodies are grown in cell cultures using tumour cells so that the B cells divide at a much faster rate than usual. This is known as the **hybridoma technique** (Fig. 7).

21 What is the importance of fusing competent B cells to tumour cells during monoclonal antibody production?

Use of monoclonal antibodies

Each monoclonal antibody is specific to a particular antigen. So, they can be used to identify cells with that antigen (Fig. 8).

Monoclonal antibodies are also used in cancer treatment. The antigens on

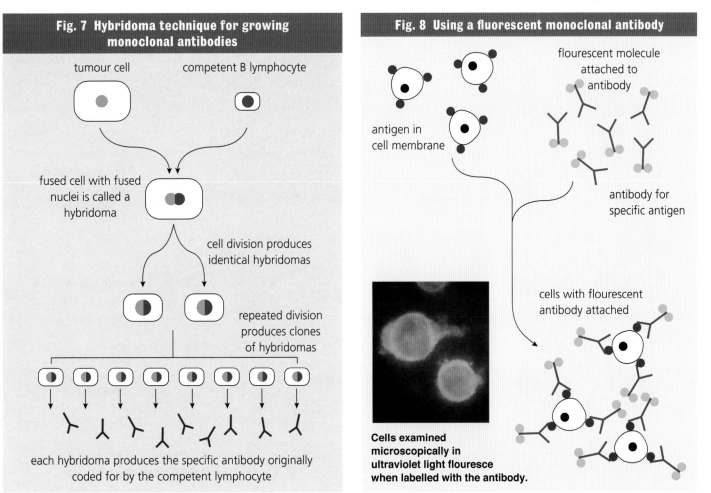

Fig. 7 Hybridoma technique for growing monoclonal antibodies

tumour cell

competent B lymphocyte

fused cell with fused nuclei is called a hybridoma

cell division produces identical hybridomas

repeated division produces clones of hybridomas

each hybridoma produces the specific antibody originally coded for by the competent lymphocyte

Fig. 8 Using a fluorescent monoclonal antibody

flourescent molecule attached to antibody

antigen in cell membrane

antibody for specific antigen

cells with flourescent antibody attached

Cells examined microscopically in ultraviolet light flouresce when labelled with the antibody.

cancerous cells are different from those on normal cells. By selecting a monoclonal antibody specific to a cancerous cell antigen and attaching a **cytotoxic drug** to the antibody, it is possible to send the drug specifically to tumour cells. (A cytotoxic drug is a drug that is very damaging to cell metabolism.) This combination of antibody and drug is sometimes called a 'magic bullet'. The same targeting technique can be used in research to discover if new drugs can be successfully delivered to specific cells.

Patients who have muscle damage following a heart attack are likely to suffer further heart problems. Such damage can be identified using radioactively labelled monoclonal antibody specific to the protein

myosin. Myosin is found in all muscle cells, but it is only exposed when the muscle cell is damaged. Damaged cardiac muscle is radioactively labelled by the anti-myosin. The label is easily detectable and doctors can then give appropriate therapy.

Q 22 What are 'magic bullets' and how do they work?

Enzyme linked immunoadsorbent assay

Enzyme linked immunoadsorbent assay (ELISA) involves labelling monoclonal antibodies with enzymes that catalyse easily detectable reactions. ELISA is widely used in clinical laboratories since it is relatively easy to perform, and does not require expensive apparatus. Hundreds of applications exist,

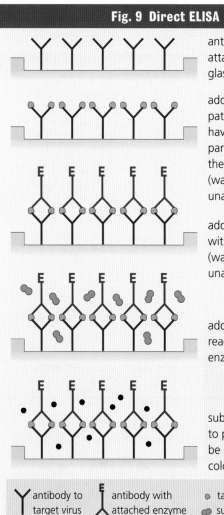

Fig. 9 Direct ELISA

antibody to target virus attached to a well in a glass plate

add sample from patient suspected to have the virus so if virus particles are present they attach to antibody (wash to remove unattached material)

add anti-virus antibody with enzyme attached (wash to remove unattached antibody)

add substrate for reaction catalysed by enzyme

substrate is converted to product which can be detected (e.g. a colour change)

Y antibody to target virus
E antibody with attached enzyme
● target virus
◖ substrate
● product

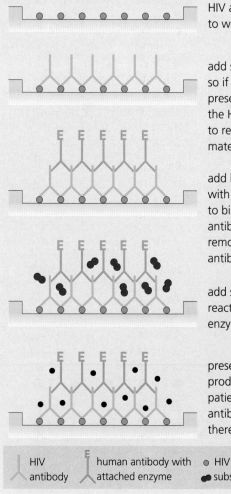

Fig. 10 Indirect ELISA for HIV antibody

HIV antigens attached to well in glass plate

add serum from patient so if HIV antibody is present it will bind to the HIV antigen (wash to remove unattached material)

add human antibody with enzyme attached to bind to anti-HIV antibody (wash to remove unattached antibody)

add substrate for reaction catalysed by enzyme

presence of the product indicates the patient has HIV antibody and is therefore HIV-positive

Y HIV antibody
E human antibody with attached enzyme
● HIV antigens
◖ substrate
● product

and new ones are constantly being developed. Two forms of the test are used:
• one for antigens (direct ELISA);
• one for antibodies (indirect ELISA).

Direct ELISA is used to detect viruses, hormones, drugs and a variety of other substances present in the blood (Fig. 9). Indirect ELISA is used to detect antibodies produced during infections such as HIV, syphilis, cholera and rubella (Fig. 10).

 23 ELISA techniques are increasingly widely used for diagnosis. Do you think ELISA supplies would be useful to include in the convoys of medical equipment sent to war and disaster zones?

Key ideas

- Penicillin was the first antibiotic. It was discovered in 1928 and first used to treat soldiers in the early 1940s.

- Different antibiotics act on microbial cells in different ways: cell wall synthesis is inhibited by penicillin, ampicillin and the cephalosporins; protein synthesis is inhibited by streptomycin, gentamicin and the tetracyclines; nucleic acid synthesis is disrupted by ciprofloxacin and rifampicin; cell membranes are disrupted by polymyxin B; cell metabolism is inhibited by antibiotics that act as antimetabolites, for example, sulphonamides.

- Bacteria are prokaryotes, fungi and humans both have eukaryotic cells. This means it is more difficult to treat fungal infections than bacterial infections. Polyoxin D disrupts fungal cell wall synthesis; nystatin damages the fungal cell membranes.

- Not all bacteria are susceptible to all antibiotics. Some bacteria have always been resistant to some antibiotics, some bacteria develop resistance to some antibiotics. Resistance to antibiotics develops when the bacteria obtain the genes for resistance. This can happen by spontaneous mutation or by gaining the genes from other bacteria.

- The genes for resistance may exist on the bacterial chromosome or on R plasmids. Resistance genes can be passed on by transformation, transduction, and conjugation. Plasmids can cross species boundaries.

- The indiscriminate use of antibiotics for 40–50 years has provided an environment for the growth of resistant bacteria.

- The reservoir of resistant bacteria found in hospitals carries resistance genes in bacterial plasmids. A single plasmid can contain genes for resistance to more than one antibiotic. Pathogens with multiple resistance cause super-infections.

- The fight against bacterial resistance includes: searching for new antibiotics; eliminating R plasmids from bacteria; preventing the expression of the resistance genes on R plasmids; stopping the spread of plasmids; reducing the amount of antibiotics that are prescribed.

- Monoclonal antibodies are revolutionising many aspects of diagnosis and treatment.

- Monoclonal antibodies are produced by the hybridoma technique.

- Monoclonal antibodies are also used in cancer treatment to target the tumour cells so cytotoxic drugs can be used. The combination of monoclonal antibody and drug is sometimes called a magic bullet because it only hits the cancerous cells.

- ELISA is easy to perform, and does not require expensive apparatus. Two forms of the test are used: one for antigens (direct ELISA); one for antibodies (indirect ELISA).

The body beautiful

'Dieting' to lose weight has been common among women for most of the twentieth century, and body building has been popular with men since the 1950s. Nowadays, both weight-reducing diets and body building are popular with men and women. In the 1990s, the 'ideal' body shape might be that of a 'gladiator' or that of a very thin model. These ideals change constantly because they are dictated by fashion rather than health. Striving to achieve an ideal body shape can be very dangerous and can lead to eating disorders such as anorexia nervosa and bulimia. Surveys of girls and women tend to show that about 75% see themselves as overweight when their actual body mass and height show only about 25% are overweight and 30% are underweight. Body builders who want to increase muscle mass might be tempted to take drugs. But a healthy body comes from a proper balance of food intake and exercise. To achieve the weight and body shape you want, you must take both factors into account.

12.1 Learning objectives

After working through this chapter, you should be able to:

- **define** basal metabolic rate (BMR), and **list** the factors which affect it;

- **explain** how BMR can be measured;

- **list** the factors which affect the body's energy economy;

- **list** the components of a balanced diet;

- **explain** why a balanced diet is essential to maintain of a healthy body;

- **understand** the principles underlying nutritional guidelines;

- **use** nutritional tables to analyse diets;

- **describe** how regular exercise can have an affect on BMR, resting pulse rate, blood pressure and lung capacity;

- **explain** how exercise and diet can lead to a reduction in the incidence of coronary heart disease (CHD) and stroke.

12.2 Energy and exercise balance

If more kilojoules are eaten than are used up by the body's activities, body mass increases. If fewer kilojoules are eaten than the body expends, body mass reduces. Both sides of this balance must be considered: the amount of food we eat and the energy we expend. In other words, diet and exercise.

How you think you look is not a good way to decide what weight you should be. The usual way to determine the range within which a person's weight should be is to calculate their **body mass index** (BMI).

$$BMI = \frac{body\ mass\ (kg)}{height\ squared\ (m^2)}$$

1 What is the BMI for a person who weighs 75 kg and is 179 cm tall?

A healthy BMI is between 20 and 25. Below 20, the person is underweight for their height, over 25 the person is overweight. A person with a BMI over 30 is obese.

2 Study the photograph. Why were scurvy and anaemia very common at the end of the 1800s?

Basal metabolic rate

In some ways the human body is a bit like a car. Both use up fuel and oxygen in a chemical reaction to release energy for doing work, both produce waste substances, and both need the correct 'diet' of other chemicals to keep running smoothly. However, when a car engine is switched off, it uses no fuel and produces no waste. Our bodies cannot be switched off. When we are asleep, life processes continue, the body still needs a supply of food and oxygen, and it continues to produce waste substances. **Metabolism** is the name given to all the chemical activity going on in the body. Metabolism is of two main types:
- **anabolism** – the synthesis of new molecules;
- **catabolism** – the breaking down of molecules.

The basic on-going needs of the body are called the **basal metabolism** and include:
- maintenance of muscle tone;
- the breathing mechanism;
- muscle contraction in the gut and heart;
- circulation of blood;
- maintenance of body temperature;
- conduction of nervous impulses;
- active transport;
- enzyme synthesis for metabolism;
- secretion;
- cell division;
- tissue replacement and repair;
- growth.

In 1899, the UK government needed more soldiers to fight the Boer War in South Africa, but over two-thirds of potential recruits had to be rejected because of poor physique. Many were poor men from towns and cities, and the urban poor lived on a restricted diet, based largely on bread. In 1880, a new process for milling flour removed the wheatgerm, so the vitamin and mineral content of bread was reduced. At the time, nobody knew about vitamins and the value of minerals in the diet was not recognised. Meat, fish, milk, and fresh vegetables were expensive and seldom eaten by poor people in towns, so scurvy and anaemia were common. The average daily labour of a working man or woman in 1899 was higher than the energy value of the food they ate. The BMIs of most recruits would have been under 20.

The energy required by these processes is called the **basal metabolic rate** (BMR). BMR cannot be measured directly, so we measure it indirectly by measuring the energy a person outputs as heat. Measurements are taken when the person is awake and at rest. The units are kJ hr^{-1}.

3 Which components of basal metabolism do you think will increase during physical activity?

Factors affecting BMR

Taking up regular exercise may not cause weight loss because the body could well be adding extra muscle tissue, but it reduces the amount of fat. This affects body shape. It is also likely that appetite increases without increasing fat levels. This is because BMR increases if you take up more active pursuits.

BMR is affected by a range of factors including:
- age;
- growth;
- exercise;
- height;
- gender;
- stress;
- pregnancy and breast-feeding.

BMR drops with age. It falls by about 50% from childhood to old age due to the decline in the proportion of lean body mass as a person gets older. People also tend to become less active as they get older.

When a person is growing, BMR is higher. This also helps to explain the decline in BMR with age, since after adolescence, growth is restricted to skin and hair, the replacement of worn out cells, and repair of damaged tissues.

Regular exercise reduces the *proportion* of fat in the body and increases BMR. A tall person usually has a higher BMR than a short person, and males have a higher BMR than females. This is partly to do with the higher proportion of lean body mass to fat in taller people and in males.

BMR rises during periods of stress. People with a pressured lifestyle are more likely to have a high BMR than those with a more relaxed way of living.

During pregnancy, the considerable rise in biosynthesis due to the growth of the baby raises BMR. If the mother then breast-feeds her baby after the birth, her BMR continues to be high until the baby goes on to other food.

Energy for other activities

About 70% of an individual's daily energy requirement supports basal metabolism, the other 30% is needed for extra activities (Table 1). Exercise affects daily energy requirement in two ways:
- extra energy is needed to carry out the activity;
- regular exercise actually increases the underlying BMR.

Table 1 Energy expenditure for a range of activities	
Activity	Energy expended above BMR kJ hr^{-1}
sitting	400
walking slowly	600–700
running	3000–40 000
bicycling	2000
swimming	3000–3700

Different groups of people have different energy requirements (Table 2).

Table 2 Energy requirements of different individuals	
Individual	Energy requirement kJ day^{-1}
child aged 1 year	3 250
child aged 8	8 500
adolescent boy aged 15	11 400
active woman aged 25	11 000
breast-feeding woman	11 700
active man aged 50	12 000
sedentary woman aged 70	8 200

4 a Why is a 15-year-old boy likely to have a higher BMR than an active woman of 25?

b What effect does taking up regular exercise have on BMR?

12.3 Energy intake: a healthy diet

Diet simply means 'the food we eat'. There is a wealth of dietary advice from the government, from TV and magazines, from professional diet writers, and from the food industry itself. Whatever body shape you want, the diet you choose must be healthy as well as result in body mass reduction or muscle mass increase. But what is a healthy diet? A healthy diet provides:

- energy;
- material for growth and repair.

The same daily food intake cannot be suitable for all people because they have different energy requirements and need different materials for growth and repair. The food we eat contains many **nutrients** – chemicals that are needed for the healthy functioning of the body. A healthy diet provides the right balance of nutrients for the individual concerned. Nutrients can be grouped into six classes:

- carbohydrates;
- lipids;
- proteins;
- vitamins;
- minerals;
- water.

Energy and the diet

The carbohydrates, lipids and proteins in our diet contain different amounts of usable energy (Table 3). Usually, our energy requirement is met by the carbohydrates and lipids in diet (Fig. 1). Excess lipids are stored as body fat for later use, and proteins provide much of the material for growth and repair.

| Table 3 Energy content of different classes of nutrient ||
Food	Energy kJ g⁻¹
carbohydrate	16
lipid	37
protein	17
alcohol	29

5 Diets designed to make you lose weight usually recommend reducing the lipid content of your food intake. Why?

The oxidation of food is called respiration, and it takes place in all living cells. The main metabolic pathway is the breakdown of glucose to carbon dioxide and water with the production of ATP. ATP is an 'energy package' that is used to power processes needing energy. (*Biology Core*, Chapter 2).

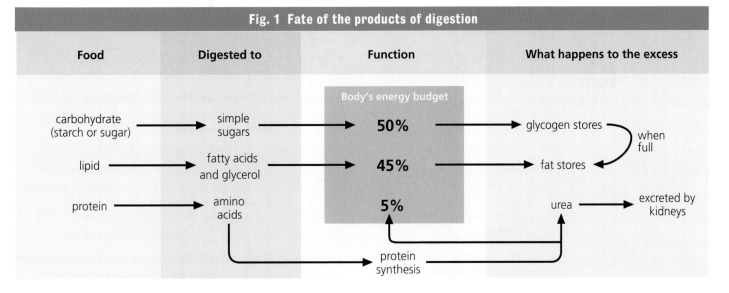

Fig. 1 Fate of the products of digestion

Food	Digested to	Function	What happens to the excess

Body's energy budget

carbohydrate (starch or sugar) → simple sugars → 50% → glycogen stores — when full

lipid → fatty acids and glycerol → 45% → fat stores

protein → amino acids → 5% → urea → excreted by kidneys

protein synthesis

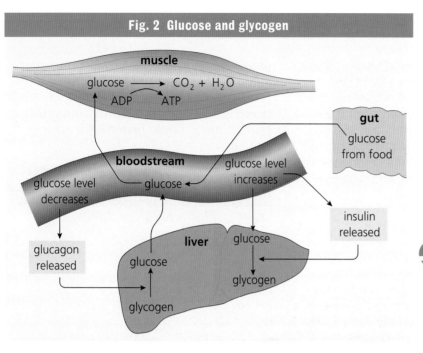

Fig. 2 Glucose and glycogen

muscle

glucose $\longrightarrow$ $CO_2 + H_2O$

ADP → ATP

bloodstream

gut
glucose from food

glucose level increases

glucose level decreases

glucose

glucagon released

insulin released

liver

glucose

glucose

glycogen

glycogen

Glucose passes into the bloodstream from food in the small intestine. The blood carries the glucose all round the body and reaches individual cells via tissue fluid and diffusion. When the level of glucose in the blood goes up, for instance after a meal, excess glucose is converted to glycogen and stored in the liver (Fig. 2). When the level of glucose in the blood is low, for instance some hours after a meal, the body rapidly converts its glycogen stores back into glucose to top up blood glucose. When the glycogen reserves are gone, the body starts to oxidise fat and protein. (Figs 2, 3).

6 Make a list of what you ate yesterday. Draw a time line to show when you were using glucose from the food you had just eaten and when you were using glucose converted from your glycogen reserves.

Fig. 3 Sources of blood glucose over 24 hours

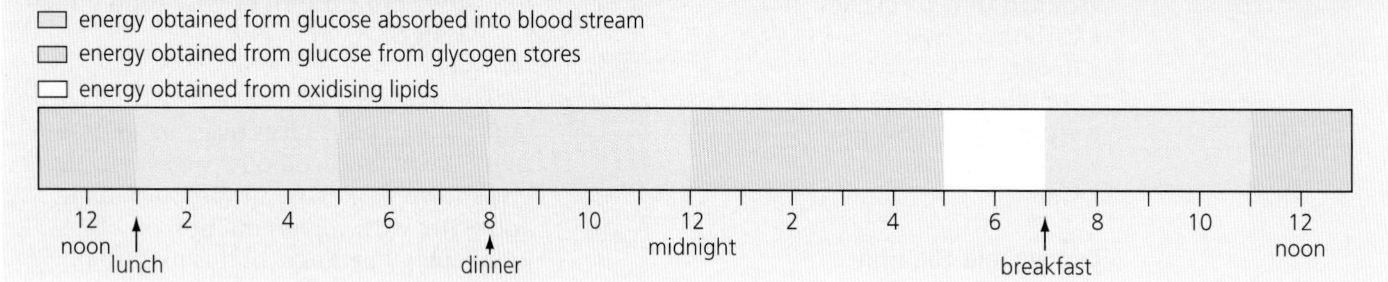

☐ energy obtained form glucose absorbed into blood stream
☐ energy obtained from glucose from glycogen stores
☐ energy obtained from oxidising lipids

12 noon — lunch — 2 — 4 — 6 — 8 — dinner — 10 — 12 midnight — 2 — 4 — 6 — 8 — breakfast — 10 — 12 noon

Key ideas

- Body mass depends on how much energy is contained in food eaten and how much energy is used in exercise.

- BMI is the way to determine in what range an individual's weight should be. A BMI of 20–25 is healthy.

- BMR is the energy required for all the basic on-going metabolic activity of the body. Any extra activity requires more energy. About 70% of daily energy requirement is to support BMR.

- A healthy diet provides energy and materials for growth and repair.

- People have different needs, so the same daily food intake cannot suit everyone.

- There are six types of nutrient: carbohydrates, lipids, proteins, vitamins, minerals, and water.

- Carbohydrates are digested to sugars such as glucose, and energy requirement is usually met by oxidising glucose to carbon dioxide and water. Excess glucose is stored as glycogen. When glucose levels fall, glycogen is converted to glucose.

- Lipids are stored as body fat and proteins provide material for growth and repair.

12.4 Nutrients

Carbohydrates

Everyone needs plenty of carbohydrates. They are one of the body's main energy sources and are composed of carbon, hydrogen and oxygen (Fig. 4). **Dietary fibre** is the name given to two groups of complex carbohydrates (Table 4). These carbohydrates are mainly polysaccharides such as cellulose and pectin, but also include substances such as lignin.

Soluble fibre seems to be important in the small intestine where it slows digestion and absorption. A meal high in soluble fibre is digested more slowly and the digestive products are released over a longer time than a meal low in soluble fibre. This is important to diabetics, because there are less extreme changes in blood glucose levels after a meal.

Insoluble fibre is more important in the colon where it absorbs water and swells. This stretches the walls of the intestines and stimulates muscular action (**peristalsis**) to keep the food moving and reduce the time it takes to pass through the colon.

Insoluble fibre probably reduces the risk of constipation, piles (haemorrhoids) and colonic cancer.

 7 Is it a good idea for a diabetic to start the day with a bowl of porridge?

Table 4 Sources of dietary fibre

Fibre type	Food sources
insoluble	wholemeal bread and wheat breakfast cereals
	corn
	rice
	pasta
	rhubarb
	cabbage and Brussels sprouts
	peas, broad beans and lentils
soluble	porridge and oat cakes
	pearl barley
	rye bread and crispbread
	most unpeeled fruit and dried fruit
	carrots and parsnips
	baked beans and kidney beans

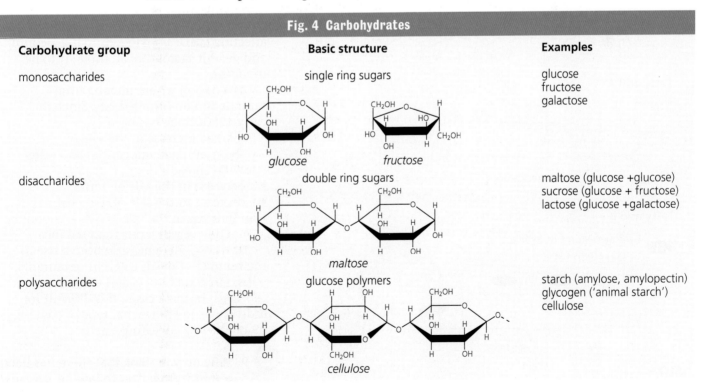

Fig. 4 Carbohydrates

Carbohydrate group	Basic structure	Examples
monosaccharides	single ring sugars — glucose, fructose	glucose, fructose, galactose
disaccharides	double ring sugars — maltose	maltose (glucose + glucose), sucrose (glucose + fructose), lactose (glucose + galactose)
polysaccharides	glucose polymers — cellulose	starch (amylose, amylopectin), glycogen ('animal starch'), cellulose

Lipids

Even people on weight-reducing diets need lipids. They are the body's second major energy source and many lipids, including cholesterol, are essential to cell membranes. Like carbohydrates, all lipids are composed of carbon, hydrogen and oxygen, but the proportion of oxygen in fats is much lower than in carbohydrates. Lipids that are solid at room temperature are called fats. Lipids that are liquid are called oils.

The majority of lipids in the diet are formed from fatty acids and glycerol and are called **triglycerides**. Triglycerides are grouped according to the nature of their fatty acids (Fig. 5). If every carbon atom in the hydrocarbon chain has two hydrogen atoms bonded to it, the fatty acid is called a **saturated fatty acid**. Sometimes a pair of hydrogen atoms from adjacent carbon atoms may be missing. When this happens, the 'spare' carbon bonds link up to form a double bond. This produces an **unsaturated fatty acid**. Fatty acids with only one double bond are **mono-unsaturated**. When there are two or more double bonds, the fatty acid is **polyunsaturated**. Most lipids from animal sources, e.g. butter and fat in meat, are composed of saturated fatty acids. Plant-derived lipids tend to have a higher proportion of unsaturated fatty acids.

Q 8 In Figure 5, what sort of fatty acid are fatty acid A and fatty acid B?

There is a link between the intake of saturated fatty acids and coronary heart disease (CHD). Government advice, based on the report of the Committee on Medical Aspects of Food Policy (COMA), suggests we shift the balance in fat consumption from saturated to unsaturated fatty acids, and reduce total fat consumption. Recent studies suggest that we should eat mono-unsaturated fats rather than either saturated or polyunsaturated fats. But fat consumption is not the only factor affecting CHD; smoking, drinking alcohol, and genetic factors are all thought to be involved.

As a nation we are moving from saturated to unsaturated fats. Since the early 1980s there has been:
- a marked increase in the sale of polyunsaturated margarines and other low-fat spreads;
- a decrease in the sale of butter;
- a decrease in the sale of red meat;
- an increase in the sale of fish and poultry (much lower fat levels than red meat).

However, there has also been a rise in the number of meals eaten in restaurants, pubs, fast-food outlets and workplace canteens. In these cases, it is difficult for individuals to know what type of cooking oil or fat they are eating.

Q 9 Why do you think that there has been a shift from butter to low-fat spreads?

Fig. 5 Triglycerides and saturation in fatty acids

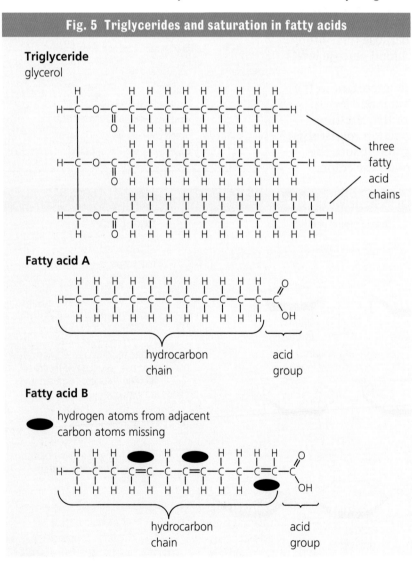

These school dinners were served in 1949. In those days there was less concern over what fats we ate and most people thought it essential that at least one meal a day contained red meat.

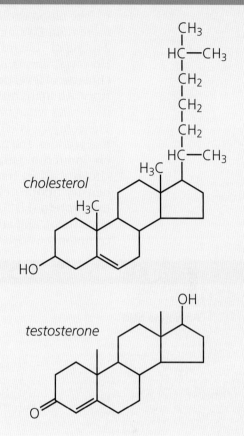

Fig. 6 Steroid hormones and cholesterol

cholesterol

testosterone

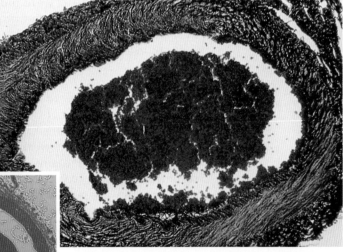

This light micrograph of a healthy artery has red blood cells in the centre. There is plenty of space for blood flow. In the coloured light micrograph of an unhealthy artery, the build up of material (red and yellow) that has reduced the central space by nearly half, is called atheroma. It is the result of cholesterol being deposited inside the blood vessel. The large mass at the centre (red) is an abnormal blood clot attached to the atheroma. Together they almost block the artery. Atheroma can occur in any blood vessel but the usual sites are the aorta, the cerebral arteries in the brain, and the coronary arteries in cardiac muscle. A coronary atheroma can lead to a heart attack. Cerebral atheroma can cause cerebral haemorrhage (stroke).

Excess carbohydrate in the diet replenishes the body's glycogen stores, which are used later during the post-absorptive phase of digestion. Less than 1% of all carbohydrate and protein eaten is converted into fat. However, excess fat is stored in the apparently ever-expandable fat reserves around the body. The fatty acid composition of the body's fat reserves is almost identical to the fatty acid composition of lipids in the diet.

It is impossible to remove fat from the diet altogether. Every cell membrane is made of proteins and lipids. Even a stick of celery contains fat. The lipid composition of cell membranes includes cholesterol and a number of fatty acids that our bodies cannot synthesise. We must get these fatty acids, called **essential fatty acids**, from our diet. Besides its role in cell membranes, cholesterol is needed to make a number of steroid hormones (Fig. 6). A single egg yolk

163

contains enough cholesterol to satisfy the recommended daily intake.

The blood cholesterol level should be no more than 200 mg dl^{-1}; a level exceeding 240 mg dl^{-1} is considered dangerous. However, simply measuring the total cholesterol level does not tell the whole story. All lipids are attached to protein molecules when carried in the bloodstream. The complex is called a **lipoprotein**. For triglycerides, the lipoprotein is **chylomicron**. Other lipids, particularly cholesterol, are transported as either **high density lipoprotein** (HDL), or **low density lipoprotein** (LDL). LDL carries the most cholesterol, and atheroma is most commonly associated with a high LDL.

However, the proportion of HDL in the blood is also significant since high HDL levels can reduce the likelihood of atheroma. Risk of developing atheroma is associated with the ratio of total blood cholesterol to HDL (Table 5).

Excess cholesterol is removed from the blood and excreted by the liver. It is added to bile, which is stored in the gall bladder before being squirted into the small intestine following a meal. If bile contains excessive cholesterol, gall stones are formed.

Table 5 Risk of atheroma and ratio of total blood cholesterol to HDL		
Risk	Male	Female
very low	<3.4	<3.3
low	4.0	3.8
average	5.0	4.5
moderate	9.5	7.0
high	>20	>10

10 a Why (even if it were possible) would a fat-free diet not be sensible?

b What are essential fatty acids?

Proteins

Proteins are necessary for everyone and body builders need a diet that is especially high in protein as it is the chief dietary requirement for anyone wishing to increase their muscle mass. Proteins are composed of carbon, hydrogen, oxygen, nitrogen and sulphur. They are polymers made up of sub-units called **amino acids** (Fig. 7). Amino acids are joined together by peptide bonds to form proteins (Fig. 7).

Proteins are essential for growth, repair and replacement. The body uses amino acids to synthesise new proteins in cell division, cell differentiation and enzyme production. Some amino acids we have to get from the diet, these are called **essential amino acids**. Some we can make, these are called **non-essential amino acids**.

Protein synthesis is an anabolic process and is assisted by steroid hormones. Some body builders and athletes are tempted to

Fig. 7 Amino acids and the peptide bond

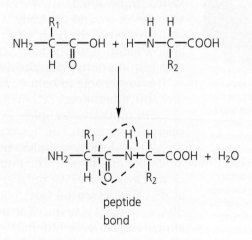

An amino acid

	R-group	Amino acid
	—H	glycine
	—CH$_3$	alanine
	—CH$_2$—SH	cysteine
	—(CH$_2$)$_3$—CH$_2$NH$_2$	lysine

amine group

acid group

the variable R-group is different in each of the 20 amino acids commonly found in living things

Peptide bond formation

peptide bond

Table 6 Source and function of some dietary minerals		
Mineral	Source	Function
Major minerals		
calcium	milk	component of teeth and bone
	cheese	essential for nerve and muscle function
	green vegetables	needed in blood clotting
phosphorous	meat	component of teeth and bone
	fish	component of ATP and DNA
	dairy produce	
	cereals	
potassium	fruit	involved in muscle and nerve function
	vegetables	
sodium	salt	important in fluid balance
	processed foods	essential in conduction of nervous impulse
sulphur	meat	component of protein
	fish	
	poultry	
chlorine	salt	important in fluid balance
	processed foods	important in pH regulation
Trace minerals		
magnesium	nuts	needed for muscle and nerve function
	soy beans	
	milk	
	fish	
	green vegetables	
	wholegrain cereal and bread	
iron	liver	component of haemoglobin, myoglobin
	meat	component of respiratory enzymes
	egg yolk	
	nuts	
	legumes	
copper	liver	component of some enzymes
	eggs	essential for haemoglobin synthesis
	fish	
	beans	
selenium	fish	component of some enzymes
	garlic	
	cereals	
zinc	seafood especially oysters	component of some enzymes
	small amounts in many other foods	
iodine	seafood	component of thyroxin
	iodised salt	

boost their increase in muscle mass by taking **anabolic steroids**, artificial steroid hormones. This is illegal, and people found guilty of taking these drugs are banned from competitions. Hormones and anabolic steroids are broken down in the liver to substances which can be detected in urine. Higher than normal levels of these substances due to taking anabolic steroids can be detected many months after the drug was taken.

11a Why do body builders need a lot of protein?
  b What is the difference between essential and non-essential amino acids?

Minerals

Although only about 4% of body mass is made up of inorganic minerals, no-one can be healthy without them (Table 6). Calcium and phosphorus make up around 75% of the body's mineral content, whereas selenium is present in minute quantities. The minerals we need fall into two categories:

- **major minerals** – needed in quantities greater than 5 g per day;
- **trace minerals** – needed in amounts of less than 5 g per day.

12a Study Table 6. A vegan does not eat meat, fish, seafood or other animal products such as eggs or cheese. What minerals might such a person be short of?
  b How do you think a vegan could overcome this shortage?

13a What minerals are found in seafood?
  b Why is it important to eat green vegetables regularly?

A healthy diet must include an adequate supply of all the minerals we need, so that the body functions properly. A deficiency of particular minerals may produce easily recognisable symptoms. For example, lack of iron leads to anaemia because the body cannot make enough haemoglobin.

Table 7 Vitamins

Vitamin	Sources	Function	Deficiency symptoms	RDA men	RDA women	Vitamin	Sources	Function	Deficiency symptoms	RDA men	RDA women
Fat soluble						**Water soluble**					
A (retinol)	fish liver oil dairy produce liver carrots spinach	maintenance of healthy membranes formation of rhodopsin (visual purple)	dry skin xerophthalmia (dry cornea) night blindness	750 µg	750 µg	B₁ (thiamine)	whole grains eggs liver red meat	co-enzyme in respiration	beriberi	1 µg	1 µg
D (calciferol)	milk butter fish-liver oil sunlight on skin	absorption of calcium and phosphorous from gut calcification of bone	osteomalacia rickets	10 µg	10 µg	B₂ (riboflavin)	yeast red meat eggs whole grain	co-enzyme in respiration	blurred vision anaemia	1.6 µg	1.3 µg
						niacin	meat fish yeast	part of a co-enzyme in respiration	pellagra	18 mg	15 mg
E	wheatgerm nuts liver egg yolk	prevention of breakdown of certain fatty acids	unknown	10 mg	8 mg	C (ascorbic acid)	citrus fruit black currants tomatoes	iron metabolism	scurvy	30 µg	30 µg
K	egg yolk liver green vegetables bacteria in large intestine	blood clotting	very slow blood clotting	no official RDA in the UK							

Food	Energy kJ	Fat g	Sugars g	Fibre g	Sodium mg	Potassium mg
Snack 1						
2 packets crisps	1121	18.0	0.2	5.9	275.0	595.0
1 chocolate bar	1260	12.8	44.5	nil	102.0	170.0
1 can drink	542	nil	34.5	nil	26.0	3.0
Totals	2932	30.8	79.2	5.9	403.0	768.0
Snack 2						
2 slices wholemeal bread	580	1.7	1.3	5.4	346.0	141.0
polyunsaturated margarine	609	16.0	0.3	nil	nil	nil
honey	483	nil	30.6	nil	4.0	20.0
camembert cheese	504	93.0	nil	nil	564.0	44.0
black grapes	214	nil	13.0	0.3	1.0	270.0
apple juice	533	nil	29.0	nil	nil	331.0
Totals	2923	110.7	74.2	5.7	915.0	806.0

Source: adapted from *Practice Nutrition*, Vol 1, no 3

Vitamins

Vitamins are organic compounds that are needed by everybody in very small (trace) amounts (Table 7). Fat soluble vitamins are absorbed by the digestive system along with lipids, water soluble ones are absorbed in aqueous solution.

14 It is not always as easy and straightforward as you might think to determine what is healthy eating. Study this table which shows an analysis of two snacks.
   a Which snack has the higher:
      salt (sodium) content?
      sugar content?
      dietary fibre content?
      fat content?
   b Which snack would you say is the healthier option?

Water

About 70% of body mass is water. It is essential because:

- all chemical reactions in the body take place in aqueous solution;
- some processes, such as digestion, have water as one of the reactants;
- water is the main component of the body's transport systems;
- water can absorb large amounts of heat and is necessary for heat distribution and heat loss.

If you exercise, you get hot. If you get hot, you sweat. If you sweat, you lose water. That's why you drink a lot after exercise. Heat produced by muscle contraction is distributed round the body by the bloodstream. Sweat, which is mainly water, absorbs heat from the skin when it evaporates; this lowers the temperature of the skin and of the blood flowing near to the body surface. Temperature control and heat loss during exercise are extremely important for the proper functioning of a healthy body.

The body also loses water by evaporation from the mouth and respiratory systems (breath contains water vapour) and through urine and faeces. Although the body can survive for up to a month without food, it can only survive for about 3 days without water.

Drinking water is not the only way the body gets water. Almost all foods contain water and the oxidation of food provides a small amount of extra water called **metabolic water**. Almost all drinks are largely water. But the body does not increase its water content from alcoholic drinks because they are **diuretic**. This means they make the body produce a large volume of watery urine.

15 **If someone quenched their thirst with a pint of beer after a vigorous exercise session, what would happen to their water levels?**

Food additives

Almost all processed and pre-prepared foods contain **food additives**. Food additives are used to enhance many products. They can be divided into eight categories:

- preservatives;
- antioxidants;
- emulsifiers;
- stabilisers;
- colourings;
- sweeteners;
- flavourings;
- flavour enhancers.

Some additives are naturally occurring substances; for example, vitamin C is an antioxidant and prevents food spoilage. However, many food production processes use high temperatures, and since many natural additives are not heat stable, artificial additives are used instead. Any additive used in the UK must serve at least one of the following purposes:

- maintenance of wholesomeness;
- extension of dietary choice;
- supplementation of dietary needs;
- improvement of preparation or storage;
- improvement of presentation;
- improvement of economic efficiency of production.

An additive that serves one of these needs is investigated by the Committee on Toxicology of Chemicals in Food, Consumer Products and the Environment (COT). COT advises the government's Food Advisory Committee whether or not to permit use of the additive.

Pre-prepared foods might contain more than you think.

Any additive used throughout the EU is given an 'E number' so that the additive can be identified in any EU country. These numbers are found on most food labelling.

16 **List the foods you ate yesterday and identify the ones that probably contained additives.**

Key ideas

- Carbohydrates are the body's main source of energy. Dietary fibre is the name for two groups of complex carbohydrates. Soluble dietary fibre slows down digestion and absorption in the small intestine. Insoluble dietary fibre maintains the passage of food through the colon.

- Lipids, including cholesterol, are necessary for cell membranes. Cholesterol is also important in naturally occurring steroid hormones. Cholesterol may be deposited inside blood vessels, especially arteries, as atheroma.

- Lipids are divided into fats and oils. Fats are solid at room temperature, oils are liquid.

- Dietary lipids are mainly triglycerides, a mixture of glycerol and fatty acids. Fatty acids may be saturated (no double bonds), mono-unsaturated (one double bond) or polyunsaturated (more than one double bond). Evidence suggests it is healthier to eat mono-unsaturates than either saturated or polyunsaturated fatty acids. Essential fatty acids are ones that we cannot make and have to get from the diet. All lipids are transported in the blood, linked to protein molecules in complexes called lipoproteins.

- Cholesterol is transported as LDL but the risk of atheroma is assessed by the ratio of total cholesterol to HDL.

- The body uses the amino acids from dietary protein to synthesise proteins. Proteins are made up of amino acids linked by peptide bonds. Essential amino acids are ones we have to get from our diet, non-essential amino acids are ones we can make.

- The inorganic minerals we need are divided into two groups: major minerals are those of which we need over 5 g per day, trace minerals are those of which we need less than 5 g per day.

- Vitamins are essential organic compounds required in small amounts.

- Water is essential because all body chemistry occurs in aqueous solution. It is also the main component of the body's transport systems, and is the means by which heat can be distributed and lost. About 70% of body mass is water.

- Additives are usually, though not always, artificial. They are intended to help preserve, stabilise, colour, or flavour processed and prepared foods.

12.5 Energy expenditure: exercise

Eating an appropriate and healthy diet only goes half-way to achieving the body shape you want. Diet must be balanced by exercise because exercise uses up energy and if undertaken regularly it increases BMR. There are also other benefits to regular exercise, it increases:
- heart efficiency;
- breathing mechanism efficiency.

Heart efficiency
Training increases heart efficiency (Table 8). The amount of blood pumped by the heart per minute is called **cardiac output** and it varies with activity. As activity increases, cardiac output increases. The difference between the resting output and the maximum the heart can achieve is termed the **cardiac reserve**. Cardiac output is

measured in $dm^3 \, min^{-1}$ and depends on the **heart rate** (the number of heart beats per minute) and the **stroke volume** (the volume of blood pumped with each beat).

$$\begin{matrix} \text{cardiac} \\ \text{output} \end{matrix} = \begin{matrix} \text{heart} \\ \text{rate} \end{matrix} \times \begin{matrix} \text{stroke} \\ \text{volume} \end{matrix}$$

Heart rate is controlled by the nervous and endocrine systems. During activity, the heart rate increases and the resulting increase in cardiac output provides muscles with an increased oxygen and glucose supply, and allows the removal of carbon dioxide and heat.

As well as beating faster, each contraction exerts a greater force on the blood. This happens because in activity, arm and leg muscles contract more and assist the flow of blood in the veins returning to the heart. So, more blood per second is poured into the heart from the main veins – the venae cavae – and the heart muscle is stretched more than usual as the chambers accommodate the extra volume. This stretching of the muscle fibre is followed by an increased contraction that applies more force to the blood as it is pumped into the pulmonary arteries and the aorta.

The main difference between an athlete and the average person is in stroke volume. Rigorous training leads to a thickening of the cardiac muscle, accompanied by an increase in the size of the heart's chambers. A trained athlete can have increased the size of his or her heart by as much as 25%. This means that the volume of blood pumped by each stroke of the heart increases. Even modest regular activity causes an increase in stroke volume and improves the efficiency of the heart.

If more blood is pumped with each beat, fewer beats per minute are needed to supply the body with the necessary oxygen and nutrients. So the average heart rate of a very active person is lower than that of an inactive one of similar size, age and sex. For most people, the resting rate is 65–80 beats per minute, but the resting rate for athletes can be as low as 40–50 beats per minute.

In exercise, the concept of maximum heart rate is important. A simple rule of thumb is that maximum rate is 220 beats per minute minus age in years. When exercising, it is advisable to set a target rate of 70–80% of the theoretical maximum; a heart rate higher than this is likely to be dangerous. So, a 40-year-old would have a maximum rate of 180 beats per minute, and an exercise target rate of 126–144 beats per minute. Any training programme should be professionally planned and should include expert advice on the target heart rate.

Table 8 Cardiac output			
Individual	Cardiac output at rest $dm^3 \, min^{-1}$	Cardiac output in vigorous activity $dm^3 \, min^{-1}$	Cardiac reserve $dm^3 \, min^{-1}$
average adult	5.0	21.0	16.0
athlete	5.25	30.0	24.75

Unless you are a sprinter, you cannot run 100 m in 10 seconds. Your legs won't move fast enough and your heart and lungs cannot supply your muscles with the amount of oxygen and glucose needed. Yet the world record for the men's 100 m sprint is just less than 10 seconds, and women's record is just over 10 seconds. What is different about world-class athletes that makes this possible? Heart and breathing efficiency.

17 a If a 25-year-old athlete has a resting heart rate of 45 beats per minute and a cardiac output of $5.25 \, dm^3 \, min^{-1}$, what is the stroke volume?

b What is this athlete's target heart rate during a training session?

Blood pressure

Regular activity also eventually lowers blood pressure. Blood pressure is the force exerted by blood on the walls of the vessels which contain it. It is measured in mmHg and differs from the aorta to the venae cavae (Fig. 8). Blood pressure depends on cardiac output and **peripheral resistance**.

$$\text{blood pressure} = \text{cardiac output} \times \text{peripheral resistance}$$

Peripheral resistance is the resistance to blood flow caused by the blood vessels. The wider the diameter of the vessel, the lower the peripheral resistance. Blood pressure is mainly determined by the peripheral resistance of arterioles as the arteries are generally much wider. However, atheroma narrows the arteries and will eventually be sufficient to increase the peripheral resistance, and therefore to increase the blood pressure.

The condition in which blood pressure is always too high is called hypertension. High blood pressure damages the inside surfaces of arteries and arterioles and increases the possibility of the build up of atheroma. This is why hypertension is a strong risk factor for CHD. Exercise is one of the main ways of maintaining a healthy blood pressure. Certain foods, particularly saturated fat and salt raise blood pressure.

18 a What risks are being run by someone who is overweight, has a desk-bound job and likes nothing better than crisps followed by a cream cake for lunch?

b What advice would you give this person?

Efficiency of the breathing mechanism

Regular exercise improves the efficiency of the breathing mechanism by strengthening the diaphragm and intercostal muscles that control breathing. At the cellular level, the number of mitochondria (organelles responsible for making ATP) in respiring cells is increased. This means the cells can oxidise glucose or lipids more efficiently.

The uptake of oxygen by the blood in the alveolar capillaries of the lungs is increased during periods of activity. This is because as well as the increase in total volume of air breathed per minute, the increase in cellular respiration causes blood oxygen levels to drop, so the oxygen diffusion gradient between the air in the lungs and the blood in the alveolar

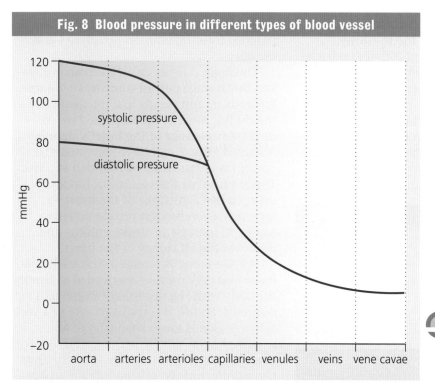

Fig. 8 Blood pressure in different types of blood vessel

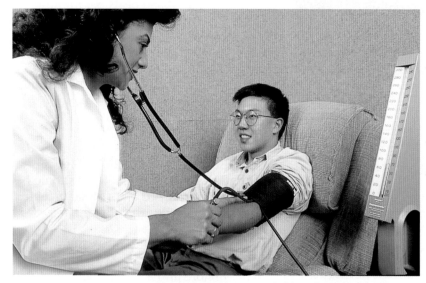

Blood pressure is measured with a sphygmomanometer. Blood is forced into the aorta during cardiac muscle contraction (*systole*) at a pressure of about 120 mmHg. As the cardiac muscle relaxes (*diastole*) and the ventricles refill with blood, pressure in the aorta falls to around 80 mmHg.

At rest we normally breathe 10–15 times per minute. Each breath draws about 500 ml of air into the lungs. This resting rate volume is called the *tidal volume*. The total volume of air breathed per minute, when at rest, is about 5–8 dm^3. During physical activity, this can increase over 20 times as the body demands more oxygen to oxidise more glucose. Increased oxidation of glucose produces more carbon dioxide that has to be removed via the lungs. As a result, breathing becomes faster and deeper.

capillaries increases. Therefore, more oxygen diffuses from the air to the blood. Increased production of carbon dioxide means the carbon dioxide diffusion gradient between blood in the alveolar capillaries and the air in the lungs increases, so more carbon dioxide diffuses from the blood to the air in the lungs. There is more carbon dioxide in the air we breathe out when active than when at rest.

19 What effect does regular exercise have on muscle cells?

20 Good body shape and fitness depend on a balance between energy intake and energy expended in activity. Is this equally true for a body-builder, a student, a model, and an office worker?

Key ideas

- Regular exercise increases BMR, heart efficiency, and efficiency of the breathing mechanism.

- Cardiac output is the amount of blood pumped by the heart per minute. Stroke volume is the volume of blood pumped with each beat. Heart rate is the number of heart beats per minute. Exercise increases heart rate; regular exercise increases heart efficiency by increasing the stroke volume and so decreasing the resting rate.

- Increased cardiac output in activity provides muscles with an increased oxygen and glucose supply, and allows more efficient removal of carbon dioxide and heat.

- Blood pressure is the force exerted by blood on the walls of the blood vessels. It depends on cardiac output and peripheral resistance.

- Normal blood pressure at systole is about 120 mmHg; at diastole it is 80 mmHg. Regular activity lowers blood pressure. Atheroma narrows arteries and eventually increases peripheral resistance, and, therefore, increases blood pressure.

- The condition in which blood pressure is always too high is called hypertension. It increases the possibility of atheroma and CHD. Certain foods, particularly saturated fat and salt raise blood pressure.

- Regular exercise improves the efficiency of the breathing mechanism by strengthening the diaphragm and intercostal muscles.

- Tidal volume is the resting rate volume of the lungs. In activity, this can increase over 20 times in order to supply more oxygen and remove more carbon dioxide. There is more carbon dioxide in the air we breathe out when active than when at rest.

- The rate of uptake of oxygen by the blood in the alveolar capillaries of the lungs depends on the oxygen diffusion gradient between the air in the lungs and the blood. More oxygen is taken up when the level of oxygen in the blood falls. There is also a carbon dioxide diffusion gradient. More carbon dioxide diffuses from the blood to the air in the lungs when the level of carbon dioxide in the blood is increased.

Answers to questions

Chapter 1

1 People would have been surprised and perhaps worried about these previously unseen organisms. You would need to explain that life exists in a wide variety of forms and that some of these are too small to be seen without a microscope.
2 The study of microbes could not advance until microscopes got better.
3 No. Viruses are too small for the resolution of even the most advanced light microscope.
4 Pasteurisation is the moderate heating of a liquid to kill any bacteria present.
5 Broth in all the flasks opened in Paris went bad, as did four of those opened on Mont Blanc. This indicated that something in the air (especially in Paris) was spoiling the broth. If microbes appeared in the broth by spontaneous generation, all the flasks would have gone bad.
6 The eukaryotic features of fungi are the nucleus, nuclear membrane, endoplasmic reticulum, Golgi body, vacuole, larger ribosomes and mitochondria.
7 Prokaryotes are the simpler cells with no membrane-bound organelles such as mitochondria, and no endoplasmic reticulum. The genetic material of prokaryotes is not enclosed in a nucleus, and the ribosomes are smaller.
8 The electron microscope brings into view the cell membrane, ribosomes, mesosomes, cell wall details, flagella, cilia and plasmids.
9 a Like other living organisms, viruses contain genetic material (DNA or RNA) to code for replication.
 b Viruses are unable to grow or reproduce outside a host cell. They have few if any enzymes.

10 **Similarities**: both are relatively small; both lack complex cellular organisation and a nucleus; both cause disease in other organisms. **Differences**: viruses are generally much smaller than bacteria; viruses lack the cellular structures and enzymes needed for growth and replication; bacteria have a complex cell wall and plasma membrane, viruses do not.
11 The number of cells would be 1 048 576, assuming there are no cell deaths.
12 a The build up of acidic waste products is the most likely cause.
 b Between 10 and 20 hours the cell numbers are increasing rapidly and the pH is falling quickly. This is due to the accumulation of acidic products. Between 30 and 40 hours the now low pH drops more slowly as the rate of cell division tails off. The product may have a pH of about 4.8.
13 The sterile medium is continuously added through the top of the vessel and stirred by the stirrer. The temperature is monitored using the thermometer so the correct temperature is maintained. As well as the product, excess medium and waste products can be drawn off through the pipe labelled 'product'.
14 Some people fear that 'monster organisms' will be created that could escape into the environment, cause damage and illness and then be difficult to control. Some people feel that genetics is an area where we should seek to understand the mechanisms but not attempt to make changes. What do you think?

Chapter 2

1 Because alcohol can effect mood and physiological functions, it is important that people are mature enough to evaluate the implications of buying it.
2 Fermentation was used as a means of preserving foods and adding flavour.
3 In the production of tempe, changes due to soaking and cooking are not part of the fermentation. After *Rhizopus* is added, the fungus produces proteases that break down the proteins to peptides and amino acids. The fungal mycelium holds the tempe together. The amounts of fibre, riboflavin, niacin, vitamin B_6, vitamin B_{12} and vitamin E increase.
4 Tempe is unusual in that it must be eaten very soon after it is produced. Fermentation usually improves the keeping qualities of food.
5 The final flavour of shoyu is the result of microbial action on the ingredients. So, adding wheat or rice to the beans alters the final flavour.
6 If the soy beans are overcooked, they lose nutritional value.
7 Yeasts grown aerobically use the tricarboxylic acid cycle to oxidise pyruvate to carbon dioxide and water. Yeasts grown anaerobically convert pyruvate to ethanol and carbon dioxide.
8 First, you should make a cell count using a haemocytometer or colorimeter. Then inoculate several series of broths (each series containing the same range of pH values) and grow each series at a different temperature. Samples from each culture should be counted at regular time intervals. The culture with the maximum cell count indicates the optimum growth conditions.

9 The differences lie in the growth temperature (top fermenters need a higher temperature than bottom fermenters) and where in the vessel the yeasts are found towards the end of fermentation. Top fermenters are used for ales and bottom fermenters are used for lagers and beers.

10 Brewers do not want oxygen in the fermentation vessels because yeasts cannot use the TCA cycle when oxygen is not available. They must ferment the pyruvate produced from the breakdown of carbohydrates to ethanol and carbon dioxide.

11 Any ethanol produced by the growth of yeast will evaporate in the ovens.

12 The fat in milk bottles is found at the top because the fat is less dense than the rest of the milk and floats to the top.

13 Samples of equal volume of different milks can be kept at a standard temperature for a number of days and then tested. Tests could include smell (not taste), direct observation, microscopic observation, the resazurin test and plating out to see the number of colonies produced.

14 Untreated milk could contain microbes harmful to health.

15 The fruit is heated to kill any microbes that might be present and could spoil the yoghurt.

16 Most microbes cannot grow at very low temperatures. Those that cause disease in humans tend to prefer body temperature.

17 Curds are the solid, coagulated part of milk; whey is the liquid component.

18 Adding fungal spores earlier in the cheese-making process could result in uncontrolled fungal growth that would radically alter the texture, flavour and colour of the cheese.

19 Vegetarian cheeses are not coagulated using chymosin from calves. These cheeses are coagulated by using only the starter culture or by using chymosin from fungi.

20 a and b Your answers to these questions depend on your views, but have you considered a taste test of traditional versus modern products? It is easy to compare prices, but what do you think of the flavours? What do the rest of your group think?

Chapter 3

1 Your answer to this question depends on your recent experience. Try examining some packaging, you may be surprised at the range of products that include citric acid.

2 a The 'tang' of citric acid makes it a useful additive to soft drinks, sweets and ice-cream.
  b Citric acid is a useful food preservative because it reacts with trace elements.

3 Enzyme 3 does not work efficiently so there is a build-up of α-ketoglutarate. This inhibits enzyme 2 and causes a build-up of isocitrate. The isocitrate inhibits enzyme 1 and results in a build-up of citrate. This leads to the excretion of citric acid.

4 In obligate anaerobes, the final acceptor in the electron transport chain is not oxygen. Facultative anaerobes have the ability to use either oxygen or an alternative final acceptor in the electron transport chain.

5 a Tube 2.
  b Tube 3.
  c Tube 1.

6 Surface fermentation methods ensure that the largest possible surface area is exposed to oxygen. This is done by using many wide shallow trays rather than fewer deeper trays.

7 The airlift fermenter is built like a coiled tube whereas the stirred ferment is like a big tank. This is because the design of the airlift fermenter aids the circulation of the medium by air, whereas the stirred fermenter needs space for the stirring mechanism and baffles. The stirred

fermenter needs a power supply to move the stirring mechanism. The airlift fermenter has a greater capacity than the stirred fermenter because the mixing is done by air not by a mechanical stirrer.

8 Sparging is passing sterile air through a vessel of nutrient medium so that it is well aerated.

9 Submerged processes have high overall yield and low labour costs even though other costs are high.

10 The design and size of a fermenter vessel is likely to be influenced by:
  • whether fermentation is surface or submerged;
  • whether fermentation is aerobic or anaerobic;
  • whether the vessel is a starter, intermediate or final fermentation vessel;
  • the nutrient requirements of the organism;
  • the oxygen requirement of the organism;
  • the amount of money available.

11 In some places, citric acid is obtained by crushing up lemons, but microbial production of citric acid has a far higher yield and is the only way of making enough citric acid to meet the demand.

12 Vinegar is made by the breakdown of alcohol; cola drinks are not alcoholic.

13 It is important that commercially useful acetic acid bacteria are acid tolerant so that they are not killed by the increasing acidity of the environment as ethanoic acid is produced.

14 The other substances present in wine, beer and cider are nutrients for the bacteria. However, pure alcohol contains nothing else, so nutrients must be added for the bacteria to grow successfully.

15 **Similarities**: both processes use microbes; both are aerobic fermentations; in both processes the fermenters have to be protected from acid corrosion.

Differences: citric acid is produced by fungi, vinegar is produced by bacteria; vinegar is produced by surface culture; most citric acid is produced by submerged culture.

16 You could say that besides producing citric acid and vinegar, microbes have been used for centuries to produce alcohol, yoghurt and cheese. It is only recently that labelling laws have made it necessary to say so on the packaging.

Chapter 4

1 a Protein production by microorganisms is efficient because they reproduce very rapidly. Other advantages include economy – microbes can be grown on cheap food substances in fermenters that take up less space than the fields and sheds needed for cattle or chickens; microbes don't have care costs like vets' bills. There are fewer ethical questions about farming microbes than mammals.

  b A rapidly growing filamentous fungus fits the criteria very well. It grows on starch, is safe to eat, is rich in protein, and will eventually produce protein at low cost. Its filamentous nature means that it can be made into fibrous lumps like meat.

2 When screening for antibiotic production, samples are screened for new chemicals produced by the microbes. When screening for a protein source, microbes are screened for protein content and growth rate.

3 Using working and stock cultures protects the stored master cultures from contamination. Master cultures are not used up too quickly. Working and stock cultures can be prepared and frozen in ready-to-use samples – the amount required is thawed when needed.

4 The purity of a culture could be damaged by contamination from the person working with the culture, the air, the apparatus used, the medium, and the bench.

5 a 60 hours.

  b Penicillin production continues to increase rapidly as biomass increase slows down.

6 a Additional nutrient increases the production phase of penicillin by providing just sufficient nutrient to support growth without encouraging a big increase in fungal mass.

  b Batch fill and draw is the more successful method because it allows additional nutrients to be added when needed, and does not encourage further mycelium development at the expense of penicillin production.

7 a Dr. Spicer's team could learn a lot about fermenter design and the growth conditions needed for fungal mycelium production.

  b First, the types of fungi used are different. Secondly, penicillin production occurs after the main growth period. So, once sufficient fungal growth has occurred, further increase in fungal mass is not required. When a fungus is grown as a protein source, mycelium growth is encouraged by aeration and addition of extra nutrients.

8 In liquid media, the fungi do not produce discrete colonies that can be measured.

9 A series of agar cultures each containing one of the carbohydrates to be tested must be inoculated with spores of *Penicillium*. The growth of the *Penicillium* should be monitored over several days by measuring the diameter of colonies produced.

10 Batch culture is generally simpler in that the culture is inoculated and allowed to ferment. At the end of the process, the growth of microbes slows or stops and product is collected. Continuous culture is more complicated and involves systems to monitor the input of medium and output of product. However, the yield from continuous culture processes can be higher because the growth phase of the microbes can be prolonged.

11 If the medium entered and left the vessel too quickly, much of it would be unused. If it entered and left too slowly, the fungal biomass would not leave the fermenter fast enough, so productivity would fall.

12 The process removes water from the cells, this decreases the overall mass and so increases the percentage of protein.

13 Samples can be washed into a known quantity of sterile water and then serially diluted. These dilutions could be plated out onto agar plates and incubated. Subsequent colony growth could be counted.

14 For penicillin, the process involves extracting a chemical from the medium. In the downstream processing of mycoprotein, the fungus itself has to be extracted from the medium.

15 A great deal of strain development, fermenter design, and research for optimum conditions has been needed. A lot of financial backing and sales promotion has also been necessary.

Chapter 5

1 To isolate a suitable strain, first look for bacteria that live in a hot or an alkaline environment, then select a strain by culturing at pH 10 and 60 °C.

2 Intracellular enzymes are inside the cell. First, the cells have to be broken open, then the enzymes have to be separated from the mixture of all the cellular contents.

3 Early techniques used moulds growing on the surface of cereals because that is what happens naturally. Later on, people developed more sophisticated methods to increase yields, but these methods may increase the cost as well.

4 a Working in a draught-free environment stops air-borne contamination of the working culture. It also stops the contamination of other areas by the working culture.

b If a loop were not allowed to cool, the heat would kill any bacteria that came into contact with it.

c If an agar plate or culture bottle is unlabelled, you cannot be certain what the medium is.

5 a Scaling-up ensures that enough actively growing organisms enter the final fermentation vessel to make the process economic.

b Take samples from the conical flask and culture them on a range of media in a range of conditions including those used to isolate the organism. Growth should occur only under the conditions specific for the strain being used.

6 The optimum pH for amylase production is pH 7.5.

7 The purpose of the starter culture is to provide a pure strain. The purpose of all intermediate phases is to grow the culture exponentially and increase the cell numbers ten-fold at each step (see also Chapter 3, p. 41). The purpose of the final fermentation phase is to grow the organisms in post-exponential conditions so that the maximum yield of enzyme is obtained.

8 a Antibiotics.

b Therapeutic enzymes, antibodies, and diagnostic enzymes.

c The more of a product there is in the broth, the easier it is to isolate and higher the final yield. Thus, it costs less to extract a plentiful product than one in low concentration.

9 a About 50% of the total production of industrial enzymes is made up of amylases.

b Amylases convert starch to sugar.

10 You could mix pectinase with cloudy fruit juice and incubate at a range of temperatures to see at what temperature the enzyme works fastest to clear the juice.

11 a *Bacillus licheniformis* and *B. subtilis*.

b The enzymes used in washing powders and liquids must work at a suitable temperature for doing the laundry.

12 You could culture the organisms on casein plates at a range of pH values and see which plates show the most clear areas where the casein has been broken down.

13 Cross linkage can damage some enzymes, but if an enzyme is robust enough to be immobilised this way, it remains very active. Entrapment does not damage enzymes, but it does slow down the speed of the reaction that the enzyme catalyses. Adsorption neither damages enzymes nor slows the reaction speed, but it holds enzymes in place by weak forces, so enzymes may become detached. It is also more expensive than the other methods.

14 After the slump in sales, enzyme technology developed a means of immobilising enzymes called micro-encapsulation. The micro-encapsulated enzyme does not cause the allergic reactions associated with the powdered form of the enzyme.

15 A stirred fermenter is more likely to physically damage the immobilising system.

16 An enzyme from *Rhizopus arrhizus* enabled chemists to use a biotechnological pathway to make cortisone – this is cheaper than the previous chemical process. Immobilising whole microbial cells and using them to produce cortisone is cheaper than isolating the relevant enzyme.

Chapter 6

1 Disinfectants and antiseptics are chemicals that inhibit or kill microbes, but antiseptics are safe to use on animal tissue.

2 Uncooked chicken can be contaminated with bacteria that can cause diseases in humans. A bactericidal soap kills bacteria.

3 Bactericidal chemicals kill bacteria, bacteriostatic chemicals inhibit bacterial growth.

4 If the ingredients are present in high concentrations, they may be harmful to the user and to the environment unless they are diluted.

5 Cultures of the microorganism could be grown in nutrient broths containing different concentrations of ethanol, then plated out using the dilution plate technique.

6 Disinfectants are non-specific and can damage all cells. Chemotherapeutic agents are more specific and kill or inhibit the growth of microbial cells without damaging the host's tissues when swallowed.

7 a The MIC is the lowest concentration that prevents growth of a microbe; MLC is the lowest concentration that kills the microbe.

b The MIC can be used to compare different chemotherapeutic agents, the MLC is important in determining the dose required.

8 The size of the zone can be influenced by the water content and solubility of the antibiotic, the diffusion rate of the antibiotic through the agar, the concentration of the antibiotic in the disc, and the sensitivity of the bacterium to the antibiotic.

9 a Mutagenesis is the process of using chemicals or radiation to produce mutations in microbes.

b It is easier to produce the antibiotic molecule and then alter it by chemical reaction than to attempt to create mutants with exactly the right genetic information to make the desired product.

10 a Antibiotics work by interfering with biochemical processes in microbial cells. Viruses have no such processes.

b A person weakened by a virus infection may be more open to infection by bacteria. This is called secondary infection. It might be better to suggest warmth and rest in order to reduce the risk of secondary infection.

11 Viruses must use the biochemistry of host cells in order to reproduce.

12 Disinfectants are less effective in that they are not specific, but they reduce the frequency of bacterial infections without the risk of increasing the number of resistant bacteria.

Chapter 7

1 Aetiology is a description of the characteristic causes of a disease.

2 In 1990, most deaths were due to heart disease or cancer.

3 Jogging, or any other regular exercise is good; smoking is not. Eating mints coats the teeth with sugar and contributes to tooth decay. A diet of pre-prepared food and fish and chips is not likely to provide an adequate variety of nutrients, and the fish and chips are high in fat. The advice: keep up the exercise; stop smoking; eat sugar-free mints (or give them up); eat a varied and balanced diet with more fresh fruit and vegetables.

4 Yes. Screening is a way of checking that good health is being maintained.

5 Screening for cervical cancer can detect early abnormalities in cells. Treatment can begin before the cancer has developed very far.

6 Fetal cells collected by amniocentesis can be used to construct a karyotype. If the fetus has Down's syndrome, an extra chromosome is present (as in the karyotype on p. 86).

7 X-rays can damage the DNA in developing egg cells. This could lead to genetic abnormalities in those individuals who develop from the fertilisation of a damaged egg.

8 Unlike X-rays, ultrasound does not damage DNA.

9 You can reduce the risk of atheroma by not smoking, avoiding stress, and eating a diet that is low in saturated fat. Taking regular exercise also reduces the risk.

10 **a** The blood clot could travel in the bloodstream to the coronary arteries. If the clot blocks a coronary artery, the blood supply to heart muscle is restricted and a heart attack results.
b An embolism.

11 Because of the reduced level of air pollution, there are fewer people suffering from respiratory diseases in the 1990s than there were in the 1950s.

12 **a** Chemicals in cigarette smoke paralyse the cilia in the bronchial tubes. The cilia normally help to clear the tubes of mucus carrying trapped air-borne particles such as dust, viruses, bacteria and fungi. Smoking also damages the bronchioles and alveoli and causes fibrous tissue to be laid down in the bronchioles.
b As a result of the damage, microbes can reach the lungs and cause infections. Lining tissues of the respiratory system become inflamed, leading to chronic bronchitis. (Eventually, the surface area for gaseous exchange is reduced – this condition is called emphysema.)

13 Cells from malignant tumours can be spread around the body by the blood and lymph systems. This is called metastasis.

14 Cancer cells often have abnormal proteins in their cell membranes. These proteins appear as foreign to the immune system and this leads to an immune reaction that destroys the cancer cells.

15 Polycyclic aromatic hydrocarbons from cigarette smoke.

16 **a** Tumours are lumps of cancerous cells. Leukaemia is a cancer that results from uncontrolled growth of white blood cells. As the cells are not attached to each other, no lump forms.
b Leukaemia sufferers have white blood cells that do not function properly in the immune response. An important defence against infection is, therefore, disabled. Bacteria are more easily able to cause infections in such conditions.

17 Skin cancer is the result of uncontrolled growth of cells in the basal layers of the epidermis. This is often due to damage to these cells caused by UVL from sunlight.

18 A holistic attitude to breast cancer recommends eating a low-fat diet and carrying out frequent self-examination.

19 Insoluble dietary fibre speeds up the passage of food through the gut, reducing the length of time substances from food (some of which may be carcinogenic) are in contact with the cells of the intestinal lining.

20 As a woman gets older, the chances of her developing aneuploid eggs with trisomy of chromosome 21 increase. An individual who develops from such an egg will have Down's syndrome. Amniocentesis can be used to collect fetal cells to determine whether or not the fetus has Down's syndrome.

21 Enzymes are proteins and they only work if the amino acid sequence is correct. This is particularly important in the active site – the area that binds with the substrate molecule. Gene mutations resulting in the insertion of the wrong amino acid into a polypeptide sequence could result in an active site of the wrong shape. If this happens, the substrate molecule will not fit and the reaction cannot proceed.

22 Liposomes are able to fuse with cell membranes and release their contents into the cell.

23 X-linked disorders are usually recessive. Women have two X

chromosomes, and one usually has the correct dominant gene to counteract the mutant gene. As men have only one X chromosome, they have no dominant gene to counteract the mutant.

Chapter 8

1 Organisms in the body's normal flora protect us against infection by competing for available nutrients more successfully than harmful microbes. Some produce substances that inhibit the growth of harmful organisms.

2 Infection is the presence of viable microbes in the host's body. Disease occurs when the host shows recognisable signs and symptoms caused by the presence of the organism.

3 Air at atmospheric pressure in the rest of the hospital tends to flow into the laboratory and thus prevent air, which might contain air-borne microbes, from getting out of the laboratory and into the rest of the hospital.

4 ORT involves drinking a solution of salts and sugars to replace those lost from the body through diarrhoea.

5 a Washing removes most of the microbes present on the surface of the skin. Unwashed hands can pass these organisms onto anything they come into contact with. Some of the microbes that can be transmitted to food by unwashed hands can cause infections such as *Salmonella* poisoning, botulism, enteritis, cholera and typhoid.

 b When you have a cold and a runny nose, mucus from the nose contains viruses. Touching your nose transfers these viruses to your hand, and they can then be transferred to other surfaces, such as food or other people's skin.

6 a Specific adherence is the process by which a pathogen becomes attached to a host cell. Molecules (called ligands) in the microbial outer coat bind with receptor molecules in the host cell membranes. Ligand and receptor must match exactly. This means that even closely related host species are often not affected by the same microbe, and closely related microbes do not have the same disease-causing properties.

 b Receptor molecules are genetically controlled. Even slight differences in the genotypes of family members can result in different receptor molecules that do not match the ligands of the microbe causing the infection.

7 Pathogens can enter a cell by endocytosis (the host cell engulfs the microbe), or by producing enzymes that damage the host cell membrane and so make entry easier.

8 All toxins are poisons. Exotoxins are released by bacteria as they grow. Endotoxins remain inside the microbe until it dies and are released as the cell is broken down.

9 Some microorganisms are not harmful if they stay on the skin. Cuts allow microbes into the body where they can cause infection.

10 a Secondary infections arise when pathogens take advantage of the weakened state of a tissue that is already infected by another organism.

 b Secondary infections are common following viral infections because of the damage done to tissues experiencing viral infection.

11 Influenza infection weakens tissues and allows secondary infections to occur. These secondary infections can be fatal to the very old and very young because these individuals are more vulnerable than the rest of the population.

12 New strains of the influenza virus are constantly arising by mutation, but vaccination only protects against the strain of the virus from which the vaccine was derived.

13 Viruses disrupt the normal functioning of a cell; they make the cell produce new virus particles and eventually kill it. Damage can also be caused when substances from broken-down infected cells enter the bloodstream and are carried round the body. These substances act like toxins.

14 The difficulty in developing new antiviral drugs is in finding remedies that can affect the virus inside a host cell, but that do not damage the host cell.

15 Drying between the toes is important because *Epidermophyton*, the fungus that causes athlete's foot, easily infects such damp warm areas.

Chapter 9

1 Tissue damage causes the release of substances (histamines) that make capillaries more permeable. This leads to an increased amount of tissue fluid in the injured area, so it swells. Arterioles serving the area dilate, and increased blood flow causes a localised rise in temperature.

2 a Interleukin is released from some white blood cells. Interleukin resets the body's thermostat in the hypothalamus.

 b A raised body temperature has an adverse effect on the metabolism of some microbes and so helps to reduce the risk of infection.

3 Body tissues provide an ideal growth medium for bacteria, so infections can develop rapidly.

4 Bacteria are found on all exposed surfaces such as skin and food, in moisture droplets in the air, in faeces, and in other infected areas of the body.

5 The body is protected from microbial infection by specific and non-specific mechanisms.

6 a Lysozyme is an enzyme that destroys Gram-negative bacteria.

 b Commensal bacteria compete more successfully than pathogenic bacteria for nutrients found on body surfaces.

7 **a** Interferons are proteins produced by lymphocytes. The interferons stimulate other blood cells to produce antiviral proteins that stop the manufacture of viral protein by virus-infected cells. Interferons also stimulate some lymphocytes to destroy virus-infected cells.

b Some of the commensal bacteria living on body surfaces protect us against infection by other organisms, such as pathogenic fungi. Antibiotics kill some of these bacteria, thus exposing us to the risk of fungal infection.

8 Macrophages ingest microorganisms. When this happens, some of the microbes' antigens become embedded in the cell membrane of the macrophage, and can be detected by lymphocytes. The lymphocytes then mount an immune response.

9 In cell-mediated immunity, T lymphocytes attack pathogens and infected cells. In antibody-mediated immunity, B lymphocytes produce the antibody to destroy the pathogen.

10 Antibodies are produced by B lymphocytes.

11 The presence of two active sites on each antibody molecule enables the formation of an interlocking antibody–antigen complex that traps the pathogen and prevents it from infecting cells. Trapped pathogens can be engulfed by macrophages.

12 **a** The primary response.

b Following a first infection with a pathogen, lymphocytes known as memory cells are produced and remain in the body. These cells are ready to stimulate a secondary response if the pathogen re-invades the body.

13 The viruses which cause the common cold and influenza exist in a variety of forms, and new forms constantly arise by mutation.

Immunity resulting from infection by one type is no use when a different form infects the body.

14 Passive immunity involves the introduction of antibodies into the bloodstream, and these are effective for a period of a few weeks to a few months. Passive immunity does not result in the production of memory cells, so no long-term immunity results.

15 You should have had a tetanus booster at age 15. Your next one will be due when you are 25.

Chapter 10

1 Yes. The HLA proteins will be identical so there will be no immune response.

2 The immune system recognises HLA proteins in the cell membranes of transplanted organs. If the donated HLA proteins are not identical to the recipient's own, an immune response occurs and the organ is rejected.

3 HLA proteins are found in the cell membranes of all humans.

4 Irradiating bone marrow reduces the production of lymphocytes. A reduced number of lymphocytes reduces the likelihood of the HLA proteins on a transplanted organ being recognised as foreign. Therefore, the risk of rejection is reduced.

5 The doctors would use drugs to help lower the blood pressure so that the new kidney is not damaged.

6 Blood group O is sometimes referred to as the 'universal donor' because it contains neither A nor B antigens to stimulate an immune response in the recipient. People with blood group AB do not produce either anti-A or anti-B antibody, so they can receive blood of any group and are sometimes called 'universal recipients'.

7

Group	Antigen in RBC membrane	Antibody in plasma
A	A	anti-B
B	B	anti-A
AB	AB	none
O	none	anti-A and anti-B

8 The second dose of Rh positive blood produces a secondary immune response. This is much more rapid than a primary response because the recipient's bloodstream already contains anti-Rh antibody, and memory cells that allow rapid production of further anti-Rh antibody.

9

Donor	Recipient			
	A Rh +	A Rh −	B Rh +	B Rh −
A Rh +	✓	✗	✗	✗
A Rh −	✓	✓	✗	✗
B Rh +	✗	✗	✓	✗
B Rh −	✗	✗	✓	✓
AB Rh +	✗	✗	✗	✗
AB Rh −	✗	✗	✗	✗
O Rh +	✓	✗	✓	✗
O Rh −	✓	✓	✓	✓

✓ = recipient accepts transfused blood
✗ = recipient has transfusion reaction

Donor	Recipient			
	AB Rh +	AB Rh −	O Rh +	O Rh −
A Rh +	✓	✗	✗	✗
A Rh −	✓	✓	✗	✗
B Rh +	✓	✗	✗	✗
B Rh −	✓	✓	✗	✗
AB Rh +	✓	✗	✗	✗
AB Rh −	✓	✓	✗	✗
O Rh +	✓	✗	✓	✗
O Rh −	✓	✓	✓	✓

✓ = recipient accepts transfused blood
✗ = recipient has transfusion reaction

10 In pregnancy, the mother's blood does not mix with the baby's blood, so no production of anti-Rh antibody occurs in the mother. In late pregnancy, mixing may take place and result in anti-Rh antibody getting into the mother's

bloodstream. This could affect a second Rh negative baby since the antibody can cross the placenta and enter the second baby's bloodstream.

11 People under 18 are still growing. People over 65 may not be able to physically cope with having blood removed. Both groups are more vulnerable than healthy adults aged between 18 and 65 who can readily make up the lost cells and plasma.

12 No. An individual infected by HIV who has begun to produce antibody to fight the virus is HIV-positive. AIDS occurs when an HIV-positive individual develops symptoms of one of the AIDS-related diseases.

13 Payment for blood donations may attract people who give blood to earn money. They may not be suitable donors, or they may give blood more frequently than is advisable and become ill themselves.

14 It reduces the risk of spreading HIV through sharing infected needles.

15 The estimates suggest that 32% of HIV-positive people have developed AIDS. The reported figures suggest that 7% of HIV-positive people have developed AIDS.

16 Lymphocytes capable of an auto-immune response are usually removed from the body by the thymus gland during embryonic development. Any lymphocytes that escape this process are usually prevented from acting by suppressor T cells.

17 a Greater publicity must also be accompanied by greater use of the donor card. Even with more potential donors and a more efficient database system, it is unlikely that the demand for donor organs can be fully met.
   b Genetic engineering can help produce animal organs which have compatible HLA proteins. However, the use of animals for such purposes is seen by some people as unacceptable.

Chapter 11

1 Without effective anaesthetics, operations had to be carried out quickly to reduce the length of time the patient suffered pain.

2 An anaesthetic is a substance given to a patient to deaden pain. Ether was the first anaesthetic.

3 Large doses of ether were required to relax the patient's muscles so that the operation could take place.

4 Shock can be caused by loss of blood or body fluids and a drop in blood pressure.

5 Sodium citrate prevents blood from clotting.

6 Bacteria could get into the wound from:
   • the surgeon's instruments;
   • the skin around the wound;
   • the surgeon's clothes, breath, and hands;
   • the air;
   • other people in the operating theatre.

7 Lister believed, correctly, that carbolic acid sprayed into a wound will kill any bacteria that settled in the wound. Carbolic acid was also used to kill microbes on surgical instruments.

8 Today, hospitals are kept very clean. Sterilisation and disinfection of all surfaces, instruments, dressings and equipment takes place.

9 Moist heat sterilisation occurs when materials are heated under pressure to temperatures above 100 °C in an autoclave.

10 Ionising radiation disrupts the microbial DNA, and thus prevents the organism from reproducing.

11 Porous surfaces such as wood, fabrics and unglazed porcelain absorb liquids. So, pathogens can penetrate the surface. This makes porous surfaces more difficult to clean than non-porous ones such as glass, glazed porcelain and metals.

12 Sterilisation involves the complete removal of all viable (capable of reproducing) microbes from a surface, object or fluid. This includes spores. Disinfection does not remove bacterial spores.

13 Disinfection is used in situations that do not require sterility, e.g. cooking utensils, or where it is impractical to achieve sterility.

14 a Penicillins are antibiotics. Antibiotics are chemicals that affect the metabolism or structure of bacteria. Human cells are so dissimilar to bacterial cells that antibiotics have no effect on them.
   b Sulphonamides act by inhibiting the production of folic acid in microbes. Since human cells do not produce folic acid, these drugs do not affect humans.

15 Fungal cells are more similar to human cells than are bacterial cells. This similarity means that antifungal agents can often also affect human cells, a problem not raised by antibacterial agents.

16 Unlike the bacterial chromosome, plasmids can cross species boundaries. This is a major factor in increasing the spread of bacterial resistance.

17 Bacteria with a gene for resistance to a particular antibiotic survive treatment. They grow and multiply rapidly because competing cells have been killed.

18 The presence of large amounts of antibiotics in the hospital environment means that although non-resistant strains of bacteria are killed, resistant strains are able to reproduce.

19 Bacteria can become resistant to more than one antibiotic. When this happens, even multiple antibiotic treatment might be ineffective.

20 Research into combating resistance includes finding ways to:
   • eliminate R plasmids from bacteria;
   • prevent the expression of resistance genes carried by R plasmids;

- prevent the spread of plasmids between bacteria.
Ascorbic acid might be a useful means of removing resistance without killing the bacteria.

21 Competent B cells produce antibodies. Tumour cells have a high growth rate. Fusing the two types of cell allows for an increased rate of antibody production.

22 'Magic bullets' are monoclonal antibodies, usually combined with cytotoxic drugs. They can be used in cancer treatment. Cancer cells have abnormal antigens in their cell membranes, and monoclonal antibodies that specifically combine with the antigens can be administered to the patient. The monoclonal antibodies attach to the cancer cells so the cytotoxic drugs attack only those cells.

23 Yes. ELISA techniques are relatively simple to carry out and therefore can be used in war zones or disaster areas where more complicated tests would be impractical.

Chapter 12

1 23.4.

2 Foods rich in vitamin C (fruit) and iron (meat, fresh green vegetables) were expensive and were not common in the diet of working people in towns and cities.

3 Physical activity will increase the energy expenditure due to:
- the breathing mechanism;
- muscle contraction in the heart;
- conduction of nervous impulses;
- secretion.

4 The 15-year-old boy is still growing; growth requires a lot of energy.

5 To lose weight, lipid intake should be reduced because lipids have a higher energy content per gram than other food types.

6 Your time line should show that for a four-hour period following each meal the source blood glucose is the food you have just eaten. From then for the next five hours, the source of blood glucose is glycogen. After that, if you still have not eaten, blood glucose is obtained by oxidising lipids.

7 Yes. Porridge contains soluble fibre which slows digestion. Glucose is absorbed by the bloodstream more slowly, so there are less extreme changes in blood glucose concentration than would otherwise occur.

8 Fatty acid A is a saturated fatty acid. Fatty acid B is a polyunsaturated fatty acid.

9 People are changing to low-fat spreads because they contain less saturated fat. Saturated fat is associated with heart disease. Low-fat spreads also have a lower energy content per gram than butter; this is useful in weight-reducing diets.

10 a Such a diet would lead to a deficiency of certain fatty acids that the body is unable to make but that are essential for cell membrane synthesis.
   b Essential fatty acids are those fatty acids that the body needs for membrane synthesis, and that it is unable to make. They must be present in the diet.

11 a Body builders strive to build up muscle mass. Protein is the main dietary need for anyone who wishes to do this.
   b Essential amino acids are those amino acids that the body needs but cannot synthesise. It is essential that they are present in the diet. Non-essential amino acids are those that the body is able to synthesise.

12 a A vegan is quite likely to be short of sulphur, zinc, iron, copper and iodine; possibly also calcium and phosphorous.
   b Vegans should eat a wide variety of nuts and beans to provide iron and copper, plenty of green vegetables for calcium, and cereals for phosphorous. The best way for a vegan to ensure a sufficient intake of sulphur and zinc is probably to take them as dietary supplements. Iodised salt provides iodine.

13 a Seafood contains zinc and iodine.
   b Green vegetables are an excellent source of calcium and magnesium.

14 a The higher contents are as follows:
   - salt (sodium) – snack 2;
   - sugar – snack 1;
   - dietary fibre – snack 1;
   - fat – snack 2.
   b Snack 1. But a varied and balanced diet requires that this sort of snack is not eaten too often.

15 First, the water level would rise. Then it would fall as the diuretic effect of the alcohol leads to the kidneys removing *more* water.

16 Any fresh foods you ate are likely to be free from additives. Most of the rest probably contained additives, unless the label specifically said 'additive-free'.

17 a 0.117 dm^3.
   b 136–156 beats per minute.

18 a This person is running the risk of developing hypertension and heart disease.
   b Someone with this lifestyle would be well advised to take more exercise, and reduce fat, salt and sugar intake while increasing starch and fibre intake.

19 Muscle cells become more efficient at respiring glucose, because exercise increases the number of mitochondria in muscle cells.

20 Yes. A balance between the energy you take in as food and the energy you expend is essential for good body shape and fitness whatever your lifestyle and occupation.

Glossary

active immunity immunity that arises when an individual produces an antibody in response to contact with an antigen 125

adenosine diphosphate (ADP) a molecule that links with inorganic phosphate to form ATP 37

adenosine triphosphate (ATP) a molecule used as a temporary energy store in respiration 37

aerated mixed with air 39

aerobic conditions growth conditions in which oxygen is present 22

aerobic fermentation the process by which microbes breakdown substances in the presence of oxygen 38

aerobic respiration the process of producing energy in the presence of oxygen 37

aetiology the list of characteristic causes of a disease 83

agglutinate (of red blood cells) to clump together when blood of different groups is mixed 132

agglutinins antibodies in plasma that cause agglutination when red blood cells containing certain agglutinogens are present (in the ABO system there are two agglutinins: anti-A and anti-B) 132

agglutinogens blood group antigens found in red blood cell membranes (in the ABO system there are two agglutinogens: agglutinogen A and agglutinogen B) 132

AIDS-related complex (ARC) a group of symptoms such as tiredness, fever, weight loss and diarrhoea that occur in HIV-positive individuals some time, often many years, after infection (it is the stage before the development of opportunistic diseases that arise as a result of the gradual breakdown of the immune system) 136

amino acids the basic building blocks of protein molecules – they are composed of carbon, hydrogen, oxygen, nitrogen, and sometimes sulphur (amino acids link together by peptide bonds to form proteins) 164

amylase an enzyme that converts starch to sugar 64

anabolic steroids hormones that assist the muscle-building process 165

anabolism metabolism that results in the synthesis of new molecules 157

anaerobic conditions growth conditions in which oxygen is absent 22

anaerobic fermentation the process by which microbes breakdown substances in the absence of oxygen 38

anaerobic respiration the process of producing energy in the absence of oxygen 37

anaesthetic a chemical used to deaden or reduce pain 143

aneuploidy the addition or removal of all or part of a chromosome from a gamete 95

aneurysm a swelling occurring in an artery wall after a reduction in wall elasticity caused by atheroma 89

antibody (immunoglobulin) protein molecules produced by B lymphocytes to combat microbial infection and provide immunity 121

antibody-mediated immunity the process by which B cells produce antibody molecules to kill an invading pathogen 118

antibody–antigen complex the lattice-like structure that forms when a number of antibody molecules combine with a number of antigens 120/122

antigen (immunogen) a substance that stimulates an immune response 118

antimetabolites antibiotics that inhibit key microbial metabolic reactions and result in a shortage of essential metabolites 149

antiseptics chemicals that destroy microbes but can be used on skin 72

aseptate (of fungal hyphae) without dividing walls 11

aseptic technique laboratory or surgical practice to reduce the risk of contamination or infection 145

atheroma the build up of fatty deposits on the inside of arteries 88

attenuated strain a non-virulent strain of a pathogen that does not give rise to a disease but can produce immunity if used in vaccination 126

auto-immune the term for lymphocytes that react to the body's own antigens – they are usually removed from the body by the thymus gland during embryonic development 139

auto-immunity the condition in which an immune response is caused by auto-immune lymphocytes reacting to the body's own antigens 139

autografts an organ or tissue transplanted from one part of an individual to another 129

autosomal dominant disorder a genetic disease where the mutant gene is dominant to the normal gene 96

autosomal recessive disorder a genetic disease where the mutant gene is recessive to the normal gene 96

B cells (B lymphocytes) lymphocytes that produce antibody molecules 118

Bacillus a genus of bacteria

bacillus a rod-shaped bacterium 12

bactericidal capable of killing bacterial cells 72

bacteriophages viruses that infect bacteria 14

bacteriostatic capable of inhibiting the growth of bacterial cells 72

balanced growth the state in which microbial cells are dividing at their maximum rate 18

basal metabolic rate (BMR) the energy required for basal metabolism measured indirectly as heat output from a person awake and at rest 158

basal metabolism the basic on-going metabolism needed to keep the body functioning 157

basement membrane a layer of fibrous material found underneath cells in epithelial tissue 99

batch culture a closed (but possibly aerated) system containing a limited amount of growth medium that was added at the start of fermentation 19

benign tumour a tumour that is harmless 90

biogas a mixture of methane and carbon dioxide produced from sewage by methanogenic bacteria 38

biomass the cell mass produced during fermentation 25

biopsy a sample of tissue taken from an organ 86

biosensors tools used by the medical profession to find out information about the body without invading the body 66

body mass index (BMI) the relationship between an individual's height and body mass that is calculated by dividing body mass (kg) by height squared (m^2) 157

broad (wide) spectrum antibiotics antibiotics effective against a wide range of bacteria 76

bulk enzymes enzymes used in large quantities in industrial processes and food manufacturing (bulk enzymes often include other unnecessary enzymes) 64

cadaver organs transplant organs taken from a dead body 130

calibration curve a graph of absorbance plotted against cell numbers that can be used to convert future absorbance readings of similar cultures to cell numbers 18

cancer a range of diseases in which there is uncontrolled growth of malignant cells 90

capsid the protein coat of a virus 14

capsomeres the individual protein units that combine to create the capsid 14

capsule a slimy layer of polysaccharides or polypeptides on the outside of the cell wall in some bacteria 13

carcinoma a tumour found in epithelial tissue 92

cardiac output the volume of blood pumped per ventricle per minute, measured in dm^3 min^{-1} 168

cardiac reserve the difference between the resting output and the maximum output the heart can achieve 168

cardiovascular system the heart and blood vessels 88

carrier an individual who is carrying a pathogen but who does not show signs or symptoms of disease (a carrier may be human or animal) 100

carrying capacity the maximum cell population that an environment can support 18

catabolism metabolism that results in the breakdown of molecules 157

cell-mediated immunity the process by which T cells attack pathogens directly 118

cerebrovascular accident (stroke) a blockage in the blood supply in the brain caused by a thrombus or embolism and resulting in damage to brain cells 89

chemotherapeutic agents chemicals used for treating disease 74

chemotherapy medical treatment involving drugs 131

chylomicron the lipoprotein that transports triglycerides in the bloodstream 164

cilia microscopic hair-like structures that are found on certain epithelial cells 99

clinical signs indications of disease that are observable by a doctor 85

coagulating clotting 35

coccus a spherical bacterium 12

coenocytic the condition in which a cell has many nuclei 11

coliform bacteria rod-shaped Gram-negative bacteria commonly found in the digestive tracts and faeces of animals 29

colostomy an operation to remove part of the large intestine in a patient with colo-rectal cancer 93

commensals harmless microbes that live in and on the body 117

compatible the term for a transplanted tissue or organ with an HLA group that matches the recipient's HLA group 129

competent the term for T or B lymphocytes that have been activated and can produce an immune response 119

complement a plasma protein that can bind with an antibody–antigen complex and destroy a pathogen 120

continuous culture a culture that is maintained in the exponential growth phase by continuously supplying fresh medium 19

continuous fermentation a fermentation in which growth medium is added continuously so that cell activity is kept at a maximum 51

cross-streak method a method of testing a microbe to see if it produces any antibiotic 76

cytoplasmic membrane (plasma membrane) the membrane that encloses the cytoplasm of a cell 10

cytotoxic drug a drug that damages cell metabolism and results in cell death 154

cytotoxic T cells (killer T cells) lymphocytes that travel to the site of an infection and attack viruses by producing a protein called perforin 120

diagnosis the process of identifying and naming a disease in a patient 85

diagnostic enzyme a very pure enzyme used to detect a chemical in body fluids 66

diastole the stage in the cardiac cycle in which the ventricles relax and fill with blood 170

dietary fibre complex polysaccharide carbohydrates such as cellulose and pectin (dietary fibre can be soluble or insoluble) 161

dilution rate the rate at which growth medium is replaced in continuous fermentation 54

disc diffusion tests tests in which antibiotic discs are placed on bacterial lawns to measure any inhibitory effect 76

disinfection treatment with chemicals that inhibit or kill microbes

diuretic a substance that makes the body produce a large volume of watery urine 167

downstream processing the process of recovering the product from the mixture in the fermenter after fermentation 42

dry heat sterilisation removal of all viable microbes using a flame 146

electron transfer chain a series of oxidation and reduction reactions that are part of respiration 37

embolism a blood clot that travels along blood vessels 88

emulsion a mixture of two liquids in which one is suspended in the other 29

endocytosis the process by which phagocytic white blood cells engulf microbes and destroy them 104

endoplasmic reticulum the folded membranes in a eukaryotic cell that are lined in places with ribosomes 10

endoscope an instrument used by doctors to look inside the body 87

endotoxins toxins produced by bacteria that are released into the body when the bacterial cell dies and the cell wall disintegrates 105

envelope the membrane of proteins and glycoproteins covering the capsid of some viruses 15

environmental resistance the ability of some organisms to survive the increasingly difficult conditions encountered during the stationary growth phase 18

epidemic an outbreak of a disease that affects a high proportion of people in a given population 84

epidemiology the study of the occurrence of disease in populations 84

epithelial tissue the tissue that makes up glands, the outer layers of the skin, the linings of the body's hollow organs, tubes (e.g. blood vessels) and the lining of parts of the body exposed to the outside world (e.g. the respiratory and digestive systems) 99

essential amino acids amino acids that the body is unable to synthesis and that must be obtained from the diet 164

exotoxins poisons released into the body by bacteria as they grow 105

exponential growth the growth phase in which cell numbers double with each generation 61

exponential increase an increase in cell numbers in which cell numbers double with each generation 16

extracellular enzyme an enzyme that is produced inside a cell but passes out through the cell walls into the surrounding medium 59

facultative anaerobes organisms that can respire either aerobically or anaerobically – they grow better in the presence of oxygen 37

fermentation the breakdown of organic substances by microbes to produce energy in the absence of oxygen (the wider biotechnological definition includes aerobic culturing of microbes for commercial or research purposes) 22

filamentous fungi fungi in which the visible fungal body is like a mass of threads 34

fimbriae (pili) short filamentous structures of bacteria that help in adherence to a surface 13

final acceptor the last chemical in an electron transfer chain 37

fining agent a chemical added to alcoholic brews after fermentation to clear them 27

flagella whip-like appendages of bacteria that are involved in motility 13

flocculate to form into larger particles 27

food additives substances added to processed or pre-prepared food to improve the shelf life, appearance, texture, flavour or dietary content 167

fungicidal capable of killing fungal cells 72

fungistatic capable of inhibiting the growth of fungal cells 72

generation time the life span of a cell; the time needed for a population to double 18

genome the complete set of genes present in an organism 14

glycoproteins molecules made from a combination of protein and carbohydrate – many antigens are glycoproteins 118

Gram-negative bacteria bacteria that appear pink following Gram's staining treatment (the complex multilayered cell wall allows alcohol to remove the purple stain used in Gram's technique) 12

Gram-positive bacteria bacteria that appear purple following Gram's staining treatment (the simple but thick cell wall does not allow alcohol to remove the purple stain used in Gram's technique) 12

granulated tissue a type of connective tissue that develops during the healing process in a deep wound – it contains a higher proportion of collagen than normal skin, has a rich blood supply, is highly resistant to infection, and lacks hair follicles and nerve endings (after healing, it remains as scar tissue) 115

haemocytometer an apparatus for counting cells 16

haemolyse to burst red blood cells 132

haemolysis the breakdown of red blood cells 30

heart rate the number of heart beats per minute 169

helical with a repeating spiral pattern 14

helper T cells lymphocytes that assist other lymphocytes to respond to pathogens 120

heterosome disorders genetic diseases caused by abnormalities in the X chromosome 96

heterotrophic nutrition nutrition that relies on complex organic molecules 10

heterozygous a genotype where the two alleles for a particular gene are different 96

high density lipoprotein (HDL) a type of protein–lipid complex responsible for the transport of some of the cholesterol in circulation (high HDL is associated with lowering the risk of atheroma) 164

HIV-positive with HIV antibody in the blood 136

homogenised mixed until the components are evenly spread; in milk, the even distribution of fat droplets 31

homozygous a genotype where the alleles for a particular gene are the same 96

host specificity the presence of specific receptor molecules in the host epithelial cells to which microbial ligands attach if there is an exact match (the difference between receptor molecules in different epithelial tissues means that the pathogen can only attack certain parts of the body) 104

hybridoma technique cell culture in which a fast-growing tumour cell is fused to a cell such as a lymphocyte so as to increase the rate at which the product of the non-tumour cell is produced (the technique is used to produce monoclonal antibodies from B lymphocytes) 153

hypha a thin filament of fungal growth 11

icosahedral with twenty faces 14

immobilised enzyme an enzyme attached to a fixed bed or membrane, or an enzyme bound to or within a particle 67

immunisation artificially creating immunity by vaccination 125

immunogen (antigen) a substance that stimulates an immune response 118

immunoglobulin (antibody) protein molecules produced by B lymphocytes in order to combat microbial infection and provide immunity 121

immunosuppressant drugs drugs used to suppress the immune system to reduce the risk of an immune response and transplant rejection 131

infectivity a measure of the number of bacterial cells needed for a disease to develop (how easily a bacterium can cause an infection) 105

interferons proteins (produced by lymphocytes in response to a virus infection) that stimulate other cells to produce antiviral proteins 117

intracellular enzyme an enzyme that stays inside the cell that produced it 59

invasiveness the ability of bacteria to penetrate cells or break into blood and lymph vessels to be carried round the body (how easily a bacterium or its toxin can spread round the body) 105

karyotype a diagram or picture of the chromosomes of an individual 86

killer T cells (cytotoxic T cells) lymphocytes that travel to the site of an infection and attack viruses by producing a protein called perforin 120

lagering the maturation and conditioning of beer 27

latent period the period between infection and the onset of the antibody production 122

leucocytes white blood cells 118

ligands molecules in a microbial cell wall or outer viral coat that bind with receptor molecules in cell membranes 104

limiting factors the factors that influence the growth of cells in a culture 18

lipoprotein a complex formed when a protein and a lipid combine together (all lipids are transported in the blood stream as lipoproteins) 164

literature search checking research journals, books and electronic media for relevant information 47

low density lipoproteins (LDL) a type of protein–lipid complex, responsible for the transport of most of the cholesterol in circulation (high LDL is associated with increasing the risk of atheroma) 164

lymph the fluid formed from excess tissue fluid that is not immediately reabsorbed into the bloodstream but flows through lymph vessels and eventually returns to the bloodstream 118

lymphocytes small leucocytes involved in immune responses (e.g. B lymphocytes, T lymphocytes, macrophages) 118

lyphophilised freeze-dried 49

lysis the rupturing of a cell and loss of cellular contents 148

macrophages lymphocytes that destroy pathogens by phagocytosis 118

main fermentation vessel the vessel in which the desired enzyme is produced after cell growth 61

major minerals minerals that are needed in daily amounts greater than 5 gram (e.g. sodium and calcium) 165

malignant tumour a tumour that spreads cancerous cells round the body 90

malted (of cereal grains) sprouted after being soaked in water and warmed 26

malting making cereal grains sprout 27

mashing crushing malted grains and mixing them with hot water 27

mastectomy an operation to remove a breast, following the development of breast cancer 93

master cultures the original pure cultures of a particular microbe 49

memory B cells B lymphocytes that continue to produce small amounts of antibody for years and enable an individual to mount a rapid secondary response following subsequent exposure to the specific pathogen 120

memory T cells T lymphocytes that remain in the lymph nodes and respond rapidly if the same pathogen invades the body again 120

meninges membranes surrounding the brain 106

mesosomes folds in the plasma membrane of bacteria that increase the surface area for metabolic activity 13

metabolic water water produced during certain metabolic reactions (e.g. the respiration of carbohydrate and lipid) 167

metabolise to produce by chemical reactions in the cell 22

metabolism all the chemical reactions going on in the body 157

metastasis the spreading of cells from a malignant tumour round the body 90

methanogenic bacteria anaerobic bacteria that produce biogas from concentrated sewage waste 38

micro-encapsulated enzyme the particulate form of an enzyme made by melting a wet paste of the enzyme at 50–70 °C with polyethylene glycol so that tiny solid spherical particles are formed 67

minimal inhibitory concentration (MIC) the lowest concentration of a chemical that will inhibit the growth of a microbe 76

minimal lethal concentration (MLC) the lowest concentration of a chemical that will kill a microbe 76

mitochondria eukaryotic cell organelles that are the site of ATP production 10

moist heat disinfection killing microbes with boiling water (some bacterial spores survive) 147

moist heat sterilisation removal of microbes from an object or fluid by heating in an autoclave (autoclaves heat water to over 100 °C under pressure) 146

mono-unsaturated fatty acids fatty acids in which the hydrocarbon chain contains only one pair of carbon atoms joined by a double bond 162

monoclonal antibodies antibodies produced by clones of B lymphocytes 153

multiple alleles multiple forms of a gene controlling a single characteristic 129

mutagenesis the production of mutants by treatment with chemicals or radiation 78

mutation treatment treatment of cells with chemicals and radiation to encourage mutation 48

mycelium an intertwined mass of branched filaments of a fungus 11

mycoses diseases caused by fungi 110

myocardial infarction a heart attack 89

narrow spectrum antibiotics antibiotics effective against a narrow range of bacteria 76

neoplasm a tumour, or mass of cells undergoing repeated cell division, regardless of the body's need for new cells for growth or repair 90

nicotinamide adenine dinucleotide (NAD) a cellular product involved in respiration and the production of energy 37

non-essential amino acids amino acids that the body is able to make and that do not have to be obtained from the diet 164

non-vascular not served by blood or lymph vessels (e.g. cornea) 129

normal flora of the body the usually harmless bacteria and fungi that live on and in the body 99

nuclear zone the area of a bacterial cell that contains the genome 13

nucleoprotein a combination of nucleic acid and protein 12

nutrients substances that provide energy and materials for growth and healthy functioning of the body 159

obligate aerobes organisms that have to respire aerobically because the final acceptor in their electron transport chain is oxygen 37

obligate anaerobes organisms that have to respire anaerobically because the final acceptor in their electron transport chain is not oxygen 37

obligate intracellular parasites parasites that can only reproduce within host cells 14

oncogene a gene which is able to transform a normal cell into a cancerous cell 91

opportunistic disease a disease that occurs because the body's defences are damaged (e.g. by HIV infection) 136

opsonisation the coating of a pathogen with complement thus making it easier for phagocytes to ingest the pathogen 120

optimum the point of any condition at which the maximum result is obtained 61

oral rehydration therapy (ORT) drinking a solution of salts and sugars to replace some of the substances the body loses in severe diarrhoea 101

oxygen requirement the term to describe whether a microbe is an aerobe, an anaerobe or a facultative anaerobe 37

pandemic a world-wide epidemic 84

passive immunity immunity caused by giving an individual antibody through vaccination or breast feeding (passive immunity rarely lasts more than a few months) 125

pasteurisation moderate heating to inhibit the growth of microbes 9

pathogenicity the extent to which toxins produced by invading bacteria can damage an individual (how toxic a toxin is) 105

pathogens microorganisms that cause disease 29

pectinase an enzyme that attacks pectin 64

percentage cover the proportion of individuals who must be immune to a disease in order to prevent an epidemic 126

perforin a protein made by killer T cells that causes cells infected by viruses to burst so preventing viral replication 120

peripheral resistance resistance to blood flow provided by the vessels through which the blood travels 170

peristalsis waves of muscle contraction that move food along the digestive system 161

phagocytes leucocytes capable of ingesting pathogens 115

phagocytosis the ingestion of pathogens by leucocytes 115

phenol coefficient test a test that compares the effectiveness of an antimicrobial substance to that of phenol 72

pili (fimbriae) short filamentous structures of bacteria that help in adherence to a surface 13

plaques clear areas on a bacterial lawn or tissue culture due to cell lysis caused by virus infection 80

plasma cells B cells that are capable of producing antibody molecules 120

plasma membrane (cytoplasmic membrane) the membrane that encloses the cytoplasm of a cell 10

plasmids small circular pieces of DNA found in bacterial cells but separate from the bacterial chromosome and not essential for growth 13

polygenic involving several genes 97

polyunsaturated fatty acids fatty acids in which the hydrocarbon chain contains two or more pairs of carbon atoms joined by a double bond 162

post-exponential phase the growth phase in which microbes continue to grow but without increasing the number of cells 61

primary metabolites substances that are produced by organisms as part of normal growth and synthesis of cell materials 25

primary response the immune response that occurs the first time an individual is exposed to a particular antigen 122

productive cough a cough where phlegm is coughed up 90

protease an enzyme that attacks protein 64

protozoan a single-celled animal (e.g. an amoeba) 103

proving (of dough) allowing to rise in a warm place 28

R plasmid a plasmid containing a gene for antibiotic resistance 150

radiographer a medical professional who uses X-rays and radioactive isotopes for the diagnosis and treatment of certain diseases 86

radiotherapy medical treatment involving radiation 131

reduced nicotinamide adenine dinucleotide (NADH) the reduced form of NAD 37

remission a period in which the symptoms of a disease seem to disappear or are greatly reduced (the return of symptoms is called relapse) 140

ribosomes particles composed of RNA and protein that are found in the cytoplasm and that play a vital role in protein synthesis 13

risk factors factors that increase the chance of an individual being affected by a particular disease (risk factors do not cause disease) 84

saprobiontic feeding off dead and decaying organic materials 10

saturated fatty acids fatty acids where the hydrocarbon chain contains no carbon–carbon double bonds 162

scaling-up the process that leads from the starter culture to the full-size fermenter vessel 41

screening (for disease) looking for signs of a disease when the patient may not be aware of any symptoms 85

screening (for new pharmaceuticals) the isolation and testing of microbes to determine whether or not they may be useful in the production of new pharmaceuticals 48

secondary metabolites chemicals that are not directly involved in normal growth and the production of cell materials 25

secondary response the immune response that occurs when an individual is exposed to a particular pathogen for the second or subsequent time – it is more rapid than the primary response and more antibody is produced, so the pathogen is usually destroyed before it can infect the body and cause recognisable symptoms of the disease 122

seed vessel (seed fermenter) the vessel in which the microbes to be used for a fermentation increase sufficiently to be put into the main fermenter vessel 61

septate (of fungal hyphae) with dividing walls 11

shock a medical condition caused by loss of blood or body fluid and a drop in blood pressure 144

sick building syndrome a situation in which reservoirs of air-borne pathogens found in the air ducts and vents of a building provide a continual source of infection for the inhabitants or users of the building 100

sparging introduction of sterile air into a tank of nutrient medium for aerobic fermentation 39

specific adherence the process by which a bacterial ligand attaches to an exactly matching receptor molecule in a host cell membrane 104

Spirillum a genus of bacteria

spirillum a spiral bacterium 12

spontaneous generation the theory that living organisms arise spontaneously from decaying materials 9

starter culture freeze-dried bacterial or fungal cells that have been carefully selected for a particular fermentation 41

starter vessel the first vessel in a fermentation process in which the microbes increase sufficiently to be put into the seed fermenter 61

stem cells cells in the bone marrow that give rise to T and B lymphocytes 119

sterilisation the removal of all forms of living matter 71

steroid hormone a hormone chemically related to cholesterol 69

stock cultures cultures made from the master culture for the supply of working cultures 49

strain selection the process of isolating a particular strain of microorganism 58

stroke volume the volume of blood pumped per ventricle per heart beat 169

submerged culture a fermentation where the bacteria grow below the surface of the nutrient medium 39

substrate a substance on which an enzyme acts; food on which microbes grow 22

super-infections difficult-to-treat infections caused by pathogens that are resistant to several antibiotics 152

suppressor T cells lymphocytes that suppress the response of other cells to antigens 120

surface culture a fermentation where the bacteria grow on the surface of the nutrient medium 39

symptoms indications of disease that the patient is aware of 85

systole the stage in the cardiac cycle in which the ventricles contract and force blood into the arteries 170

T cell receptors protein molecules found in the cell membranes of T lymphocytes that recognise antigens 119

T cells (T lymphocytes) lymphocytes found mainly in the lymph system that attack pathogens directly 118

therapeutic dose the dose of antibiotic needed to kill or inhibit bacteria 76

therapeutic enzymes enzymes used for treating disease 66

therapeutic index the ratio of the therapeutic dose and the toxic dose (an effective antibiotic has a low therapeutic dose and a high toxic dose) 76

thrombus a stationary blood clot found in an artery 88

thylakoids folds in the plasma membrane of photosynthetic bacteria that increase the surface area for photosynthetic activity 13

tidal volume the volume of air taken in with each breath when the body is at rest 171

tissue type the particular set of HLA proteins present in the cell membranes of an individual 129

toxic dose the level of antibiotic that causes damage to the host cells 76

toxoids modified toxins used in vaccinations – toxoids are harmless but can give rise to an immune response 126

trace elements trace minerals found in food that may make food 'go off' if not stabilised by reacting with citric acid 35

trace minerals minerals that are needed in daily amounts of less than 5 gram (e.g. iron and zinc) 165

transfusion reaction an immune reaction caused by giving a patient an incompatible blood transfusion 132

transmission the transfer of pathogens from one individual to another 100

transplantation taking an organ or tissue from one person and putting it into another 129

tricarboxylic acid (TCA) cycle part of a series of reactions that enable a cell to produce energy from glucose 36

triglycerides lipids formed from the combination of three fatty acids and a glycerol molecule 162

trisomy having three copies of a chromosome rather than the usual two 95

turbid cloudy 18

unsaturated fatty acids fatty acids in which the hydrocarbon chain contains one or more pairs of carbon atoms joined by a double bond 162

use-dilution test a test that attempts to mimic realistic conditions so as to find the lowest effective concentration of a disinfectant 73

variolation the technique of introducing infected material into a scratch in the skin to produce an immune response 124

viable capable of reproducing 146

Vibrio a genus of bacteria

vibrio a curved or comma-shaped bacterium 12

virulent able to cause disease 126

working cultures cultures made from the stock cultures for use 49

wort the sugary solution extracted from malted barley after mashing 27

Index